New Writing of East Europe

New Writing
of East Europe

edited by

GEORGE GÖMÖRI and CHARLES NEWMAN

Chicago

QUADRANGLE BOOKS

1968

116013

Contents

New Writing of East Europe

Introduction

CHARLES NEWMAN

" . . . mad Ireland hurt you into poetry.
Now Ireland has her madness and her weather still,
For poetry makes nothing happen: it survives
In the valley of its saying where executives
Would never want to tamper; it flows south
From ranches of isolation and the busy griefs,
Raw towns that we believe and die in; it survives,
A way of happening, a mouth."
                                        –W. H. Auden
                                        In Memory of W. B. Yeats

OUR COUNTRIES hurt us in different ways, though rarely into poetry. For those "executives" whom Auden dismissed so airily in 1940 have had a way of securing even the "valleys of saying" for themselves. Further, it is blindly condescending to celebrate art only in terms of its dissidence, as if madness, public or private, were a prerequisite for its happening.

Auden's well-intentioned elegy for an Irish nationalist prefigures the West's patronizing attitude toward recent writing from East Europe, where the work of adventurous writers is given extra dimension as it involves danger to their persons, and conjures up those "hurts" commonly associated with the creative process. But the artist's craft, unfortunately perhaps, cannot be evaluated in terms of his own personal courage, nor does it deserve our attention simply because it has been repressed. In our country, for example, the greatest efforts of aesthetic courage may go utterly ignored, while in others, the slightest deviation may bring punitive attention. It is difficult, in any case, to determine whether popular indifference, commercial ignorance, or official censorship is more injurious to art, though it is historically clear which is more dangerous to artists. But the genuine artist, after all, is known ultimately by how he makes use of his obstacles; and these artists should be notable for their aesthetic accomplishments before their suffering.

We in the West have preferred social commentary in our literature willfully opaque—didacticism has been the paramount aesthetic sin since the fifties—

so it is instructive to experience in East European writing protest which is necessarily oblique. But the strain in both cases springs from similar motives: the desire to create a private language that can cut through official cant, aesthetic and otherwise. In this sense we hold a mirror up to each other.

With the lessening of tensions, however, and, more importantly, the mutual re-examination of our respective traditions, we seem to have more in common, aesthetically, than ever. Perhaps this is because dissidence itself has taken on a more universal character—that is, we have come to associate the enemies of civilization not so much with ideologies or nation states but rather with a technocratic mindlessness which increasingly knows no geographical bounds. (It is also interesting to note that as our politics have deteriorated, our arts reflect a new didacticism, while as their regimes have been liberalized, their art grows more subtle and detached.)

More positively, we have both simply become more sophisticated—drawing on techniques and models outside our own cultures. George Gömöri illustrates the common theme of East European artists' spiritual return to Europe—a return which implies much more than just "looking west"—and it is certainly true that American writers of this generation have learned more from foreign writers than any of their immediate predecessors. So at the simplest level, East European literature reflects the internationalization that we have all undergone in the last twenty years.

This is all by way of saying that the selections herein have been chosen on their aesthetic merit alone, though I personally have been partial to those writers from whom I think American writers might learn the most. The "politics of translation" are inescapable, and I can only refer the reader to George Gömöri and Tymon Terlecki, whose erudition qualifies them to confront this complex problem more directly. I would simply emphasize a few matters for American readers.

The shared, contemporary experience of East Europe—an experience no less crucial for us because we have had to deal with it at several removes—is that of the coextensive German and Russian occupations. While there is hardly a selection herein which does not relate directly to those historical circumstances, it would be a mistake to take any of them as strict allegory. Indeed, the genius of most recent East European writing is its multileveled richness—the manner in which its folk-mythic, political, and interpersonal relationships become, for all purposes, symbiotic.

Moreover, it is the stylistic aspects of the work which are frequently most interesting. Note, for example, Déry's revivification of the great tradition of European realism, a tradition of which most young American writers seem totally ignorant, as well as the amplification of techniques of the new French novelists—particularly by Bocheński and Linhartova—techniques which seem to work best when adopted by those who use them pragmatically, as they do. Similarly, the reader should be alert to the unique blend of Western poetic traditions—imagism and surrealism particularly—as exemplified in the work of, say, Popa and Holub.

East Europe has also produced a number of minds universal in scope—Witkiewicz and Gombrowicz, Weöres and Jószef are writers whose concerns are in no way limited provincially by geography or theme, though obviously they pose immense problems for the translator.

Nevertheless, universal themes, if they are persuasive, spring from particularized circumstances, and Jan Kott, Laco Novomesky, and Ted Hughes (with regard to Popa) point out how the struggle for artistic freedom must be grounded in a local context, a genuinely engaged audience, rather than in metaphysical generalizations about the sanctity of art which we in the West fall back on so easily. E. M. Cioran, a Rumanian-born philosopher now living in Paris, sums up well the problem of comparative "freedom" in his "Letter to a Distant Friend":

> Freedom in the West, in order to manifest itself, requires a void—and succumbs to it. The condition which determines is the very one which annihilates it. This freedom lacks foundation; the more complete it is, the more it overhangs an abyss, for everything threatens it, down to the principles from which it derives. Man is so little made to endure or deserve it, that the very benefits he receives from it crush him, and freedom ultimately brings him to the point where he prefers, to its excesses, those of terror. To these disadvantages are added others: a liberal society, eliminating mystery, the absolute, order, and possessing the true metaphysic no more than a true police, cast the individual back upon himself, while dividing him from what he is, from his own depths. . . . Imagine a society, overpopulated with doubt, in which, with the exception of a few strays, no one adheres utterly to anything; in which unscathed by superstition, certainties, everyone pays lip service to freedom and no one respects the form of government which defends and incarnates it. . . . You are disappointed after promises which could not be kept; we, by a lack of any promises at all. . . .

Finally, perhaps the most persistently instructive and enviable aspect of East European literature is the engagement it reflects between writers and their society. Critics like Georg Lukács raise questions about the relationship between expository and imaginative forms, and the function of art within a society that we are only beginning to consider, and thinkers like Kolakowski and poets like Weöres have shown us the importance of recognizing the continuity of our aesthetic and philosophic traditions, at the very point when we are dismissing them out of hand. Kolakowski, of course, must be reckoned as potentially as important to an understanding of European intellectual history as, say, Sartre or Jaspers.

It is high time we stopped patronizing these writers with our Cold War rhetoric, and gave their work the guiltless aesthetic discrimination it warrants. Respect of this sort is, indeed, independent of official madness and our common weather.

CHARLES NEWMAN was born in St. Louis, studied at Yale University, and did graduate work at Oxford. He is editor of *Tri-Quarterly,* a national journal of arts, letters, and opinion published at Northwestern University. His first novel, *New Axis,* published in 1966, was received with unusual critical acclaim. His second, *The Promisekeeper,* will appear this year. Mr. Newman had also edited *The Art of Sylvia Plath* and contributed short fiction and articles to various reviews. He is currently spending a year in Europe on a Rockefeller grant for creative writing.

Literature deprophetized

New trends in East European literature

GEORGE GÖMÖRI

I T IS DEBATABLE whether there has ever been such a thing as 'East European literature'. Perhaps one should regard it as a vague definition at best, something like the literature of 'the Soviet people'. There is still no such thing as the Soviet people, although the Soviet Union has been in existence long enough to leave its imprint on modern history, and we can speak about the literature of 'the Soviet period' in Russian or Georgian literature. Whatever uses the term 'East European' may have, it gained wide currency only after the Second World War when Poland, Czechoslovakia and Hungary, countries which for a long time thought about themselves as being "central" to Europe, forming a "bridge between East and West" or an outpost against "the Eastern hordes", suddenly found themselves firmly implanted in *Eastern* Europe. The centre of European gravity has shifted further West, and those countries within the Russian sphere of interest underwent a social revolution and an 'Easternization' at the same time. Since then, this "Easternness"(which is not necessarily a result of Russification) inflicted upon them by history, has become part of their consciousness and forms a part of their everyday life. In this respect, the small nations of Eastern Europe are more or less in the same boat. This is not to say that they gave up their particular national prejudices or that they have dropped their conditioned reflexes towards authority or history, but they have changed in subtle ways—their allegedly immutable national characteristics were caught and transformed in the flux of history. After 1956, a joke circulated that the Hungarians were behaving like the Poles, the Poles like the Czechs, and as for the Czechs....Since then, the tables have been turned more than once; it is now the Hungarians who behave like the Czechs, and the Czechs that began to exhibit 'Polish' symptoms, not to speak of the rebellious Slovaks who sound almost 'Hungarian'. All this proves a certain interchangeability in Eastern Europe: shared experience supports a tendency to behave similarly in similar psychological, economic and political situations, irrespective of traditional national traits.

When I speak of Eastern Europe, it is first of all Poland, Czechoslovakia and

Hungary that I have in mind, although I think that the northern part of Yugo-slavia also belongs to this cultural region; what lies further South is the Balkans. For a variety of reasons, I do not regard Rumanians as 'East Europeans', whereas Yugoslavia is a more complicated case. Croats and Czechs have a great deal in common; so do Serbs and Hungarians, Serbs and Poles. Yugoslavia is not only mixed ethnically, but linguistically speaking, it could also be divided into three or four primary cultural zones. One of these is part of my 'Eastern Europe' if not geographically, at least in a cultural sense. Krleža is a typical product of a Central-Eastern European culture and the poems of the Serbian poet Pavlović would sound authentic in Czech or Polish as well.

What I want to trace in this essay is the development of individual literatures in Eastern Europe, and the new trends which they have displayed in recent years. In spite of their linguistic and other differences, there is one thing all East Euro-pean literatures have in common: the strong wish to return into the mainstream of modern European culture. A spiritual return into Europe - this is perhaps the most widely shared ambition and the most important *common denominator* of Polish, Hungarian, Czech and Slovak literature.

In the presentation and evaluation of East European writing in the West, two extremes should be avoided. There is a danger of uncritical acceptance of the opinions and preferences of the official cultural spokesmen, or of politically reliable critics of the country in question. This problem did not arise in the years of the cold war when no Western critic in his right mind could take seriously the elaborations of a Révai or a Stoll on the extraordinary merits of Soviet Socialist Realism. Since 1956, and especially in the last few years, things have changed: an increasing number of East European books appeared on the English and American market. Some of these were translated by competent, native or emigré translators and became a success; others were put out in Budapest or Prague by special foreign-language publishing houses to serve 'informative' (and often propaganda) purposes. The influence of such publications as the Hungarian-sponsored "Landmark," edited by Miklós Szabolcsi, is admittedly very limited. Still, potential readers should be warned against judging contem-porary Hungarian literature on the basis of such politically 'screened' selections. The editors of such anthologies are not really interested in literary values; what they are after is the loyal reflection of the officially recognized hierarchy in literature at that particular moment.

The other excess, that of political overestimation, is in some ways more dangerous. It grows out of the sensationalist attitude so common in the Western press—a sensationalism towards anything—policies, personalities or books—East of the Elbe. In a competitive system one cannot sell unless one exaggerates; sales-manship breeds an unhealthy tendency to blow up every literary bubble into a minor sensation. Of course, an *element* of sensation is involved in some literary works produced in Communist countries—*Dr. Zhivago* struck many intelligent people as truly exceptional, even sensational in the best sense of the word. The same can be said to a lesser extent about Marek Hlasko, Tertz-Sinyavski and Arzhak-Daniel who were commendable not only for the political nuisance value (or truth value) but also for the literary merits of their work. Those who remember the first publication of Tertz's and then Arzhak's writings, might recall a third author hiding under a pseudonym as well—a certain I. Ivanov. Reading his play "Is there life on the Mars?" one could not help feeling that it was the work of a dilettante or in the best case of a very weak writer. All the same, it was published in Paris in Polish, Russian, and in goodness knows how many other languages. Ivanov's play (a parody of Stalin's paranoid Doctors' Plot) was clearly published for extraliterary reasons; *not* because it was good literature. This precedent could be repeated any time whenever a clandestine manuscript reaches the West, whether it come from the Soviet Union or any of the P.D.'s (people's democracies) and, in my opinion, such an absolutely non-literary approach is not really helpful to anyone. It obscures the real values that Eastern Europe has to offer to Western readers, and dismays the genuine writers in those countries whose works are *not* being translated into Western languages for lack of critical political allegory[1]

Does this mean that we can blissfully ignore the social and political problems with which Polish, Hungarian or Slovak writers have to cope? Far from it. Literature should not be viewed as an isolated subject; the literary work may be investigated "in itself" but it is doubtful that purely formal or structural analysis will make it less opaque to the inquisitive glance. In the literatures of Eastern Europe, familiarity with the social and political background often provides a key to understanding, a chemical substance to bring out those parts of the work which were written in invisible ink, what the Poles call *podteksty*. Poems like Weöres's 'Mural of the 20th century' or the better known 'Poem for Adults' by Ważyk, are hard to grasp without some measure of 'background information', in this case about the Second World War and the Stalinist era in Poland often called by Party *aesthetes* as the 'past period' (*miniony okres*). How could one discuss the achievement of that brilliant but short-lived comet, Attila József, without pointing to the nature of his total alienation—which meant not only rejection by one or more women, but also rejection by society and excommunication from his chosen sect, the Communist Party of the thirties?

All the same, many facets of the literary work are inaccessible to the straightforward sociological approach. For the critic Arthur Sandauer, the most admired contemporary Polish authors are Schulz, Gombrowicz and Bialoszewski —writers concerned with myths, patterns of behaviour, psychological arche-types, or with the inadequacies and ambiguities of language. There is no sociological short-cut to understanding the solipsistic philosophy and obsessive linguistic games of a Bialoszewski. As for Gombrowicz, he can be treated as a 'social case' but such a treatment would amount to an appalling simplification, something like defining a tiger with the phrase: "after all he is also a cat". Is there then a *correct* critical approach? I, for one, would advocate some kind of a 'per-

---

[1] I may be wrong but I feel that Mihajlo Mihajlov would have benefited from somewhat less publicity in the West before his ill-fated press conference in Zadar. He is a talented critic and journalist (*Moscow Summer* gave ample proof of that) but not yet an important writer, even less a typical representative of contemporary Yugoslav literature.

spectivism', as suggested by Professor Wellek in his essay 'Some Principles of Criticism',[2] although I am not convinced that the practical application of his method would yield similar results in the hands of different critics. A critic living in Eastern Europe would probably emphasize different things than his more 'detached' colleague living in the sheltered world of an American campus. 'Perspectivism' means to me simply a comprehensive viewpoint and resistance to vulgarization, be it sociologically or aesthetically motivated.

In editing this collection I was partial to such trends manifest in East European literature which in one way or another link up with modern trends in the rest of Europe. I have sought contributions on writers and poets who, even if they did not belong to the then 'Avantgarde' movements, were precursors to the literature of the nineteen-fifties and -sixties (Witkiewicz, Gombrowicz, Attila József) and writings by or about such authors who while seeking for new means of expression, have already established themselves in their respective countries as important continuators of the critical and demythologizing tradition of Western Europe (Déry, Háy, Andrzejewski). This collection does not pretend to offer a complete picture of *all* interesting trends and major writers in Eastern Europe; selectiveness inevitably meant exclusion of some obvious names, and the reluctant omission of valuable material which seemed to have less relevance to the central preoccupations of contemporary European literature.

Since 1956 East European literature has moved away from uniformity, emerged from that grey fog of unmitigated boredom which now is looked upon as the distinguishing mark of the Stalinist period. This breakthrough did not come everywhere at the same time: in Poland it happened in one long haul between 1955 and 1959, in Hungary it began as early as 1954, was interrupted in 1956 and got a new impetus around 1962. In Czechoslovakia there was a glimmer of hope around 1956, but the real reassessment of literary judgements and values had to wait until 1963 and longer. These dates are given here to account for the sometimes amazing dissimilarities (one may say discrepancies) between different East European countries. Their drive for 'liberalization' (read: Europeanization) has proceeded under varying political conditions. Until quite recently, it looked as if those countries would be sealed off from each other by impenetrable frontiers, as if each country was making a special effort to contain its own home-grown revisionism or existentialism or modernism. To mention just a few examples: the best essays of Kolakowski have not been translated into Hungarian, Mrożek's plays were not allowed on the Hungarian stage until 1964; on the other hand, József Lengyel, the 'Hungarian Solzhenitsyn' was for a long time unprintable in Poland.[3] In the last few years, however, perhaps responding to the spread of polycentrism within the Communist camp, there has been an increasing interchange of unconventional ideas and literature between all East European countries. Kolakowski begins to influence the Czechs, and those Poles who are fed up with the censorship look towards Yugoslavia, which of all Communist

---

[2] In *The Critical Moment*, Faber and Faber, London

countries, is nearest to 'cultural normality'.

As for new literary trends, the Poles are still in the lead. Much can be said against Polish literature, except that it has failed to be provocative during the past twelve years. It has successfully provoked the attention not only of the native reader but also of countless foreigners who had never before read a Polish book in their life. Lec, Mrożek, Andrzejewski, Gombrowicz. . .For the success of Polish literature abroad a fair share of credit should be given to the emigrés. There is no other European literature (with the possible exception of Spanish) in which emigré writers play such an indispensable role. To mention just a few names: Gombrowicz, Milosz, Herling-Grudzinski, Wat, Marek Hlasko. The influence of the first two has been enormous on young writers in Poland; it helps them to resist 'Sarmatian' provincialism and 'committed' primitivism, even when those two join forces as a new [Sarmatian] edition of Socialist Realism.

Years, decades, after the last war the Poles are still obsessed with and haunted by the stark image of those years when their country "ceased to exist". Many war novels have appeared in the United States and in other countries since V-day, but it is amazing how hard war-themes die in Poland. Since 1956 there has been a noticeable shift in the handling of the subject—the straight-forward journalistic account and the usual combination of realism and romantic patriotism has given way to a more sophisticated approach, or at least a more differentiated one. While in the first post-war decade, writers with few exceptions wanted to communicate simple "blocks of feeling", now interest has grown in psychological analysis, fringe-situations and even in the grotesque that in those years co-existed with the macabre. J. J. Szczepański's "Boots" is a remarkable example of the psychological approach, whereas Kazimierz Brandys's "How to be loved?" deals with an unusual and unheroic situation which was also part of the strange reality of the occupation years. Stawinski's scenario of the "Eroica" exploits the grotesque, often comic situations in which such a tragic event as the Warsaw Uprising of 1944 abounded. Some young writers who were children at the time of the war, but lived it through with eyes and ears wide open, have lately managed to evoke those years with frightening clarity. Even in the difficult genre of concentration camp stories, where Borowski is the undisputable master, something new can be achieved - see "Handcart", a recent novel of the talented Janusz Krasiński.

The war is an important theme in Czech literature as well, and here again, we can observe certain attempts at 'deheroization'—I have in mind Skvorecky's much discussed novel "The Cowards", in which the last days of the war are shown just as they were: chaotic and ridiculous. Still, it could be argued that Skvorecky's attitude is brave but atypical, and perhaps the stories of Arnošt Lustig and Ladislas Fuks give a better idea of the virtues and limitations of Czech prose which is now trying to probe war and camp experiences with more emphasis on psychological effects.

---

[3] Lengyel's novel on Siberian camp-life was published in Budapest a month before Solzhenitsyn's 'Ivan Denisovitch'. It is now available in English; *"From Beginning to End"*, Peter Owen, London, 1966.

Until recently, Hungarian literature has shown a curious reluctance to evaluate or to re-evaluate war experiences. In 1945 a few poets of the Left (Gyula Illyés, Benjámin) tried to spell out the meaning of Hungary's collapse, while assessing the responsibility of the intelligentsia in it. Some deeply-probing essays were written by István Bibó, the most enlightened and most lonely political thinker in Hungary, but far too few people listened to his thorough analysis and well-substantiated warnings.[4] Soon political passions flared up again, and in about 1948, literature was given tasks other than to answer the question: what made Hungary's political and moral catastrophe inevitable? This vital question was shelved for more than a decade, but at the beginning of the sixties it has emerged with a new force and now younger writers are trying to confront it. Novels by Sánta, Cseres and others establish guilt, for the first time, at different levels: those who gave the orders were guilty, but so were those who carried them out, and even those who did not do anything but only turned the other way. What happens when 'patriotic duty' and 'common decency' clash? Are widely accepted ethical norms acceptable in 'dehumanized' situations?

Perhaps the most interesting phenomenon of this self-searching trend is the poetry of János Pilinszky. Pilinszky is a Catholic existentialist who writes very little, but the great evocative power and crystal-like finality of his works is undisputable. He regards the tragedy of European Jewry "the most universal scandal of our age" and one of his central concerns is to show in his poems and written for a KZ-oratorio, entitled "Dark Heaven", the extreme, inhuman loneliness of victim *and* murderer inextricably bound together in the act of 'depersonalized' murder. Pilinszky's is one of the most authentic voices in contemporary Hungarian poetry, yet for a long time he was not published at all and even now he is more tolerated than appreciated by officialdom.

The new look at war themes and at questions of individual moral responsibility was clearly influenced by the study of Existentialist philosophy and literature. As for the second trend, which has many characteristics of a critical realism, it is closely connected with various 'Revisionist' tendencies amongst the creative intelligentsia. As a matter of fact, "Revisionism' had its *Sturm und Drang* period in 1956-1957, but that was mainly a direct answer to the political challenges of the day. This period brought forth works such as Hlasko's stories, Ważyks's 'Poem for Adults,' and in Hungary, Déry's 'Niki' and Benjámin's 'reckoning' poems. Once that wave had abated, there was a time for 'more balanced' but still rather critical work about the 'mistakes and abuses' of Socialism —such as Kazimierz Brandys's 'The Mother of Kings'. Angry books, like Hlasko's 'Graveyards' were not published— Hlasko had to become a political defector to get it published in Paris. It was the Poles who first reached the third stage in the metamorphosis of 'Revisionism'—by returning to historical allusion and the parable. The first novel of this kind was probably Andrzejewski's *Ciemności*

---

[4]His collected essays were published in Hungarian in London: Bibó István, *Harmadik út*, Magyar Könyves Céh, 1960.

kryją ziemię translated into English as 'The Inquisitors', a short novel about the dialectical mind of that remarkable man, Torquemada. It is interesting to note that in a speech some time around 1962 Gomulka actually compared Stalinist terror with the methods of the Spanish Inquisition. Did he, by any chance, read Andrzejewski?

When I am speaking about 'Revisionism' what I have in mind is any definite disagreement with the basic tenets of institutionalized Marxism. That would include mistrust in the 'objective laws' of history and unimpeded progress, doubts about the benefits of complete state control and greatly centralized personal power, as well as an assertion of one's own personality against 'the will of the masses', a concept of doubtful authenticity. It is no wonder that once the initial shock of destalinization was over, many Communists or ex-Communists began to speculate about history, only to reach rather sceptical conclusions. What emerged from this soul-searching was a new belief in the value of the human personality; some of the ex-Communists writers could indeed be described as "Marxist personalists".

Amongst the historical-social parables written in Poland in the last few years one can find such gems as Jacek Bocheński's "The Divine Julius" and Woroszylski's "Dreams under the Snow" a sharp-cutting biographical novel on Saltykov-Shchedrin. It was clear for anyone who has read Bocheński's book that in throwing light on the mechanism of totalitarian power in the age of Julius Caesar, it also "formulates views about freedom which are also valid today".[5] Although he has no Marxist roots, I would mention the affinity of Zbigniew Herbert with the historicism of the 'Revisionist' writers. Herbert - whom many believe to be the most important poet now living in Poland—contemplates history from many angles. His view is always ironic, though in certain cases, for instance when writing about contemporary Polish history, his irony has tragic undertones. In poems like 'Fortinbras's Elegy' (printed among other places in Alvarez's "Under Pressure") Herbert manages to put a well-known literary theme into a modern political context. History, culture and literature, Herbert seems to say, provide us with patterns of behaviour, with models that have a validity even centuries later. Not only Shakespeare is our contemporary, but anybody whom we choose to be "the past - is today, only a bit further" wrote Norwid, and Herbert derives part of his strength from the recognition of the same truth. He is a poet of historical continuity.[6]

Herbert has no counterpart in Czechoslovakia or Hungary, although the Czech poet Holub clearly has points of contact with Herbert's themes, if not his style. Both poets are analytical in their approach to their subject-matter, but while Herbert often reflects upon cultural formations and objects, Holub, being a scien-

---

[5]Stefan Żółkiewski in *Z problemów literatury polskiej XX wieku*, Warsaw, 1965, p. 24

[6]Many of Herbert's poems are available in English translation; see *Postwar Polish Poetry* edited and translated by Czeslaw Milosz, Doubleday, 1965. Penguins are now preparing a selection of his poetry. Apart from poetry, Herbert is known as a playwright and an essayist, a collection of his essays ("Barbarian in the garden") was sold out within days after publication.

tist by training and occupation, is interested in the microcosms of the living world. What they certainly share is an interest in the shifting scene, in the 'dialectics' of history. In the first collection of Holub verse to come out in English,[7] I found a few poems which I think Herbert would not disown either. Take that curious poem, "Polonius". Holub's Polonius is as up-to-date as Herbert's Fortinbras, he is not simply an over-zealous elderly courtier and intriguer, but in Holub's imagination, a nameless functionary, an unscrupulous informer ("walls are his ears / keyholes his eyes"), a symbol of that servile opportunism which is the mainstay of *every* totalitarian system. The poet's attitude towards him is that of infinite contempt. When he falls:

> the whole continent will be lighter
> earth's axis straighten up
> and in night's thunderous arena
> a bird will chirp in gratitude

The historical parable as a guise for contemporary problems has appeared in Hungarian literature time and again. This applies above all to the theatre where it seems to have become something of a tradition. Lately two such plays have been written, the guise being in both cases Roman: "The Minion" by Gyula Illyés and "The Horse" by Gyula Háy. Thanks to the peculiar system of censorship now applied in Hungary, both plays (by implication strongly anti-Stalinist) could appear in *print* but neither of them got a clearance to be *performed*. Recently the ex-Communist, ex-Revisionist and ex-prisoner Tibor Déry wrote a book entitled 'The Excommunicator', a half-historical, half-debunking novel on St. Ambrose, a terrifying farce which has a chapter reproducing the absurd confession of a certain Innocentus, a heretic accused of plotting against the saintly pontiff. For Innocentus, read any accused of the Rajk trial.[8] What is remarkable is that this parallel was pointedly referred to in a review of the book in the Budapest literary journal *Uj Irás*.

The third important trend—and here again most credit should go to the Poles —is that of the absurd drama (anti-theatre) and the literature of the grotesque. This is perhaps the most exciting trend for critics and theatre-goers in the West, as it has connections with the drama of Beckett and Ionesco and that of the modern English anti-theatre. In Poland the anti-drama is flourishing mainly thanks to the talents of two authors: Mrożek and Różewicz.

Mrożek's career began around 1956 and the problems he tries to solve in his plays indicate his 'Revisionist' orientation. His individuals are caught in the huge iron hands of the System and squeezed dry (*Strip-tease*) or haunted to death

---

[7]Miroslav Holub, *Selected Poems*, Translated by Ian Milner and George Theiner.

[8]László Rajk, Hungarian Communist leader was executed in 1949 for heading alleged Titoist plot against the Hungarian Communist regime. Rehabilitated and reburied in 1956, he was fully rehabilitated in 1962.

by Authority which discovers a tiger in their bathroom (*Piotr Ohey's martyrdom*). He creates a world of absurd laws and logic that superimpose themselves upon the world of 'normal' human existence. If Ionesco in "The Bald Soprano" was mainly interested in the 'absurdity of everyday speech', Mrożek is intrigued by the deadly absurdity of social stereotypes. In his plays the chain of schematization is laid bare through a peculiar logic inherent in the plot. Mrożek sees reality being organized and controlled through schemes which eventually begin to live a life of their own, resulting in the degradation of people into mechanistic agents. Mrozek's world is one of social and political alienation; his last play "Tango" does not indicate any more faith in political progress than his first play "The Police" did.

Rózewicz's plays are different from Mrożek's because of their "nihilistic humanism" and their desperate search for values. Rózewicz's alienation is total like that of Beckett: his plays have hardly any plot and are usually built around a lyrical hero and his tortured monologues. The hero is tormented by the absurd normalcy of 'being', but he is unable to propose a solution. The world is 'out of joint' but there is no way to put it right. As in his poetry, so in his plays, Rózewicz expresses a not entirely unjustified despair and disgust over the state of affairs in the world.

Both Mrożek and Rózewicz have been widely translated into Western languages but Kolakowski is less known as a playwright. Leszek Kolakowski is a brilliant young philosopher who (apart from strictly philosophical works) has written essays on sociology, sarcastic and 'modernized' versions of biblical tales, and two plays as well. The more recent of these, "The System of Priest Jensen, or Entrance and Exit", published in the June 1966 number of *Dialog*,[9] is of particular interest, as it produces a new genre, something between a 'historical reckoning' and a 'philosophic parable'. The play takes place in the waiting-room of a dentist where the patients are nervously discussing the chances of painless and quick cure. Yet nobody seems to have left the surgery through the entrance door— when the patients enter, sometimes after years of waiting, they disappear for ever, while from the operating room heart-rending cries of pain are heard. Finally the whole population of the waiting-room is quietly transferred to another dentist while the mellifluous Father Jensen confidently announces his supreme axiom: "Each dentist is better than the previous one." Although Kolakowski's subtitle to the play promises an 'optimistic polemics' with Beckett, in fact it turns out to be a farce directed against high hopes attached to political change, "but it surely will be better for our children". Each political regime is better than the previous one, because we wish it to be better. But is it really better? Will pious dialectics ever make up for unfulfilled expectations?[10]

---

[9]*Dialog* is an excellent theatrical monthly published in Warsaw. It has published texts by all the leading Polish playwrights and also translations of Dürrenmatt, Beckett, Ionesco, Albee, Pinter, Shvarts, etc.

[10]This play, incidentally, is open to a different, more metaphysical interpretation. Boleslaw Taborski, in his bibliography on the modern Polish theatre, published in T35 of the *Tulane Drama Review*, claims that Kolakowski's play explores "attitudes towards, and conceptions of, after-life". Nevertheless, Priest Jensen seems to have the mind and use the arguments of a shrewd dialectician and though the possibility of 'going to another dentist' might stand for consolation offered by another religion, I would rather stick to my interpretation. Anyway, the play was written in 1957 but allowed on the stage only for three performances and then banned—surely, not for fear of offending Catholic believers.

The absurd drama has found its champion in Czechoslovakia as well in the person of Václav Havel. His fame rests on two plays, "The Garden Party" and "The Memorandum". The first play, written in 1963, is based on the acid proposition that thoughtless dogmatism and mechanistic obediency to orders suits "the petty-bourgeois" like a glove. "The petty-bourgeois" in this context are the old-style functionaries, those dear old and middle-aged fellows in the apparatus. Havel's second play, "The Memorandum" is extremely funny in a frightening way; although it borrows in technique from Ionesco and perhaps from Mrożek, it is unmistakably rooted in Czech reality. It is about a new language, the *ptydepe*, invented in the "Centre" and introduced suddenly and without explanation in all offices. Nobody knows why this new language is necessary but everybody tries to pretend to be in favour of the innovation and to speak the language, however absurd "of the times". At the end, the introduction of *ptydepe* turns out to be a mistake and it is withdrawn. Czech critics hesitate whether to call Havel an 'absurdist' or a 'realist' - in fact, he is both, or probably a 'realist of the absurd'. The catchword is again: "alienation" and Havel's message to the audience could be summarized as: "I know you know they know *we* know". Alienation in the capitalist West? Certainly. But from time to time its language is still used for communication. Reading Havel one is not quite sure whether this is so in Czechoslovakia.[11]

In connection with Havel's successes it should be noted that there has been a parallel movement in Czech prose as well—a tendency to the grotesque, sometimes on the slightly facile level of an Anouilh, sometimes in a grimmer, more nightmarish version. In this genre Karel Michal's "Ghosts for Everyday" (1961) was a landmark, but more recently it has been Hrabal's stories that have won the warmest critical acclaim. Hrabal apparently manages to rise above the 'micro-realism' of contemporary Czech prose; his stories are a strange mixture of the grotesque and the lyrical, not without a touch of Surrealism. Czech literature is changing: one of its post-war myths, the myth of the 'decent little man' has crumbled under the onslaught of the grotesque. Hrabal is a writer standing somewhat apart, but the novels and stories of Skvorecky and Michal, the plays of Havel and Topol have all but demolished "the little man" as a hero - they have shown his cowardice and snivelling opportunism disguised by bureaucratic cant. And that is a lot to say in a country where Schweik is still a national hero.

We see, then, three interesting trends in the literatures of Eastern Europe: the new look at war and occupation themes, the need for historical parables and a more 'historicist' than 'salvationist' outlook, and, finally, the still growing fashion for the grotesque and the absurd. Many fascinating authors and books are left unmentioned—I have not mentioned the linguistic trend in Polish poetry, or the monistic 'biological myth' or anthropological structures of such outstanding Hungarian poets as Ferenc Juhász and Sándor Weöres. The Czechs could

---

[11]There is a striking lack of 'absurd drama' in Hungary. Only one author—Miklós Mészöly—wrote two plays that could be defined as anti-dramas. These were printed in provincial periodicals and partly ignored, partly furiously attacked by critics. For the sake of reference: "Waiting for Godot" was first performed in Hungary in 1965.

reproach me for omitting any reference to Holan who is a more accomplished poet than Holub. Yet from what I have said certain conclusions can be drawn which are actually corroborated by articles appearing in the Polish and Hungarian literary press.

The traditional posture of literature in Poland and Hungary is that of a constant alertness to national (and consequently, social and political) problems. This is less so in Czechoslovakia, though the social and educational role of literature has also been stressed there more than often. Since the mid-fifties, this traditional attitude has been slowly changing; the Soviet variety of Socialist Realism has been discredited beyond repair, and with it went the cruder, more direct form of national romanticism. With the "little stabilization" setting in both in Poland and in Hungary, literature has lost its political (largely anti-Stalinist) appeal to the masses. This is obviously less true for Czech and Slovak literature—with Mňačko's "The Taste of Power" the Slovaks have now reached, if not surpassed the Poles in the intensity of [their] attacks on the arbitrary policies of 'the past period'. But in Warsaw and Budapest no such novels are written any more. Literature has become more literary, inverted, professionalized.

This state of affairs was recently described in an outspoken article by the Polish critic Wlodzimierz Maciąg.[12] He believes that the post-1956 escape or liberation of literature from dogmatic control created new dangers. "Literature is free, but it is free *from* something, not *to* something, it is free from programmatic doctrines, but not to create its own programs for itself." In Maciąg's opinion Polish literature has regained its autonomy but only at the cost of its social influence and effectiveness. "It cannot speak in the name of society, it cannot appeal to the essential ideological and social interests of society"; in other words, literature has opted out of 'the construction of socialism', or for that matter from the debate to define what socialism should be like. Maciąg's accusation that everything that is important happens *outside* literature and it does not find its reflection in literature contains a germ of truth: after engagement in the service of certain ideals, came disengagement and *deprophetization*. After October the writer made a bargain with the authorities - he was given freedom to write as he pleases, as long as he refrains from questioning basic political decisions. Which is to say, he lost his status of a 'bard' of a 'prophet'.

The same phenomenon can be observed in Hungary where in a recent Party document[13] the leading and 'prophetic' role of the writer was emphatically denied and branded as an anachronistic and dangerous concept. This indicates that the concept still enjoys a certain amount of popularity in Hungarian intellectual cricles, in clear contrast to Poland where (as Maciąg implies) the writers' 'leading role' was completely renounced. There are political reasons behind this, to give just one: as long as the Oder-Neisse frontier hangs in the balance, the Poles have no alternative to Gomulka's foreign policy, whereas

---

[12] *Miesięcznik literacki*, October, 1966.

[13] The mission of literature and arts in our society', *Társadalmi Szemle*, July-August 1966

the Hungarians *do* have the alternative but fail to take it up. Also, the freedom of the Hungarian writer (as far as literary techniques go) is still much more limited than in Poland, although the discussions of the past few years about the meaning of "realism" might have softened the ground for a more generous approach to "modernism" (e.g. Garaudy's "boundless realism" might have won some supporters in official circles). The Hungarian attitude towards such modernist tendencies as abstract painting or Surrealism has been until now rather conservative; the only concession to the 'modernists' was to allow them to publish abroad, namely in the Hungarian language monthly *Hid* at Novi Sad (Yugoslavia) and in *Magyar Mühely*, an emigré review in Paris. In spite of various restrictions, as in Poland and Czechoslovakia, so in Hungary a workable but tenuous compromise has been reached between the writers and the authorities.

As for 'deprophetization', which is not a bad thing in itself, it can be successful only if it is linked with a visible increase in the practice of civic courage. 'Professionalization' and letting the writer loose in the field of technical experimentation is not enough. From a literary point of view, absurd dramas and historical parables are welcome, but unless the press is capable of taking over the militantly critical function of "engaged" literature, this one-sided freedom of literature is less than satisfying. It might breed isolation from the real problems and interests of society; writers would then find themselves writing for each other and posterity, in a sort of literary pseudo-world revolving in a vacuum. Lest this should happen, writers in Eastern Europe should regard the present arrangement for what it is—a temporary compromise—and should never give up their birthright: the insistence on full creative freedom. If one can take the Kolakowski affair and Mňačko's intransigence in publishing his last book abroad[14] for a cue, there are many writers in East Europe who have not forgotten this fundamental obligation of their profession.

---

[14] *The Taste of Power* was published both in German and English but so far its publication has not been permitted in Czechoslovakia. Since then, Mňačko has decided not to return from a visit to the West as long as the Czech government is not revising its policy *vis-à-vis* Israel.

GEORGE GÖMÖRI was born in 1934 in Budapest, Hungary. He studied Polish and Hungarian literature at Eotvos Loránd University, Budapest, leaving his native country in 1956. In the following years he was awarded two degrees; a B. A. Hon. in London (Polish Language and Literature) and a B. Litt. in Oxford where he did research as a member of St. Anthony's College. In 1960-1961 he spent an academic year at Jogjakarta, Indonesia on a grant of the Paderewski Foundation. In 1963-1964 he taught Polish and Hungarian at the University of California, Berkeley, and the following year he was Research Fellow in the Harvard Russian Research Center, working on 19th century Polish literature. He is presently Senior Research Associate at the Centre for Russian and East European Studies at Birmingham University, England. His publications include two books of poetry in Hungarian and a book of translations in Hungarian from Boris Pasternak's postwar poetry; numerous essays in Hungarian, Polish and English, and a full-length study of the social and political pressures that shaped post-war poetry in Eastern Europe, *Polish and Hungarian Poetry 1945 to 1956*, Oxford University Press, 1966.

translated by Kathleen Szasz

The Portuguese Princess

TIBOR DÉRY

ONE HOUR after the German evacuation, in the lowland village of B., on a hot summer day that tenderly wrapped and steeped in its brightness the big peasant houses of the quiet side street, one of the greenpainted gates burst open suddenly and a boy of ten or twelve flew out of it in a wide arc. He turned two somersaults in the air, then lay stretched out on the ground with wide-spread arms. Behind him, the green-painted gate swung slowly to, its hinges squeaking cheerfully.

By the time the tiny clouds of dust had settled around the small body lying on the ground and the young acacia tree it had hit tilted back to its original graceful position, a fair-haired little girl had scrambled out of the roadside ditch, walked up to the sprawling boy and squatted down by his head.

'They kicked you out?'

The boy made no reply.

'So they kicked you out,' the little girl repeated wagging her head.

The boy lifted his hand above his face and in the precipitous sunshine examined his small, dirty fingers one by one.

'You noticed?' he murmured.

'You nearly uprooted that tree,' said the little girl looking at the acacia tree; its feathery shadows were still vibrating on the shimmering dust-carpet of the street.

'Why did they kick you out? Did you pinch something?'

'Shut up!' the boy growled.

For a moment the little girl gazed silently in front of her, then she lifted her hand and slapped the boy quickly. Then, like a little frog, she jumped away. After two or three jumps she stopped and, her head tilted, glanced back curiously. The boy hadn't moved.

'You can add that to the others, you worm!' the little girl said. 'And next time you are cheeky I'll stamp on you like an old shoe. You aren't worth a rotten fig! You don't get on with the peasants, you are kicked out of every house, and you are cheeky into the bargain.'

The boy sat up, beat the dust from his long, black hair with his palm, then suddenly, he burst into tears.

'You've got a dirtier mouth than my mother and she was bad enough,' he sniffled, wiping away his tears. 'A lot of comfort you are—all you can do is scold.'

'Shut your trap!' the little girl said.

The boy got to his knees and explored his back and hipbones with both hands.

'You don't even ask me if I'm hurt,' he said plaintively.

The little girl rose from her squatting position—they were of the same height—and looked him up and down contemptuously.

'Who cares?' she said curtly, 'I jumped out of a first-floor window once and nothing happened except that I limped for a week. There's nothing to whine about. Little worms like us don't get hurt. Wait till we grow up.'

Another tiny, fair head rose from the ditch.

'Can I come out?' the third child asked.

He seemed somewhat shorter than the other two and a year or two younger, but his face was clean as if a woman's hand had washed it.

'Shall I bring the luggage?' he asked.

The little girl turned to him immediately, her thin, freckled face with the two precocious, flashing dark eyes suddenly softened and filled with a rush of tenderness. In a second, as if the wind had blown her there, she stood beside the ditch.

'Are you hungry, Johnny?' she asked.

'Not very hungry yet,' the small boy replied.

The little girl wiped the child's nose with her skirt.

'Then leave the luggage where it is, we'll try another house or two.'

'Shall I go?' Johnny asked.

'Certainly not!' the little girl said. 'That dog-catcher hasn't earned a bean today.' She bent to the ear of the small boy. 'Cross my heart, I wouldn't mind if they caught him,' she whispered her forehead turning suddenly red, 'he hasn't got any more sense than a plate of tripe. Look at him brushing his hair!'

The unpaved, dusty street ran between two rows of bushy-topped acacia trees which, bending close, like the two blades of a pair of scissors, caught between them the brilliant summery horizon. There wasn't a soul on the pavements, nor a cart in the road, not a single hen scratched about along the fences. When, at times, a lazy little breeze flitted among the trees it caused such a cloud of dust that it lingered for the next hour. The arid heat swallowed up every sound, even the tiny crackle of the cow-dung drying in the middle of the road. There was so little shadow left in the street that it would have found room under the wing of a sparrow.

'Johnny, let's go on,' the little girl said, jumping with her two quick, bare feet into the ditch. 'This street is no good, it isn't worth a horse dropping.

Peter!' she called out to the dark, long-haired boy who stood leaning his back against the acacia tree and staring in front of him darkly, frowning, 'We are going on, pick up the traps!'

'Not me,' the boy growled. 'My shoulder hurts.'

The little girl threw back her head.

'Dirty fascist,' she said.

'They broke my shoulder!'

'They broke your nut!' the little girl cried in her fresh, ringing voice that spattered so coolly on the dusty, June ground, like a jet of cold water. 'If you don't come here at once I'll squash both your shoulders as if you were a bug!'

The three children trudged along the deserted street, one behind the other. Johnny walked in front. On one shoulder he carried a big overstuffed rucksack made of camouflage material that bumped against the backs of his knees, from the other a pair of huge leather slippers hung on a long string; he had covered his fair hair against sun and dust with a red scarf. Peter, walking behind him, balanced a green patched rucksack on his back, round his neck he carried the wire noose with which, after dark, he was wont to strangle any dogs and cats that came his way. His elbows stuck out from his torn shirt, his knees from his trousers. Behind the two of them walked the little girl, also with a full ruck-sack on her shoulder from the mouth of which a long wooden spoon stuck out. She swung a birch-rod in her hand and a full-blown poppy hung from her mouth. Neither spoke to the other, only Johnny, walking in front, muttered to himself the way old women and children wrangle, echoless, with their own loneliness.

Round the corner of the next crossroads a red brick Lutheran church loomed above the one-storey houses and a large, open area became visible beyond the mouth of the street.

'Turn in here, Johnny,' cried the little girl from behind. This street was also completely deserted, only a slowly descending cloud of dust showed that a dog must have run across the road a short while back. In the middle of the yellow lawn in front of the church a lonely sumac stood playing with its shadow. Further on, on the edge of the lawn, a broken rusty tank squatted on its wheelless axles; Johnny spat on it as he walked by. Peter stopped and examined it, but there was nothing left to strip off.

'Johnny, aren't you hungry?' the little girl cried from behind.

'Why shouldn't I be?' the child said.

'Do you want some cherries?'

The child frowned.

'If there are any maggoty ones,' he said after deliberating, 'I'll have them.'

The little girl ran forward. From the pocket of her skirt she palmed a handful of salmon-red cherries into the little boy's hand. The boy glanced at them suspiciously.

'I don't want them,' he said. 'They aren't maggoty.'

'You can still eat them,' the little girl murmured.

The boy made a face.

'I won't,' he said. 'I don't like them empty. Give them to Peter.'

A peasant in top-boots advanced towards them; he was there before them as suddenly as if he had risen out of the sun-warmed dust. He had a tiny, fair moustache, shaved closely on both sides, a vest and a blue flannel shirt and he carried a small basket, tied in a red kerchief, in his hand. The moment he reached Peter he stopped in his tracks and muttered an oath.

'Johnny, run!' the little girl screamed a second later.

The child looked back, then jumped into the air and broke into a run. Peter was too late; his long, black hair was caught in the peasant's hand. The little girl ran towards the other end of the street but as soon as she reached the opposite pavement she turned and tore back like the wind.

'Leave go of him!' she shouted, panting. Peter was sitting on the ground, the peasant had wound his long hair around his hand like a hemp-rope.

'I've caught you, you dirty scamp,' he growled, reaching with his right hand for the little girl who jumped up and down around him like a mother hen, defending her chickens, round a cat. The basket in its red kerchief sat in the dust a few feet away.

'Leave go of him!' the girl screeched, 'because if you don't I'll bring down the whole street on you, you filthy butcher! Let him go, do you hear? Or do you want us to pay for that horrible sour soup you gave us for supper last night? God will punish you, you sweaty-head, you won't die in your bed, don't count on it. . .'

The peasant pulled his hand out of Peter's rucksack and made a grab for her but by then the little girl was dancing behind his back.

'Let him go, you Hitler-moustache!' she screamed bringing the birch-rod down on the peasant's back. 'Aren't you ashamed to attack three fatherless-motherless orphans who earn their own living? Look how skinny we are, you pot-bellied swine! I bet you have bacon for breakfast, you grunting pig!

The man couldn't run after her without letting go of Peter's hair who sat motionless, in a heap on the ground. He reached back with his hand but by then the little girl was swinging her skirt at the other side of him.

'Give back what you stole from me!' the peasant growled, his face bloated and blood-red.

'Filthy capitalist!' cried the little girl jumping back.

Big drops of sweat gleamed on both sides of the peasant's moustache. Sticking out her tiny behind the little girl bent forward mockingly.

'Melon-head!' she shouted in her crystal clear, sharp voice, 'Brood animal! Shit-on-the-ground! Big brute!'

The peasant looked at Peter sitting at his feet and with a jerk pulled him up by his hair.

'Let him go!' the little girl screamed at him, 'May your mother never speak to you again if you don't let him go!'

'What did you say?' the peasant growled and again he dug into Peter's rucksack. 'Give me back what you stole from me!'

The bells of the Lutheran church behind them were chiming midday; each chime churned up a little dust on the roofs of the houses and mixed it imperceptibly with the sunlight which then—like the pink cheeks of a bride under her veil—momentarily lost its colour and brillance. A cart came clanking towards them from the end of the street with two skinny cows harnessed to its pole. The little girl threw a quick glance backwards, then she brought the birch rod down hard on the peasant's snatching hand.

'What do you want us to give you back?' she cried. 'The dollars? We've torn them up and thrown them away long ago. If we tell the police that we found dollars in your bed they'll keep you in prison until you go mouldy. You can bet your life the police wouldn't do anything to an orphan like me whose father and mother were taken away by the fascists! Only yesterday I sat on the sergeant's knee; he even gave me a cigarette!'

The boy sitting on the ground began unexpectedly to moan and whine. As if driven out of her mind by the sound the little girl leapt forward, her head bent, caught the man's hand and bit it with all her strength. A second later Peter was galloping away on the other side of the street while the peasant, swearing loudly, his face distorted with pain, ran in pursuit of the little girl. But in spite of the rucksack dancing on her back she raced along with such speed that the clumsy and heavily limping man soon lost sight of her.

Even as she ran the little girl kept her eyes peeled. She was not scared, her heart beat faster only from the strain put upon it by her speed, her fair hair fluttered gaily out behind her. She watched both pavements carefully and had enough presence of mind left to dispatch a cherry from her pocket to her dried-out mouth. A few minutes later she caught sight of Johnny in a distant doorway with the red kerchief, winking from afar, on his head.

'This way, Tutyu!' the little boy shouted waving both arms wildly.

The little girl glanced behind her but her pursuer had submerged behind the dust.

'Here, hide in this doorway!' the child cried. 'Where's Peter?'

'I saved him,' the little girl panted.

'How?'

'I bit the peasant.'

Johnny stared with round, shining eyes into the little girl's freckled face.

'Where did you bite him?'

'In the throat,' the little girl said. 'I bit through his throat.'

'Did it bleed much?' Johnny asked. 'How much blood came out of it? . . . Ten litres? . . . Why isn't your mouth bloody?'

'I wiped it,' the little girl said. 'But inside it is still red. Can you see it?'

She opened her mouth, the little boy tilted his head to one side and inspected it carefully.

'It isn't very red,' he said in a disappointed voice after a while. 'A dog bit me once and I bit back but it stank and my mouth was all full of hair.'

They met Peter an hour later at the Market place where they were holding a National Fair on that very day.

'You dog-catcher,' the little girl said. 'I nearly got caught because of you!'

'Because of me?'

The little girl nodded angrily.

'Didn't he have you by the hair?'

Peter flushed with fury.

'Wait till I have you by the hair,' he cried stamping his feet. 'I don't need your help, I can do all right without you! Don't you pick on me!'

'The devil picks on you,' the little girl said and turned away.

There were many people in the market but there was little to buy. The towns-women sat side by side in a long row with the sad leftovers of their households displayed at their feet, here and there among them a few peasant women caught the eye with a variety of junk, cherries, vegetables and cottage cheese in their baskets. Nobler products, eggs, bacon, poultry, were offered for sale only by those who wanted to settle their bank loans with the price of a pair of chickens or exchange twenty five eggs for a suit of clothes. In keeping with the slow supply, business was only just limping along and grew livelier only on the edge of the market, behind the backs of the stallholders; here a few showpeople had set up their tents who would let you in even for money.

The three children stopped at one of the tents. It was a big one, made of camouflaged canvas, with a narrow wooden platform in front of it and a tiny box-office also built of boards. On the facade of the tent, in red letters on a black background, stood: BLOODY ADVENTURES OF THE PORTUGUESE PRINCESS.

'We're going in,' Peter said. Johnny held on tight to the little girl's hand.

The Portuguese king sat on the platform with long, grass-green hair streaming down to his shoulders from under his golden crown. His brows were also green in his aristocratically pale face and sombre corals, the colour of blood, hung from his ears on silver chains. His nose was somewhat fleshy and decorated with a few warts.

'That's the king,' the little girl explained.

'What kind of dress is he wearing?' Johnny equired.

The little girl examined the costume closely.

'I don't know,' she said. 'A royal dress. The kind my sister wore when men came to see her at night.'

The child regarded the royal costume with awe. They were standing in the first row, a large crowd was pressing forward behind them, curious but close-fisted. There was hardly any sound except the stamping of feet in the soft dust, a suppressed fidgeting and, from far away, the organ of the merry-go-round. But in the eyes of some of the younger spectators the Portuguese king grew immense and flashed like a diamond.

'What is he doing out here now?' Johnny asked. 'Ruling?'

The king's ear must have caught the question because he threw a furious glance at the child who, frightened, drew closer to the little girl.

'No,' she said, 'he can rule only inside, in the tent. There he is master over life and death, he can even have people beheaded if he wants to.'

'Us too?'

'Yes,' the little girl whispered, 'if we go in, us too. But out here the police won't let him.'

'Let's go in,' Johnny said, turning pale.

'Will you pay? ' Peter asked the little girl.

At that moment the executioner appeared behind the king on the platform. He wore a blood-red coat with black buttons, red jersey pants ran down his spindly legs all the way to his red shoes, with curly tips like Venetian gondolas. He leaned with both hands on a blood-smudged, gold-hilted sword; the broad blade flashed in the sunshine as if it were interpreting for the people cruel and poetic messages from a distant heavenly body. Also the executioner's face was transcendentally pale and evil; in keeping with the rules of his craft he wore a big black beard which was moth-eaten in several places.

'Isn't he ugly!' a female voice exclaimed. Peter gave a frightened gasp and held on with both hands to the wooden platform. The people shifted their weight from one foot to the other in their amazement, someone dropped his cane.

'What does he have in his hand?' Johnny asked.

'A sword,' the little girl explained. 'He cuts people's heads off with a sword.'

'Why doesn't he make the king give him a sub-machine-gun?' Peter asked. 'You can work much faster with that.'

The little girl shrugged her shoulders.

'It's expensive,' she said. 'He probably doesn't have enough money. Besides, this looks better.'

'That's true,' Peter said biting his lips with excitement. 'Still, when I have money I'll buy a sub-machine-gun. With that you can liquidate a whole village in half an hour.'

The flap of the tent parted for a moment and out stepped a man in shirt-sleeves, with a top hat on his head and a red-ribboned drum resting on his belly. He had very long white fingers that worked the drumsticks with extraordinary speed. Immediately the throng turned to him and the cheerful quarrelsome rat-a-tat of the drum attracted people from the other, shadier side of the square as well. A Russian soldier stopped in front of the tent, tilted his cap back on his head and submitted the actors to careful scrutiny.

'Walk up, walk up,' the drummer cried, putting a temporary stop to his precise and playful dialogue with the drum. He spoke with a foreign accent which dressed his words in a guise as attractive and exciting as that worn by the king and the executioner; the king's scarlet cape which, in its off moments looked like a woman's dressing gown, blazed up suddenly as if ignited by the light out of the foreign-sounding words.

'Walk up, ladies and gentlemen,' cried the drummer from under his top-hat, 'come and see the bloody adventures of the Portuguese princess, based on historical data, word for word just as they happened in the sixteenth century, with the original cast. The performance begins right away. This is the only stage that offers real art because we are acting this historical event on the basis of original documents and the young lady playing the Portuguese princess is even more beautiful than the original as everyone can establish from contemporary photographs. The king is played by Don Basilio, the most famous actor in the world, entirely free of charge, moved by his selfless enthusiasm for art. As for the executioner, he is not an actor, ladies and gentlemen, but a genuine executioner, whom we won away from the royal court of England after his five hundredth execution. As you can see, our performance surpasses reality in its historical authenticity, a hall-mark of real art. Walk up, ladies and gentlemen, we shall make an exception and accept cash which, in these days, is also a unique opportunity in its way. An egg per head will be accepted instead of cash for the Portuguese princess.'

The drummer resumed drumming with devilish speed, then the flaps parted again and another man in a top-hat stepped out onto the platform. He lifted a huge brass trumpet to his lips and blew so hard that the thunder-and-lightning tones made an old woman's nose bleed and the sparrows, bathing in the dust of the market-place flew off terrified in all directions. Several people made their way towards the box office.

'Are you going to treat us?' Peter asked in a shaky voice and shook his long black hair.

Johnny squeezed the hand of the little girl who turned pale with excitement.

'How much is a ticket?' she asked.

'Five million,'* Peter, who could read, replied.

All three fell silent.

'It isn't much,' Johnny remarked after a while. 'Go on, fork out. We've done enough today.'

The throng stamped about enthusiastically in front of the box-office. A lad counted down banknotes on the sill of the narrow window with the anxious seriousness of a dog relieving himself. Behind him stood three peasant girls in starched skirts, shyly smiling; one of them wouldn't raise her eyes from the ground. Some paid in eggs or a little tobacco, and one old woman commuted art's levy for herself and her grandson into a pound of white bread.

'Where's the Princess?' a voice shouted in the background. 'Why don't you show her as well?'

The drummer pointed behind him with one of his drumsticks.

'The Princess won't show herself free of charge,' he cried in his impressive accent. The king, on the platform, broke into uproarious laughter. The crumbly sounds of gipsy music floated towards them from behind the whirling dust.

Holding on tight to each other the three children approached the box-office.

'Please let us go in for nothing,' the little girl said. A fat, yellow-haired woman sat behind the window.

'No,' the woman said.

'Please, let us in,' the little girl begged in a sing-song voice, 'we are orphans, everyone lets us in free.'

'No,' the woman said.

---

*After the war there was a serious inflation

The little girl raised herself on tiptoe.

'If the king acts free of charge,' she said, 'you could let us in free of charge too.'

'No,' the woman said for the third time. A red-cheeked peasant woman in a black shawl holding a scrubbed-faced, freckled child in her arms stood behind the children.

'Let one in,' she suggested, 'so it can tell the others about it.'

The cashier shook her head in silence. The drummer released the running-belt of drumming. Peter took hold of the box-office window and shook it with all his might.

'I want to go in, lady!' he cried, his eyes overflowing with tears, 'please, let me go in!'

As the people behind them were getting restive, the little girl reached into her bosom and pulled out a large man's wallet from which she picked a sheaf of carefully folded bank-notes. She put them down on the window sill.

'How much is that?' she asked. 'Is it enough yet?'

'What's that in your hand?' the cashier asked. 'Let me see!'

'Dollars,' the little girl said. 'A five dollar note.'

The lady held out her hand.

'Give it here!'

The little girl deliberated for a while, then held out the banknote. 'But you'll let all three of us in?' she asked.

Inside the tent it was dark, only through the slits in the canvas did blade-sharp beams of light stab in, revealing here the back of a chair, there a pale, moustachioed male face. The outlines of objects emerged slowly, reluctantly, from the solemn sawdust-smelling obscurity as if they had grown tired of exploiting human bodies and wanted to be left alone. After several jerky attempts, the curtain opened.

The Portuguese King sat on his golden throne in the left corner of the stage, dipping his thick feet in the scarlet cushions of the foot-stool. From the other corner of the stage a Knight, clad in black from top to toe and with a black plume on his helmet sped forward rattling his sword. In the background, through the wide open door, the park of the royal castle became visible, with an avenue of palms running straight towards the brilliant blue sea. At least a hundred palms stood one behind the other, growing smaller in the distance, but even the smallest was sharply separated from the others in the wonderful shell-blue light, and the avenue was so long that it would take at least half an hour to reach the shore, even on horseback.

'God almighty,' a deep, amazed voice said.

A female figure, walking along dreamily, appeared among the palms, one could see her slowly approaching the castle. At first she was no bigger than a thumb and yet one could clearly distinguish her nail-sized face with the tiny mouth, nose, eyes, and the brown hair streaming down to her shoulders. On her head she wore a thimble-sized green crown. Advancing slowly she grew larger and larger until, at last, she entered the door, life-size and smiling.

'It's the Princess,' the little girl whispered.

'But she isn't bloody!' said Johnny.

'Not yet,' she whispered back, 'she will be later.'

The audience was completely enthralled by the resplendence of the alien maritime landscape; there wasn't enough movement even to shake a cobweb. In the distance, diminutive sailing ships rocked on the tousled, sparkling sea, the sails whipped around like the corners of a handkerchief. Microscopic sailors sunned themselves on the miniature decks, under match-stick masts. By now the Princess was standing by the throne. She was so beautiful that the little girl felt her heart contracting.

'What language are they speaking?' Peter asked. 'German?'

The little girl shrugged, she didn't feel like answering. Johnny was watching with his whole body, bent forward in his seat, his fist pressed to his lips.

'What language are they talking?'

'Shut-up!' Johnny whispered beside himself, 'Portuguese!'

'Why not Hungarian?'

'It wouldn't be so beautiful . . .' the little girl panted.

The conversation between the King and the Knight obviously concerned the Princess who stood trembling by the throne in her wheat-coloured dress. The two great men were eating from a large golden tray.

'Just look at that, they're eating sausage!' exclaimed a surprised voice behind the children. And indeed, the King was holding a long sausage between his fat fingers. At the sight of the familiar food the whole audience drew a relieved breath.

'It isn't true,' Johnny whispered, 'it isn't sausage!'

'What then?'

'A banana.'

The little girl gave the child a grateful look.

'You're right,' she confirmed, 'banana. One eats only bananas and birds from a golden plate.'

'What birds?'

'Eagles, and ostriches, and suchlike,' the little girl said.

The Black Knight asked the Princess to marry him but she only stamped the ground with her gold slippers and turned angrily away. So the good King, though he was sorry, refused the suitor who hit his sword, threatened the king with his fist, then departed swearing. The Princess blew her little nose into a reseda-coloured handkerchief. The curtain was drawn.

It grew dark again in the tent, people began to fidget in their seats but nobody felt like talking. Here and there a young couple would exchange a few whispers, boots creaked, the older peasant lads stared woodenly at the curtain. The little girl sat frowning, gazing quietly before her, like someone watching a dream taking shape beyond space and filtering it into life; her facial muscles tensed, her large, serious dark eyes shone ecstatically and her toes curled in tensely. The actors performed with such unequivocal, clear gestures that there was no need for the explanatory ribbons of words; every movement they made spoke straight to her excitedly thumping heart. Her back was covered in goose pimples, her little stomach and thighs in sweat. She became aware of the two boys only when the curtain parted again and Johnny moaned with happiness.

When the second act began the sun was still shining, the King sat on his throne sleeping. He slept in Hungarian, his snores were intelligible to all. The Princess was again walking among the palms.

'It smells good,' Johnny whispered, 'it must be the smell of those trees.'

'It isn't,' Peter corrected him, 'it's the sea.'

'How do you know?'

'I've been on the sea,' the boy informed him. Johnny groaned and tugged at the little girl's dress plaintively.

'He is lying again,' he whispered. 'Only Jews travel on the sea, isn't that right?'

'Look!' the little girl said excitedly.

Beyond the Princess, deep within the avenue of palms, a tiny black shadow fell on the road and then, from behind a distant minute palm, the Black Knight emerged on tiptoe. It was obvious that he was planning to abduct the Princess but for the time being, because of the distance between them, he seemed less than half as tall as the lady. His black armour gleamed like the wing of a fly.

'Look out, he is coming!' Johnny exclaimed half aloud. 'He is coming fast!'

The little girl clasped his hand in hers. 'She doesn't notice!'

Peter jumped up from his seat. 'I should hope not!'

'Why?'

'Let him abduct her!' hissed the long-haired boy viciously, 'Let him abduct her!'

In her excitement the little girl pressed her hand to her stomach. Johnny rose.

'If she reaches the castle in time her daddy will protect her.'

'She won't reach it,' Peter muttered, 'she won't reach it, she won't reach it! He is coming fast as hell!'

'And she still hasn't noticed him!' Johnny complained.

The little girl emitted a little scream then, pressing her palm on her lips, she too rose from her seat.

'He's got her!' Peter growled between his clenched teeth. 'By the hair! Hold her by the hair! Put your hand over her mouth!'

The audience sat in petrified silence.

'Mr. King, wake up!' Johnny shouted at the top of his voice. The little girl, pale as death, pulled him down on his chair and held his hand tight.

'You mustn't shout!' she whispered bending to the boy's ear. 'You'd protect me . . . you would, wouldn't you, if someone tried to abduct me?'

In the distance, in the shell-coloured light, a somewhat larger ship appeared among the white schooners, with blood-red sails and gleaming brass cannons on its deck. It glided towards the shore, swift as the wind, growing rapidly as it advanced until its pirate flag with skull and crossbones covered the whole blue sky. As soon as it reached the shore, an ant-sized human figure jumped from the deck.

'Who is that?' Johnny asked.

The little girl shook her head. As there were no sea pirates in the lowlands, no one for the moment could answer his question.

'Perhaps it's Horthy,' Johnny whispered uncertainly, 'he goes everywhere by boat!'

The Pirate had a long, fair moustache and long, fair hair just like the Princess. He drew his sword with a movement so proud that the blood froze in the audience's veins. The duel was fought at the foot of the first palm tree, immediately in front of the castle gate; the little red lips of the trembling Princess were sealed with a black kerchief and inside, in the throne room, the good King snored stertorously, untroubled. The blades clashed like eagles' wings.

'Kill him, blackie!' Peter cried.

Now one retreated, now the other, the children stamped their feet, their faces livid, their nostrils quivering.

'Jesus Christ, save me,' the little girl prayed silently. If the Black Knight wins she is lost, she thought.

On her left Johnny wheezed like a threshing machine, on her right Peter beat the back of the fat peasant woman sitting before him with his fist.

'Go on, blackie, kill him!' he shouted uninterruptedly; he was frothing at the mouth.

The little girl began to cry:

'What a wicked boy you are,' she told him and closed her eyes.

After a while she had to shut them again: when the executioner dragged the Black Knight to the scaffold and then, in full sight of the audience, cut his head off with his broad sword. Before his execution the Black Knight raised his index finger, rattled his chains and laughed like a devil.

'Wham,' said Johnny, 'he's cut it off. Like a chicken. Why are you shutting your eyes?'

The little girl opened one eye and stole a glance at the castle, the good King was watching the execution from his throne and drinking wine from a bejewelled chalice. The huge red globe of the setting sun hovered close above the surface of the sea and steeped the slender avenue and the friendly throne room in the colour of blood.

'Look, the executioner is swinging the head!' Johnny said. 'Bam, now he's thrown it into a basket.'

'Is he no longer alive?' the little girl asked, her eyes still shut.

'No,' Johnny said, 'he fell behind the table. Only his feet are sticking out.'

The little girl took a deep breath and let go the arm of the chair. Peter was sitting at her side humped, his elbows on his knees, gazing before him with dull eyes. The little girl turned her eyes away stiffly. She looked closely at Johnny: the boy's pale face was flushed, his eyes shone with tears, his upper lip had grown wet with all the excitement. The little girl wiped it with her skirt and kissed him, and her heart swelled with great courage.

Up there, in the throne room, the last big scene was unfolding. The good King forgave the Pirate his innumerable crimes. He took him by the hand, led him to the Princess, and put their hands into each other's. The Princess smiled shyly. The palms swayed gently in the evening breeze dropping small dates onto the pebbles of the walk. The Pirate . . .

The little girl cried out in pain.

'What is he doing?' she whispered pressing both small fists on her heart. 'What's the matter with him?'

The two boys were also watching these events uncomprehendingly. The Pirate stepped back, bowed deeply before the Princess, then, straightened up and shook his head vigorously.

'Why is he shaking his head?' Johnny asked.

'He is shaking his forefinger as well!'

Peter stiffened. 'Doesn't he want the skirt?'

'Is he ill?' the little girl asked, panting.

Again all three jumped up from their seats.

'He must be ill,' Johnny said, 'because he is beating his heart.'

'But why is he pointing to the sea?' the little girl whispered.

'He is pointing to his ship.'

'That isn't true,' Peter said, 'it isn't his ship, he is pointing to the whole sea, look how he waves his arm.'

'And now he is pointing at the sun!' Johnny cried.

The little girl's mouth filled with saliva, her knees tingled.

'He doesn't want the Princess,' she stammered in a dying voice and big tears sprang to her eyes.

'Well, what does he want?'

'The sea,' said Johnny. 'He doesn't want to sit at home all the time in a big stone castle.'

'Is that why he keeps slapping his chest?'

'Hell . . .' Peter growled discontentedly, 'what is he doing now? He has spread his arms wide and is looking up to the sky.'

'He'll fly away!' Johnny cried excitedly.

'Where to?'

'Far away! . . . To the negroes.'

The little girl sank back, exhausted. She did not believe that the beautiful, wavy-haired, fair Pirate would take to wings and fly away but she did see that he wanted to be his own master.

'You can see now,' Peter whispered gloatingly, bunching his fists with anger, 'it was a pity to execute the Black Knight. What did they gain by it? Damn all! . . .'

Once more the Pirate pressed his hand to his heart then, waving his hat, he marched away towards the distant home of freedom! The Princess's tiny reseda-coloured hankerchief fluttered after him like a chained butterfly. A moment later the departing figure disappeared in the golden dust of the sun. The curtain closed.

'There you are,' a thick voice said, 'he showed her!'

Shuffling, people were slowly getting ready to leave. Their palms were wet, their feet leaden, the cold ashes of snuffed-out excitement settled on their hearts. Robust terrestrial light and dust streamed in through the open flap of the tent. The women blinked, the men cleared their throats. The three children remained last under the overheated canvas, fumbling with their rucksacks and staring at the impenetrable green velvet curtain. Coming out of the tent they stopped for a moment; in the strong sunshine the wide market-place appeared immense and stupid, the air was lustreless, the acacia trees disorderly, Hungarian words flat. They tramped on side by side silently, their eyes on the ground.

'Where are we going?' Peter asked.

'We are getting out of this town.'

'Fine,' Johnny said. 'Do you know the way?'

'We go where the wind blows,' the little girl said.

The street ran straight toward the railway station, then, skirting it where the warehouses stood, opened, at the turnpike, onto the high street. It was a concrete road, its accumulated heat burned one's bare soles.

'Put on your sandals,' the little girl told Johnny.

'Tutyu,' he asked, 'have you ever been to the theatre?'

The little girl shook her head. 'That was the first time.'

'I've been,' Peter informed them.

'Where?'

'In Budapest,' the boy said. 'I went to the theatre every day there.'

Johnny looked at the little girl, she winked back at him. They understood each other. Neither replied to the long-haired boy; his fate was sealed.

'The Knight wasn't dead,' Peter said. 'When the blonde sailor was talking to the Princess, he moved his feet twice.'

A small, dusty whirl-wind rose before them, chasing its own tail like a dog. In the steep rays of the sun the black shadows of the poplars stood like puddles around the feet of the trees; the little girl dipped her foot into them.

'Don't you believe me?' Peter asked.

'No,' Johnny answered firmly.

Peter broke into an ugly laugh.

'Dope!' he said. 'If he had died who would act at the next performance? Eh, Tutyu?'

Half an hour later they reached a cross-roads one corner of which was decorated with a toppled crucifix and a rusting German tank. The little girl stopped by the tank.

'Aren't you talking to me?' Peter asked.

'No,' the little girl said.

'Why not?' asked the long-haired boy.

The little girl's eyes suddenly narrowed, her forehead turned old.

'This is where we part,' she said curtly.

'Who?'

'We . . . from you!'

'How come?'

'We don't need you,' the little girl said.

The boy stared rigidly before him, his long black hair fell over one eye.

'You don't need me?' he repeated unbelievingly. 'Why don't you need me?'

The little girl swung her birch rod.

'You are just as evil as the Knight,' she said in a toneless voice. 'You have strangled three dogs since we've been together. I don't want anyone like you.'

Peter turned livid with fury.

'And you thought of this today?' he screeched, 'on this blessed day? Why today of all days?'

'I don't know,' the little girl said. 'I've just decided.'

They stared at each other silently. The boy's lower lip shook, he turned blue with anger, the wire loop around his neck threatened to snap.

'We blew all our money this afternoon and there's nothing else to share, right? Get going, worm!'

'Go to hell,' Peter said making a face. 'You're not serious, are you?'

'I am ,' the little girl said.

Peter began to swear. He swore so filthily that Johnny blushed with shame. The little girl listened in silence.

'I won't beat you up,' she said, 'because you don't belong to us any longer. But get going now!'

Johnny and she waited at the shot-up tank until Peter's rapidly diminishing figure with the swollen rucksack on its back disappeared behind the dust. Johnny was chewing a piece of dry bread indifferently, the little girl brought out a comb and a brush from her rucksack and combed the boy's hair. They then took each other by the hand and set out.

'Was the Princess more beautiful than me?' the little girl asked.

'Much more beautiful,' Johnny said firmly.

The little girl meditated for a while.

'She had beautiful big breasts,' Johnny explained,' and you haven't got any. In her ears she had diamonds as big as eggs, there wasn't a single freckle on her nose, and her dress was all silk and velvet.'

'Then it's all right,' the little girl said, relieved, 'then it wasn't me, after all.'

Johnny laughed loudly, heartily.

'Of course it wasn't you!' he laughed. 'Your legs are dirty and hers were as white and lovely as cotton wool.'

'Did you see those tiny sailors on the ship?' the little girl asked. 'All of them would have served her.'

'There were Chinese among them and Russians and French,' Johnny hummed. 'And negroes. And they had a soccer team, too.'

'On the ship?'

'Yes,' Johnny said. 'Between the masts there was a little football pitch and that's where they played with a tiny golden ball.'

The little girl looked out over the fields burned yellow by the sun; there was not a single soul in sight for miles. For a while she dug around in her pocket absent-mindedly, then she took a cigarette from a tin box and a brass lighter and lit the cigarette.

There was a golden bird on top of one of the masts. It sang,' she said blowing ribbons of smoke from her snub nose.

Johnny nodded.

'I heard it,' he said. 'The centre-half was Hungarian.'

They advanced slowly, comfortably, the wind kicked up tiny clouds of dust before them.

'A big red, crested fish swam round the ship,' Johnny said, 'and when the ball fell into the water he threw it back.'

'It was a Persian chin-chin fish,' the little girl said drawing on her cigarette.

Her thin, little freckled face was serious and passionate like a child's at a feast. The rucksack had bruised her shoulder but apart from that she didn't feel her body; though she didn't know it herself, she was busy reforming the world. Between two rows of whispering poplars the road ran straight as an arrow towards a fleecy cloud.

'Where are we going to sleep tonight?' Johnny asked.

'On the ship,' the little girl said.

'Fine,' the boy murmured. 'We'll sign up as sailors. Can I have a piece of bread?'

TIBOR DÉRY was born in 1894 in Budapest. For many years he lived outside his native country, in Czechoslovakia, Berlin and Vienna. In 1934 he returned to Hungary, but was not allowed to publish his first important novel *The Unfinished Sentence* there until after the war. A leading spokesman of the Hungarian 'Revisionist' writers, he was imprisoned for alleged 'anti-state activities' in 1957, and was released in 1961. The following books of Déry are now available in English: *Niki*, a short novel, *The Giant*, stories, and *The Portuguese Princess*, stories. This story will be included in a collection of the same title to be published by Quadrangle Books and Calder and Boyars (London) this year. KATHLEEN SZASZ is a translator living in London; she has translated many Hungarian authors into English, including Déry and Németh.

translated by Joy N. Humes

Witold Gombrowicz

K. A. JELEŃSKI

FERDYDURKE is a novel about immaturity and form. Man, Gombrowicz tells us, is an opaque and neuter being who must express himself through certain attitudes and poses and thus becomes for others much more defined than he is for himself. From this stems the tragic disproportion between his secret immaturity and the mask which he must don to deal with others. He ends in adapting inwardly to this mask, as if he really were what he appears to be. It is thus a question of two forms of immaturity, one innate and consubstantial with man, the other imposed from the outside—by others, by social conditions, by culture. The hero of *Ferdydurke*—a grotesque transposition of the author himself—is a man of thirty years who, "infantilized" by the terrible Professor Pimko, is forced to re-enter school, only to leave it for other adventures, always progressing further and further into this process of "immaturization." Instead of being themselves, the characters of the novel act as functions of diverse social myths, which Gombrowicz defines as ideas grafted onto the intimate reality of man (the myth of the stable boy, of the modern school girl, of the aunt, etc.). Hence the problem of sterotyped forms which run the gambit of human expression, engendering "styles" which do not correspond to any interior reality and which exert a determining influence one upon the other. The man of *Ferdydurke* is created by others, for according to Gombrowicz, men create themselves among themselves and impose forms, or what we might call, "ways of being" upon one another.

Is *Ferdydurke*, then, a novel? It seems to me rather an existential inquest and also a poem, from which stems its unique character. Like Sartre, and five years before *l'Etre et le Néant* (*Being and Nothingness*) Gombrowicz insists on the importance of the *moment,* on the potentialities of a sudden change in orientation, of a new position taken in regard to a past which cannot, in itself, change. I have found passages in *L' Etre et le Néant* which read like abstract formulations of certain existential themes in Gombrowicz. Thus: "Every act made against another may, necessarily, become for the other an instrument to be used against me." (See the two duels between Mientus and Siphon, Philifor and Anti-Philifor, the first of which is presented in the extract which follows this essay.) [1] Similarly, Sartre's *regard d'autrui* (the look of the other) and the famous phrase from *No Exit*, "Hell is other people," could serve as an exergue for *Ferdydurke*. One must not, however, exaggerate the intellectual significance of *Ferdydurke*. Today, thirty years after the publication of *Ferdydurke,* all these themes can be translated in terms of existential psychoanalysis, Marxism, behaviorism. What is unique in Gombrowicz is an anthropomorphic style which expresses abstract ideas in such a way as to make them painful and almost obscene. The role which the different parts of the body play in the work of Gombrowicz can hardly be overemphasized: hands, mouth, fingers, legs, all have in *Ferdydurke* a symbolic autonomy, while the essential mechanism of social life is summed up in the categories of "mug" and "bottom."

The *gueule* which the characters of *Ferdydurke* wear as an uncomfortable mask, which the hero is condemned to take with him in his ultimate flight, we too must wear at the slightest error in the direct expression of ourselves. The limits of translation weaken the Polish word, *pupa*, the fat pink bottom of the good bourgeois baby which man becomes in *Ferdydurke* under the pressure of social idealisms.

In his *Journal* Gombrowicz permits us a glimpse of his creative technique. On first inspiration, it seems to rest on automatic writing: "Enter into a waking dream. Begin to write whatever comes into your head." But Gombrowicz is not satisfied with such accidental poetry. After three successive drafts: ("You will perceive new associations which will more clearly define your field of action . . .") he will become aware of the obsessive current in the work: "Before you have realized it, you will have created certain key scenes, you will have in hand a free and symbolic structure—like the parts of the body in *Ferdydurke* ..." These parts, detached from the body, detached from being, particles of the universe, oscillate between the temptation of unity represented by crystallized form but always suspect of immaturity, and the temptation of green adolescence, budding, luxuriant and viscous. The terms, "adolescence" and "immaturity" have a significance for Gombrowicz which goes beyond the individual and is applicable to peoples and "minor" cultures, less definitively "formed" than the "adult" cultures. *Ferdydurke* is attached by an umbilical cord to the Poland that resembles him. Gombrowicz expresses this idea at the beginning of the book. "How, I wondered, had I become so subjected to, so fascinated by the green and the unripe? Perhaps because I was the native of a country in which collars do not suit anyone and the countryside is haunted by the lamentations of laziness and incompetence rather than those of a Chopinian melancholy."[2] Perhaps this explains the paradox that although he emigrated in 1939 Gombrowicz is the greatest influence—even extra-literary influence—in Poland today.

This universal spirit has its origin in traits which are archetypically Polish. Gombrowicz comes out of that rich provincial nobility whose inconsistency and opacity he so effectively exposes in *Ferdydurke*. In revolt against his own class, without roots, he nevertheless draws his verbal richness from 18th century Poland, from the latinized Macaronics of his ancestors—senators drunk on Hungarian wine and "liberum veto." Gombrowicz' first book, *Memoirs from a Time of Immaturity*, was welcomed in 1933 with a mixture of astonishment and mis-

---

Translator's notes
[1]Philifor (representing Synthesis, or love of form) and Anti-Philifor (Disparity) are rival scholars who decide to settle their quarrel by a duel. The victims of the duel, however, are two non-combatants, the respective wives of the men, both of whom are killed.

[2]This passage appears in Jelenski's text in English translation by Eric Mosbacher.

trust. When, five years later, *Ferdydurke* appeared, it was a if a concrete block had been tossed into the tranquil waters of Polish "literary" literature. The controversies around *Ferdydurke* were impassioned: Gombrowicz seemed destined to be, if not the *poéte maudit*, at least the Eternal Outsider. When a weekly literary magazine asked Jaroslaw Iwaszkiewicz, in 1958, what Polish writer he most admired, he replied: "Gombrowicz," it was as if in the United States John Steinbeck should declare that William Burroughs was the greatest American writer.

A few days before the outbreak of war in 1939, Gombrowicz embarked for Argentina, where he has lived for twenty-five years in Buenos Aires. Thus a curious destiny seemed to condemn the hero of *Ferdydurke* to another "green" and indefinite world—that of Latin American, where he has earned his livelihood giving courses in philosophy in cafés, and so preserving the adolescence of genius in the mature man he had become.

The beginning of the Argentine experience, the drama of a far-off war, Polish emigration, all this led to the *Trans-Atlantic*, (published in 1953 in *Kultura*), a fantastic biography which grafts onto the South American baroque of 1940 a Polish super-baroque of the 18th century, culminating in a carnival in the streets of Buenos Aires. The work to which Gombrowicz himself attaches most importance is his poetic drama, *The Marriage* (also published in 1953). In it he again treats the principal problems of *Ferdydurke*: the problem of form, the eternal conflict of human content and form.

Who would have thought that *Ferdydurke*, this almost confidential work written for a thousand readers, a hundred fervent admirers, would penetrate into Poland and become an acting force there? Of a very limited edition, how many copies could have survived the destruction of Warsaw or the bonfires of public libraries under the Stalinist regime?

What struck me in the course of my first encounters, since 1955, with young Poles coming from Poland and belonging to the post-war generation, was the natural way they would use (with no reference to Gombrowicz) expressions taken from Ferdydurke, expressions which have passed into the daily language: "What a mug they gave us," "The whole country is assholed," "Rape (violation) by the ears."[3]

Mysterious diffusion of a book which has disappeared! The fact is that intellectual Poles recognized in *Ferdydurke* the image of their own situation in the face of that monstrous Sunday School which Stalinism was imposing upon them. In 1957, Jan Jozef Lipski, a young communist, in *Nowa Kultura*, told how at the end of a writers' conference during the Zhdanovian period he had, with his friends, re-read Ferdydurke. "This consoled us. Imbecility is immortal, it only changes in form, intensity, scale. But why isn't Gombrowicz among us here in Warsaw? Why can't he attend a meeting at the Institute of Literary

---

[3]The sense of these expressions, (Ils nous ont fait une gueule . . . le pays entier est cuculisé . . . le voil par les oreilles . . .) is the infantilization through the pressure of social idealisms—carried to the extreme by Stalinism.

Studies, listen to a speech at the Union of Socialist Youth, study the ideological training, the press conferences, the gala academic events? He would simply have to write without hope of being published (in the same way that Tacitus described the crimes of the Caesars.) What a great difference: the lessons of Rabougri and the powerful ideological machine of Stalinism. It's like the difference between a coffee mill and an atomic center. It is only with that Gombrowicz would be able to find his great theme."

The only contemporary Polish work to have acquired an international reputation, the work of Gombrowicz is firmly anchored in essentially Polish realities. It is not surprising that the action of his two other novels, *Pornography* and *Cosmos*, published respectively (in Polish) in 1960 and 1965, should be situated in that Poland which Gombrowicz has not seen since 1939.

Gombrowicz has thus contributed to the preservation of a sort of catharsis in Poland, determined by intelligence and humor. It is significant that *Ferdydurke* should have been republished in Poland a month after the political ferment of October 1956—and the edition sold out in two weeks. The reappearance of this work was greeted in a way which could hardly have failed to surprise Gombrowicz himself, spying on the literary game from behind a tree just as his hero in *Ferdydurke* spies on the games of his comrades. Gombrowicz, the predestined Outsider! The foremost Polish avant-garde critic, Arthur Sandauer, has written: "It is difficult to understand how a writer who is the glory of the Polish nation could have been so long condemned to exile." And in another of his critiques: "The work of Gombrowicz, considered an eccentricity before the war, today takes on the qualities of a triumph, unifying the Polish nation." One is reminded of the words of André Malraux: "It has happened, it happens, that artists are stoned by the good intentions of their defenders."

Ferdydurke is a revolt against immaturity, or rather against the social system which makes access to real maturity so difficult. Nevertheless, one sees in it the parallel cult of youth, of a freer, undetermined and "green" world. This evolution is accentuated as Gombrowicz himself becomes further removed from his own youth. That he himself is aware of the problem is shown in his *Journal*, as for example in this passage on the Retiro Park in Buenos Aires: "Youth appeared to me as the highest value in life ... but this 'value' has a peculiarity, no doubt invented by the Devil—being young it is beneath the level of any value." The same theme re-appears in *Pornography*. Immaturity is not always innate or imposed by others. There also exists an immaturity toward which we are pushed by the culture (society) when it engulfs us, when we don't manage to raise ourselves to its level. "We are infantilized," writes Gombrowicz, "by any superior form. Man, tormented by his mask, makes, secretly and for his own use, a subculture: a world constructed from the debris of the superior world of his society, the realm of trash, of childish myth, of unavowed passions, a secondary realm of compensation." It is there, Gombrowicz tells us, "that is born a certain shameful poetry, a certain compromising beauty."

One must not forget that Gombrowicz wrote in his Journal: *I do not believe in a non-erotic philosophy.* Eroticism is the base of his entire work, and his profound conception of the erotic is very close to that of George Bataille: it comprehends horror, degradation, death and—the only modern key to a time which is *sacré*[4]—it demands at least a counterfeit of the sacred. *Piety is ab-so-lute-ly and ri-gor-ous-ly demanded, even the smallest of little pleasures cannot do without piety*, says the terrible and derisive Léon in *Cosmos.* It would certainly be absurd to reduce *Ferdydurke* to homosexuality, *Pornography* to a "mise-en-scène" of the erotic, *Cosmos* to onanism. But in the genius of Gombrowicz, the most abstract ideas are expressed in relation to eroticism.

The narrator watches, in *Cosmos,* all the interworkings of the body. The hands, the mouths, the fingers, the legs which in *Ferdydurke* have a symbolic autonomy, are here otherwise examined, as if Gombrowicz had become conscious of what Freud had neglected: the participation of the body, of the whole body, in imaginative life; the correspondences which, obscurely and almost without our knowing it, are established within this misted zone between the physical and the psychic which is at the very base of our existence.

Even in Poland, Gombrowicz is always interpreted in terms of *Ferdydurke.* Thus, Gombrowicz is regarded as an explorer, investigating the themes of Superority/Inferiority, Maturity/Adolescence, Formal/Informal. These themes, apparently new in *Pornography* and *Cosmos,* are nevertheless already present in his first book of short stories, *Bakakaj,* published in 1933.[5] We find in it a nonexistent crime, the evidence of which is based on such clues as a dead louse, a rancid bit of butter. In another story, *Events on the Sailship Banbury,* the menacing reality is announced through certain "signs" which foreshadow *Cosmos: To tell the truth I avoid all conversation, for I feel that the design of the anchor of the great sailing ship is most uselessly curved in the form of an S. The letter S begins a word of my own invention which I should have preferred not to know. It is not just the anchor either. There are on this ship other forms, other disagreeable cracks and crevices.* Finally, and still in the same collection, *Virginity* is one of the most obscene texts that I know (with a Gombrowiczian obscenity which escapes censure). If *Pornography* and *Cosmos* are more grave in tone, more menacing than his first works, this is not alone due to the evolution of Gombrowicz' genius. There is in *Bakakaj* a juvenile humor, an insouciance which exorcizes the death which already, however, is oozing from every crevice and fault. This death, and the death of God, Gombrowicz now examines in "mortal" seriousness, while the everyday, the banal—which he deforms with such profound fidelity—while even the derision only serve, by contrast, to augment the gravity of the "Ceremony."

We have seen that Gombrowicz often hesitates between maturity and immaturity, between the role of *form* and the yet-undetermined world. One might risk the hypothesis that the conflict itself, and inside the conflict, the hesitations of the writer, stem from a certain lack of equilibrium: as adult as Gombrowicz may be intellectually, he seems to suffer from a psychic im-

---

[4] *sacré* may mean either "holy" or "damned". It is probably used here in both senses at once.
[5] It was republished in Warsaw in 1957.

maturity. In speaking about the intellectual maturity of Gombrowicz, I am not alluding, of course, to his sharp and original intelligence: as buoyant as this may be, it could very well lack maturity. I mean, rather, that Gombrowicz is capable of an astounding mimesis of psychic maturity—that he sees its "superiority," its necessity, in the work of human "salvation." It would have been easy for Gombrowicz to consider his work as a struggle for real maturity. But his intelligence has nothing exterior. It is the natural respiration of his entire being, and could not admit a false note. His enormous pride would not permit him, on the other hand, to pretend anything whatsoever. Thus—although the conflict between maturity and immaturity, between form and indetermination, remains the central motif of his work— we have an alternation of motifs. It is true that Gombrowicz has written: "No historic pressure will draw important words from men fixed in immaturity," but he is already tending toward something else: to cast in bronze his own immaturity, to fix his indecision, to set up his indetermination as an oracle. Such an enterprise—to take entire cognizance of one's own self, accepting full responsibility, to draw the ultimate consequences from that which one has chosen to be—always has an heroic aspect, and is familiar to us in poetry. Jean Genet used a similar method to impose the pederast, the thief, the traitor. But ordinarily it is a question of the sacralization of extreme passions, a form of black mythology. Gombrowicz' undertaking is new in the sense that he is trying to lead up to a paroxysm of those traits which are themselves opposed to paroxysm: "There is hardly any psychic position," he writes, "which, pushed to the extreme, does not command respect. Force can exist in weakness, security in indecision, coherence in inconsequence as well as grandeur in mediocrity; cowardice can be courageous, weakness as cutting as steel, and flight, aggressive."

This moral program of Gombrowicz leaves us perplexed. Is it a question of "pushing to paroxysm" a complex of traits opposed to form and maturity, or is it merely a question of becoming aware of them? In what concerns him personally, Gombrowicz leans toward the latter position: "I think I have shown by my own example that awareness of a 'lack'—lack of form, lack of evolution, immaturity—not only does not weaken, but may even give more strength." This "my own example" is linked to a heroic, poetic undertaking. Whatever Gombrowicz may think of himself, his work is neither "indeterminate" nor "un-evolved". In rejecting maturity and form Gombrowicz feels freer, but he cannot forget that he has only made, at the most, a particular transfer: in his work he tends—with what efficacy!—towards maturity and towards definitive form.

Note: This essay posed a triple problem. Jeleński quotes from the English translation of *Ferdydurke*, French translations of *Cosmos, Pornografia,* the *Journal*, etc. Since the original Polish texts were inaccessible, it has been necessary to rely, in the one case, on another translator's work, and in the other, on our own judgment. This fact explains whatever discrepancies of terminology exist between the Gombrowicz extract and the critical commentary.

FERDYDURKE: an excerpt

'Professor!'

'What is it?' Pimko replied, also in a whisper.

'Don't stay there, professor! They've written a bad word on the other side of the tree, and that's what they're laughing at. Don't stay there, professor!'

While talking this rubbish I felt myself to be the very high priest of idiocy. I was startled at what I found myself doing—muttering from behind the back of my hand to Pimko standing behind the tree in the school playground.

'What did you say?' the professor asked from behind his tree. 'What did they write?'

There was the sound of a motor-horn in the distance.

'A bad word!' I said. 'A bad word! Come out from there!'

'Where did they write it?'

'On the other side of the tree! Come out from there, prof, professor! That's enough! Don't let them make a fool of you! Sir, you tried to make them out to be naïve and innocent, and they've written a four-letter word.... Don't go on provoking them, professor, it's gone far enough. I can't go on talking into the air like this, professor, I shall go mad! Come out from there, please! I can't stand it any longer!'

While I said this summer declined slowly into autumn and the leaves fell silently.

'What's that?' the professor exclaimed. 'What's that? You expect me to doubt the youthful purity of the youthful generation? Never! In all matters of life and pedagogy I am an old fox.'

He came out from behind the tree, and the boys, seeing him standing there in the flesh, let out a yell.

'My dear young people,' he said after they had calmed down a little. 'I am not ignorant of the fact that among yourselves you use very coarse, indecent expressions. Don't imagine for a moment that I don't know what goes on. But you have no cause for anxiety. No excess, however lamentable in itself, will ever affect my profound belief that at bottom you are innocent and pure, and that is what you are to me. Your old friend will always believe you to be pure and innocent, and he will always have faith in your decency, your purity, your innocence; and, as for bad words, I know that you use them innocently, without understanding, just for effect—no doubt one of you picked them up from

From Witold Gombrowicz's *Ferdydurke*,
translated by Eric Mosbacher, Harcourt,
Brace & World, New York 1961.

his nurse. That's quite all right, there's no harm in it at all, it's far more innocent than you think!'

He sneezed, blew his nose and, feeling very pleased with himself, went off in the direction of the headmaster's study to talk about me to Mr. Piorkowski. Meanwhile the mothers and aunts on the other side of the fence flung themselves into each other's arms and exclaimed with delight:

'What wonderful ideas the professor has! What a wonderful faith in innocence!'

Among the boys, however, Pimko's speech caused consternation. Silently they watched him walk away; and it was not until he was out of sight that the storm broke.

'Did you hear that?' Mientus exclaimed. 'Did you hear that? We're innocent! Innocent! He thinks we're innocent! Whatever we do we're innocent! Innocent!'

The word was a thorn in his side; it paralyzed, tortured, killed him, imposing naïveté and innocence upon him. At this point a boy named Pylaszczkiewicz, but known to his intimates as Siphon, seemed to succumb to what had become the prevailing atmosphere of naïvete; he said to himself, but in a voice which resounded in the pure and limpid air as clearly as a cow-bell:

'Innocent? Why not?'

And he stood there plunged in thought. Why not, indeed, be innocent? He could not have asked a more sensible question. For who is more mature, he who flees from sin, or he who seeks it out? But the thought, though rational and mature, sounded innocent, and Siphon realized this himself, because he flushed.

He tried to slip away, but Mientus had heard what he said, and was not going to allow it to pass.

'What?' he said. 'You admit you're innocent?'

Mientus was so startled by the innocence of what he had just said that he stepped back. But now Siphon was upset too, and was not prepared to allow this remark to pass either.

'Admit it?' he said, 'Why shouldn't I admit it? I'm not a child!'

Mientus laughed sneeringly in the diaphanous air.

'Did you hear him?' he jeered. 'Siphon's innocent! Wah! Wah! Siphon the innocent!'

'*Siphonus innocentus!*' boys started calling out. 'Has our worthy Siphon no knowledge of women?'

Others took up the chorus of this green raillery, and the world became disgusting again. The growing hubbub infuriated Siphon. He glared all round.

'And even if I were innocent, what of it?' he exclaimed. 'What's it got to do with you?'

'So it's true, then!' they jeered back at him. 'So it's true!'

And the unhappy lads did not realize that the further they went, the more deeply they engulfed themselves in innocence.

'Would you believe it?' they sneered. 'He doesn't even know the facts of life!'

They started jeering and booing again.

'And even if I didn't, what business is it of yours?' Siphon burst out. 'What business is it of yours, I should like to know?'

There was such a strange, icy tone in his voice that for a moment they were intimidated, and silence prevailed. Then voices started calling out:

'Come off it, Siphon! So it's true that you don't know, is it?'

And they stepped back a pace. Siphon would obviously have liked to have stepped back too, but could not. Then Mientus called out:

'Of course it's true! Look at him! It's obvious!'

And he spat. Bobek called out:

'But that's disgraceful, he ought to be ashamed of himself. I'll tell you everything, Siphon, you really ought to know!'

Siphon: 'But I don't want to!'

Hopek: 'You don't want to?'

Siphon: 'I don't want to, because I don't see the necessity.'

Hopek: 'You don't want to? You don't want to? But it isn't just a matter of what you want or don't want, it's a matter that concerns all of us. It's not a situation we can be expected to tolerate. If we did, how could we ever look girls in the face again?'

'So that's what's getting you, is it?' Siphon burst out angrily. 'Girls! Girls! You want to cut a dash with the girls! I don't give a fig for your girls! So you want to be boys with the girls!'

He had realized that he could no longer retreat, and, moreover, he no longer wanted to.

'Girls!' he exclaimed. 'Girls! And why not decent girls? Why not adolescents and decent, respectable girls? So you want to be boys with the girls! Well, I like being an adolescent for decent girls. Why should I be ashamed of using words which are decent and honourable? Anyway, that's how it is, I want to be an adolescent for decent young women.'

He stopped. But what he said was in reality so true, sensible, and convincing that many of his listeners were left perplexed.

'Doesn't he speak well?' some of them said, and others remarked:

'He's quite right, purity is better than girls!'

'One ought to have some ideals, after all!' another pointed out, and someone else remarked:

'If he wants to be an adolescent, let him!'

'Adolescents!' Siphon announced. 'Up the adolescents! Let us found a society to preserve the purity of youth and oppose everything that soils it! Let us swear never to be ashamed of beauty, purity and nobility! Forward!'

And before anyone could stop him he raised his hand and swore a solemn oath, with a grave, inspired expression on his face. Several juveniles, surprised by his gesture, raised their hand and followed suit. Mientus rushed angrily at Siphon in the pure and transparent air; Siphon's blood was up too, but fortunately they were separated in time.

'Why don't you fellows kick his arse?' said Mientus, struggling with those who were restraining him. 'Have you no blood in your veins? Have you no ambition? Only a good kick in the arse can save you! Just let me get at him!'

He was in an ungovernable rage. Sweating and pale, I looked at him. I had had the shadow of a hope that with Pimko out of the way I might somehow manage to recover my adult personality and explain myself in everybody's eyes. But what chance was there of this while innocence and naïveté were increasing and multiplying in the fresh and limpid air? The backside was split between Boy and Adolescent. The world was being shattered and re-formed on the basis of Boy and Adolescent. I stepped back.

The tension increased. Boys, redfaced and furious, set on one another. Siphon stood motionless, with his arms crossed, while Mientus shook his fists. The mothers and aunts on the other side of the wall were in a highly exalted state too, though they did not have too clear an idea why. But most of the boys remained undecided. They went on stuffing themselves with bread and butter, reciting remorselessly:

'Can the *dignissime* Mientus be a *sensualus luxurius*? Can Siphon be an *idealistus*? Let us work hard, or we shall fail in our exams!'

Others, who did not wish to compromise themselves, talked sport of politics, or pretended to be interested in a game of football. But every now and then one or other, unable to resist the fascination of the heated and piquant controversy, would break away, start listening to it: he would ponder, blush, and join either Mientus's or Siphon's party. Meanwhile the usher sat drowsily on his bench, feasting himself from a distance on the spectacle of youthful naïveté.

'Ah! the pretty little backsides, the innocent little backsides!' he muttered.

In the end only one boy failed to be dragged into the superheated ideological conflict. He stood aloof, quietly sunning himself, wearing a shirt and white flannel trousers, with a gold chain round his left wrist.

'Kopeida, come over here!'

Everyone seemed to want him, but he took no notice of anybody. He raised one leg and dangled it in the diaphanous air.

Meanwhile Mientus was struggling in the net of his own words.

'But don't you realize that we shall be an object of contempt to every working-class lad, every hall-porter's son and apprentice and agricultural labourer of the same age as ourselves? We must defend the Boy against the Adolescent!' he declared with passion.

'We're not interested in what apprentices, hall-porters' sons and street boys think of us, they've got no education,' replied Gabek, who was one of Siphon's friends.

Mientus went over to Siphon and spoke to him haltingly.

'Siphon, this has gone far enough,' he said. 'If you withdraw what you said, I'll withdraw what I said. That's fair, isn't it? Let's drop it! I'm ready to withdraw everything I said on condition that you withdraw everything you said . . . and agree to be told everything. It's not a matter that concerns you only, after all.'

Pylaszczkiewicz gave him a look that was full of light, dignity, and inner strength. After looking at him in this fashion, it was impossible to reply other than in vigorous fashion. He stepped back.

'There can be no compromising with ideals,' he announced.

At this Mientus dashed at him, with clenched fists, shouting:

'Come on! Come on! Death to the Adolescent!'

'Adolescents, rally round me!' cried Pylaszczkiewicz in a penetrating voice. 'Rally round me, rally to the defence of your purity!'

This appeal caused many to feel the Adolescent in themselves rising against the Boy. They formed a thick barrier round Siphon and faced up to the partisans of Mientus. The first blows were exchanged. Siphon leapt on a stone and shouted encouragement to his supporters, but the Mientus party began to gain the upper hand, and Siphon's men beat a disorderly retreat. How dreadful! The Adolescent seemed lost. But Siphon, faced with inevitable defeat, gathered his last strength and struck up the innocent, adolescent song:

Youth! Lift the world
On your shoulders . . .

This made his supporters shudder. Was this a song to sing in this situation? Surely it would have been better not to sing that song. But they could not let Siphon go on singing by himself, so they started joining in, and the song grew, spread, multiplied, became enormous and took wing. . .

* * *

Gabek, looking slightly pale, then read out the rules of combat, in a voice that sounded simultaneously menacing and ironic:

'The two contestants will stand facing each other and will make a series of faces. Each and every constructive and beautiful face made by Siphon will be answered by an ugly and destructive counter-face made by Mientus. The faces made will be as personal and as wounding as possible, and the contestants will continue to make them until a final decision is reached.'

He fell silent. Siphon and Mientus took up their positions. Siphon tapped his cheeks, Mientus rolled his jaw, and Bobek, with his teeth chattering said:

'You may begin!'

At these words reality burst from its frame, unreality turned into nightmare, the whole improbable adventure became a dream in which I was imprisoned with no possibility of even struggling. It was as if after long training a point had been reached at which one lost one's own face. It would not have been surprising if Mientus and Siphon had taken their faces in their hands and thrown them at each other; nothing would have been surprising. I muttered:

'Take pity on your faces, take pity on my face, for a face is not an object but a subject, a subject, a subject!'

But Siphon had already put his head forward, and he made the first grimace so suddenly that my own face was suddenly as distorted as if it were made of papier mâché.

Siphon blinked, like somebody suddenly emerging from the darkness into broad daylight, looked right and left with an expression of pious astonishment, rolled his eyes, looked up, opened his mouth, made a slight exclamation, as if he had noticed something on the ceiling, assumed an expression of ecstasy, and remained still in that inspired pose; then he put his hand on his heart and sighed.

Mientus collected himself and retorted with an alarming and derisive counter-grimace. He too rolled his eyes, then raised them to heaven, glared, opened his lips in idiotic fashion, and rotated the face that he had thus composed until a fly fell into his cavernous mouth, whereupon he swallowed it.

Siphon paid no attention to this pantomime, which seemed to make no impact whatever on him (he had the advantage over his opponent of acting for the sake of his principles, not just for his own sake). He burst into tears, pious, bitter tears, floods of tears, that reached the heights of remorse, revelation, and ecstasy. Mientus burst into tears too, and sobbed and sobbed until a tear trickled down to the end of his nose—whereupon he caused it to drop into a spittoon, thus reaching a new level of disgustingness. This assault upon the most sacred feelings was too much for Siphon; it shook him; and, in spite of himself, still sobbing, he looked daggers at his opponent. But this was unwise of him, for it was just what Mientus had been waiting for. Realizing that he had diverted Siphon's attention from the heights, he stuck out his face in such an obscene fashion that Siphon, touched to the quick, groaned. Mientus seemed to be gaining the day, and Bobek and Hopek sighed with relief. But their relief was premature; they sighed too soon.

For Siphon, realizing that he had allowed himself to be excessively distracted by Mientus's face, and that irritation was making him lose control of his own, beat a hasty retreat, recomposed his features, and once more elevated his eyes towards heaven. He advanced one foot slightly, slightly ruffled his hair, caused a lock to droop over his forehead, and froze into a position of unshakeable unity with his principles and ideals; then he raised one hand, and pointed towards the stars. This was a powerful blow.

Mientus thereupon pointed his finger too, spat on it, put it up his nose, scratched himself with it, did everything in his power to debase and ridicule Siphon's noble gesture, thus defending himself by counter-attack. But Siphon went on remorselessly pointing towards the sky. In vain Mientus bit his finger, rubbed his teeth with it, scratched the sole of his foot with it; in vain he did everything he could think of to make his finger odious and contemptible; Siphon stood there remorselessly and impregnably pointing upwards, and yielded not an inch. Mientus's position started becoming untenable; he was using up his stock of insulting gestures, and Siphon's finger still pointed remorselessly towards heaven. The seconds and the umpire were petrified with horror. In a last desperate effort Mientus dipped his finger in the spittoon and waved it at Siphon, covered as it was with sweat and spittle. Not only did Siphon fail to take the slightest notice, but his face became diffused with seven colours, like a rainbow after a storm, and lo! there he stood in seven colours, the Boy Scout, Purity Incarnate, the Innocent Adolescent.

'Victory!' Gabek exclaimed.

Mientus looked dreadful. He retreated to the wall, fuming with rage, took hold of his finger, pulled it as if he were trying to pull it out of its socket, in order to destroy this link that bound him to Siphon, to enable him to recover his independence. But he could not pull out his finger, though he tried with all his strength, in spite of the pain. Impotence hung once more in the air. But there was nothing impotent about Siphon, who stood there as calm as the heavens, with his finger pointing upwards, not for himself, but for the sake of his principles. What a ghastly situation! Here was I, the umpire, between two boys each of whose faces was distorted into a horrible grimace, imprisoned between them no doubt for ever and ever, slave of the faces, the grimaces, of others. My face, the mirror of their faces, was distorted too; terror, disgust, fear, left their ineradicable marks on it. A clown between two other clowns, what could I do except grimace? Sadly my toe accompanied their fingers, and I grimaced and grimaced, well knowing that I was losing myself in my grimaces. Never, never, should I be able to escape from Pimko, never should I be able to return to my old self. What a nightmare! Oh, horror, oh, dreadful silence! For there were moments of dead silence, when the clash of arms was stilled, when there was nothing but silent grimaces and gestures.

Suddenly the silence was broken by a wild yell from Mientus.

'Go for him! Get him!'

What was this? So it wasn't over yet? Mientus dropped his finger, leapt at Siphon and struck him in the face, and Bobek and Hopek did the same to Gabek and Pyzo. A moment later an inextricable heap of bodies was writhing on the floor, with me, the umpire, standing over it.

In a flash Gabek and Pyzo were overpowered and tied up with their braces; and Mientus was sitting on Siphon.

'So, my fine young adolescent, you thought you'd got the better of me, did you?' he boasted. 'So you thought that all you had to do was to stick your finger in the air and the trick was done, did you? So you thought, my fine fellow (here he added some disgusting expressions) that Mientus wouldn't be able to get the better of you, did you? You thought he'd let himself be tied round that little finger of yours, did you? Well, then, for your information, when there's no other way out, fingers have to be brought down by force!'

'Let me go!' Siphon gasped.

'Let you go? I'll let you go! I'll let you go soon, but not in this state! Not till I've dealt with your adolescent in my own way. You'll have cause to remember Mientus. We're going to have a little talk. Come here with your ear. Fortunately it's still possible to get at you through your ears. Come here with your ear, I tell you! Come along, my little innocent, I'm going to tell you some things!'

He bent over and started talking softly. Siphon went green in the face, yelled like a pig in the slaughterhouse, writhed like a fish out of water. Mientus was suffocating him. Siphon turned his head this way and that to move his ears away from Mientus's mouth, and Mientus poured his filth first into one ear and then into the other; and Siphon yelled to prevent himself from hearing Mientus's filth; he yelled gravely, dreadfully, he froze into a quintessential yell. It was difficult to believe that the ideal could yell like this, like a wild beast in the primeval forest. His tormentor started yelling too.

'Gag him! Gag him! What are you waiting for, you fool? Stuff a handkerchief in his mouth!'

I was the fool to whom he referred. It was I who was supposed to stuff a handkerchief into Siphon's mouth, for Bobek and Hopek, each of whom were holding down one of Siphon's seconds, obviously could not move. But I would not, I could not, there I stood, rooted to the spot, disgusted with words, gestures, disgusted with every kind of expression. Alas, poor umpire! Where, oh! where were my thirty years? Vanished . . . But, suddenly there was Pimko standing in the doorway, with his yellow buckskin shoes, his brownish overcoat, and his walkingstick, standing there in a manner as definite and absolute as if he were seated.

WITOLD GOMBROWICZ was born in Maloszyce, a Polish country house, in 1904. He left Poland in August 1939 and spent fifteen years in Argentina, which he left in 1964, invited to West Berlin on a stipend of the Ford Foundation. He now lives in Vence, in the South of France. Author of *Bakakaj* (short stories, 1933), *Yvonne, Princess of Burgundy* (a play, 1936), *Ferdydurke* (1937), *The Marriage* (a play, 1946), *The Trans-Atlantic* (novel, 1948), *Pornography* (novel, 1963), *Cosmos* (novel, 1965), *Operetta* (a play, 1966) and of a *Diary* (1953-1965). Almost unknown in the United States, his impact upon Poland has been such that phrases from his novel, *Ferdydurke*, have passed into the everyday language. This, despite the fact that the book has been published only twice, in limited editions, in 1937 and 1957, once forgotten in the upheaval of war, and again "forgotten" by the Communist regime in Poland. When, twenty years after its original appearance, the Gomulka government permitted the re-publication of *Ferdydurke*, the entire edition of 10,000 was sold out in days. The success of *Yvonne* in Warsaw was followed by sudden and complete silence: a scheduled premiere of *The Marriage* in Cracow was cancelled, and overnight Gombrowicz' name disappeared from publishers' lists. He has just received the Prix International de Litérature. K. A. JELENSKI, a Polish critic living in Paris, is on the editorial board of "Preuves". Editor of an anthology of Polish poetry in French translation (Editions du Seuil, Paris, 1964), author of monographs of painters (*Leonor Fini*, Milan, 1963; *Hans Bellmer*, Denoël, Paris, 1966), he has contributed essays and articles on literature and art to numerous European and American magazines. JOY N. HUMES is presently an instructor in Romance Languages at Northwestern from which she holds her M.A.

translated by Paul Neuburg and Donald Davie
SANDOR WEÖRES

Salve Regina

Henceforward let me remain in your offing
though you promise no passing away of your veil,
nor more than the parching of dews in a storm of wind
        when your two green stars
        flare into a glowing dawn
and a cruder gold comes over your lucent night,
and over the monster-mask through which I discerned
        your traces in the inclement wood;
        yet here is a permanent landscape
on which your bare brow opens a colonnade.

Yours the decrepit rocks I sit among
past the pinewoods where your snows have drifted.
Marble-cool, the haunches of the Powers
        depend into their
        Pulverizing, soles of ice still moving;
up from the knees their frames are hidden in sky;
out of the valley-cleft smoke peters upward,
        votive smokes
        wreathing the ankles,
sacred pyre consuming a liveness of masques.

If, Lady, the star that beams upon my lot
you pluck for me out of a fire of dominoes,
and if into militant hands you deliver the shield, the sword,
        stepping out from your overlooking
        thus by way of a course of life that is over,
I fear the daylight of your bounty, Mother,
so benign the night was of your weaving,
        odorous with your mercies:
        the breadth and light of space
have shuddered back among the pulsing petals.

Rude the crossing where your Son has charge
yet home, since here, wound off your spool, is home.
Sieved through your veil, the cold and the heat are tempered;

the year turns, chimes at your finger;
    the apple that it cannot see, it proffers.
With that you cheat me, Woman who dazzle the eye;
spiced breath you are of a Golden Age that would hold us,
    seeing millennia persuade themselves
    that here is more than a bootleggers' trading-post
where a naming of Names shuts off, opens before us nothing.

My masquerade has been in hotter kitchens,
a shadow-shape of many claws and horns,
soaked in the blood of others and its own,
    loitering for its hire.
    Maidservants there abruptly
scudded across (In a broken mirror I saw you);
the breasts of the cook were wagging down unclothed;
    the heifer cooked, and the he-goat;
    I was the meat in the juices
softened, the marrow boiled out, and clawed-out cavities of eyes.

Now that the half-light lays me a table of stone
and the first inconsequent beam
over earth and sky and skyline beckons
    to a bodiless repast
    me, the cracked socket,
comes over it your comeliness in spate
and under the brilliance in flow the stump
    splits open its source deep-down,
    yawns into the brimming love-cup,
and you above it, afloat, a white bird, pinions spread.

I say my creed: walled in your living body
uncertain-distant, yet within my flesh
you are entire in lip, hand, breast and eye
    body material Spirit
    Spirit a pure body
its every member in the teguments of veil and gems
passes through bone, withholds itself from me;
    you call me, and no voice rises
    dance and stillness in the one rhythm
as the tent of your hair in vociferous silence roofs me.

Your black locks out of Canaan
flash with blue lights into the further dark;
with a luring glint, a-burning with more beauty
    than Eve's red mane

or the blonde crown
of enchanting Lilith blanching every face,
this basin-full of embers fanned by tempest;
        the many strands of your plaits
        hang down to the dragon-racked deep
and, round and round the brute, turn, and at last compose him.

From behind the flying wands of the pigtails
through a mother's rocking play of tress and tassel
the skeleton whimpers and will find no rest
        till it flags into sleep
        like a fog scattered;
but hearing the song of the unending vintage
the organum drowning all things in its voice
        the foison is ground in the mill
        and the inebriate breath
responds from the height in descant.

All are aware of you, favoured of God,
you mighty mother here from the beginning
the omnifluent Woman in her youth
        as your blue thin shoes
        brush turf or a flower,
they see rose-silver the bodice
the golden cloak with its green dragons
        and every your garment
        your being inwoven with it
and you in a red robe straight before bare flame.

Among your celestial figures night has passed,
come dawn I see the garden of your valley;
Look! the tip of a marvellous rosehip!
        Its bountiful own blossom
        has grown back in, not fallen;
it waves, the everlasting, Rose of Spring,
its nature fights the winter easily:
        this your small and earthy body
        the overflowing of your mighty
essence gulfs over, and it shall not perish.

Stocky smiling brown-skinned girl,
in the frame of many hanging soot-black plaits
the round face is brilliantly white,
        blood shadows it lightly;
        thinly drawn mouth,

soft arch of the nose, dark eyes wondering:
simple beauty, everyday charm
                you're tiny, My indulgence
                but tinier is space,
fate and existence: a tip of your veil has filled it.

May the skeleton be a kneeling effigy
before you, tender phantom; for this larva
has known and loved you longer than I have,
                I know your name from him;
                profoundly excited, seethes
the beggarly family of brain, eyes and heart,
at the Queen's coming into their dwelling;
                a moonlight in their cellar,
                you scatter your light inward
on the people of the house and on me, lost in their shadows.

Among their thick, blood-branching shapes
gliding, a Madonna's silence, you inform
the fever of their dry dumbfoundedness
                you are no longer alone,
                in your lap your Babe.
You rock him there, of a sudden you cradle a corpse.
He it is prostrate behind each shroud;
                your regard is composed:
                your Father who is your Son
dissolves in himself the thirst of their implorings.

Let me confide my world to you, Mother of God
under the dead that embraces it, falling upon it
as it casts off the soft loins of the beasts,
                the ganglia of the tributaries;
                stirring up shadows,
the scattering dawn is vexed more than the night;
already my Lord's directive sends me abroad,
                who is your Lord also:
                on the road of the riders
am going where ancestral steps are knocking.

Whom your heel bruises, the craving snake
perishes, but in rapture, feeling your footfall press him;
old bonehulk drains his yearning yellow night;
                there too you are consuming, amorous:
                and he will swear that way is a good way

is moved to tears, the resin in him clots;
if on my nightmare's shamefulness your blinding
                    passage should traverse,
                    holy Virgin, bruise it with your heel
that the pearl of sweat in its sleeping bless you.

But my peculiar lot in life take off
soon as I merit. I don't hanker for it,
it shuts me from you, casts me into a small caul
                    which like a floating island
                    is adrift on your veil foaming;
and though a sweet sea, amorous dream, it is,
a hundred bubble-glass in you rejoicing,
                    be you my Death,
                    give me your Life,
heap on my cinders, burn them, they are yours.

Clear morning is prodigious to the night,
the arch of your brow is emptiness to twilight,
where centuries in arms are still in motion,
                    flickers among the hills
                    a valley-song of vintage.
These, though in arms, anticipate no guerdon
nor look upon you, though they bear your blazon
                    who are more fair than if your wing should shimmer
                    above a spring, or than those weavers are
of filaments which sway you down, the stars.

translated by Richard Lourie

Mural of the 20th Century

Castles in the air,
filled for three thousand years with decorations and junk,
with chests bearing inscriptions—"mine" "I" "for me" "me"
their walls bulging with "my treasure" "my fever" "my salvation"
it finally toppled
and fell into the dung piled up below.

Its inhabitants
throng in the dirt down there,
not understanding what happened, not seeing in the night,

struggling on the garbage with heavy moans or
scurrying tread on each other
carrying their broken, creaking belongings
they want to build by devastating the ruins—

But there is one among them who can see
and rolling himself in tar he sets himself on fire
that they too should see:
desperate light, live torch.

Some point at him: "Look at the fool,
he dipped himself in tar and now burns to ashes
instead of helping us salvage".
Others yell: "We can see by his light"
and they drag and pull the broken junk still faster.

What could they see? What could the live torch show them?
the ruins, the dung
and above it the black nothing
where the castle in the air has already vanished
and the angels also have vanished,
the Angels of Security, of Freedom, of Truth, and of everything else
even the Angel of War is gone, for what they take down there for war
is a ceaseless squabbling in the dark
of people tumbling against one another;
where is the time when free decision declared the war?
and even the Angel of Hatred is gone—
everybody bites any leg he can—
where is true hatred now?

One remains in the sky, an idle, indifferent soul
the Angel of Disgust, for now only that which has a soul
can feel disgust.

If they could see by the light of the live torch
they would see him, the Angel of Disgust,
as he dangles his legs for dogs or whistling
urinates on the ruins,
and would not believe he is an angel
that he is love in a new shape, who smiles and does not anger
and if they saw him close up they would not believe
he is the Angel of Disgust, for he is as beautiful
as the woman carried in the depths of our dreams,
the murderer falls into ecstasy, throws himself on his fists
and makes solemn promises, and the pure man too is startled:
what is beauty that it has such sway?

And the shouting torch of fire and the final sweetness
are one and the same—

If they ask him, he answers:
"Don't fret" pouting his lips he says "Don't fret."
And he says it a third time, "Don't fret." And grows silent.

The live torch runs around and shouts—
"Have you heard—don't fret.
These two words are the word flown to you, they are the Great Book,
these two words could smooth the convulsions of the world.
Don't fret, don't long to sway banners,
nor to fling up your arms with the motions
of building, of destroying, of salvaging,
leave slogans alone, self-important principles, convulsive ideas.
Listen—demand no advantage,
don't believe for the sake of advantage
and the hundred madnesses which promise advantage
will fall away from you,
and you will be like the heart-beat:
its calm is activity and its activity a calm."

Having shouted this, the live torch collapsed,
ashes and soot pour from his mouth,
even his bones are black.

The Angel of Disgust
dispassionately plays
above the ruins.
He is waiting.

translated by Richard Lourie

Profusa-Selections

The View Penetrates the Spectator

A russet rock lifts its stubby horn into the blue—at its foot purple
thistle swaying in the wind—this image lies softly between half-closed
lashes where the instant sprays it with a gentle red—and in the darkness
behind the eyes in the forehead, a bodiless snake dances, and as the
instant snaps, this winding thing vanishes in the blood.

Theatre

As soon as the performance begins the lights fade out, a creaking
scurries along the lines of chairs and everybody takes out a face
which a moment before he would wear only among his bones.
Through their eyes and ears their selves roll onto the stage, the
actors dance on them softly and gently. This is how they dance out
their love, desires, suffering, deaths, heavens and play on the
orchestra.
The spectators are naked: coats, hats, umbrellas are left in the
check room.
It is much the same with the readers of scandal sheets, baseball fans
and lonely men eating in restaurants; they pay to be projected into a sham
world where they are at last identical with their dream-self. But gratis
they begrudge each other their true faces.

Antithin

At last it has leaked out—thin men are the cause of everything.
They wait in ambush on streetcorners and if an old woman comes by,
they don't even greet her. They are more concerned with exchanging their
straw hats for lottery tickets, and with naturalising crocodiles in
the waters of Europe, so that even there there should be no safety.
They always begin their fishy deals in their beds at dawn, and
afterwards go to the street. Some work in offices, others ostensibly
are waiters or locksmiths—they all disguise themselves. But their
true trade is thinness. At last it has leaked out—thin
men are etc.

SANDOR WEÖRES (b. 1913) is an extremely gifted Hungarian poet whose real stature
became apparent only after the publication of his collected poems, *The Tower of Silence*
in 1956. Weöres is little known in the West, but *Penguins* is soon going to publish a small
selection from his poetry in English translation. PAUL NEUBURG is a young Hungarian writer and scholar, living in England since 1956. He took a degree in Cambridge
and is presently doing graduate work at New York University. His first English novel was published this year. DONALD DAVIE is a well-known English poet and critic; amongst others
he translated Mickiewicz and Pasternak into English. At present he is Professor of English at
the School of Comparative Studies, Essex University, England. RICHARD LOURIE is an
American poet who studied at Berkeley and is now living on the West Coast.

Conversation with Weöres
Conducted by LÁSZLÓ CS. SZABÓ

Cs : Where were you born? In the western part of Hungary?
W : There, in Transdanubia. In Szombathely.
Cs : Where did you spend your childhood?
W : In a village, called Csönge, west of Szombathely.
Cs : Did you make up poems as a child?
W : In the same way as every child does. Whether or not he is aware of it, every child's speech has some rhythm. It was the same with me. And I remember quite well how this rhythmic prattle grew into versification.
Cs : How old were you then?
W : I learnt to write, in capitals, at the age of four. I learnt handwriting later.
Cs : You wrote poems in capitals? Was this the period of transition you were hinting at?
W : Yes. The prattle which started in the cradle was gradually transformed into conscious versification at the age of four or five.
Cs : Tell me: do you write nursery rhymes on one level—or on several different ones? I mean: are they simply nursery rhymes, or is there some complex rhythmic experimentation behind them? Could you tell us something about that?
W : They are, usually, experiments with rhythms. At the time of writing I don't even think whether they are going to be nursery rhymes or poems. It is only later that a lot of my poems are classified as 'nursery rhymes'.
Cs : Could you show us an example of these experiments with rhythms—how a rhythmic problem made you write a poem which turned out to be a nursery rhyme?
W : For example

> *Fut robog a kicsi kocsi, rajta ül a Haragosi,*
> *din don diridongó.*
> Part of a cart rattles and rolls,
> Its guard is a bard who hums and falls
> Down don diringo.

A little game with short syllables.
Cs : Does it require a particular state of mind—or is it something extraneous that urges you, occasionally, to write nursery rhymes, play little jokes with syllables,—instead of writing seriously? Is it the result of a psychological pressure—or of some external circumstance?
W : Well, rhythmic experiments, nursery rhymes: they are little exercises. It's not a question of mental attitudes. The painter with his pencil or pastel or whatever he has will sometimes draw little sketches—and sometimes trace large compositions.
Cs : Let us turn to the large compositions. The greater part of your work has a dark and sombre, if not depressing tone. Are you in a dark and sombre mood when you write these poems?
W : In most cases, not all. For the large compositions one needs such inner peace and serenity... from which the material of the poem will suddenly emerge, defined in sharp contours. Whether that material is sombre or gay does not depend on me, on my mood.
Cs : To a certain extent I have always felt the same. You have the reputation of being a pessimistic poet—but the pessimism I find in your poems has, one might almost say, cosmic, and not social, motives. And that kind of pessimism is a component of all great religions and all great myths—isn't it?
W : I think it is.
Cs : In other words, the darker quality one finds in your poems—whether or not intentional - is, in fact, related to the same universal pessimism which all mankind shares and has shared whenever contemplating its own predicament throughout the ages?
W : When religion, philosophy or poetry faces the ultimate questions, it somehow becomes, in a sense, misty, barren, obscure, dark. It is so difficult to cross the thresholds beyond the limits of everyday, practical life.
Cs : Perhaps you were influenced by those archetypal songs which seem to be full of religious or metaphysical references to man's predicament. It would appear from your poems you were.

W : To a very great extent. The connections are quite obvious between my poetry—and folk-poetry, myths, primeval and modern religions.

Cs : What was the greatest influence? Babylonian, Indian or Egyptian poetry?

W : It would be difficult to say which influences me most. Ancient Chinese poetry, the Tshu-Tse collection or the Te King of Lao Tse influenced me as well as the Upanishads, the Bhagavad Gita or the Babylonian epic of Gilgames and the tale of Istar's descent to Hell; the Egyptian hymns, the Polynesian Rabie Hainuvele cycle of myths, Negro Mythology... and other things.

Cs : In what language have you read them?

W : Some in Hungarian translations. Others... from German, French or English sources.

Cs : And who interests you most among modern poets? In European literature. Let us say from the Middle Ages to our time. With whom do you feel a particular affinity?

W : From the Middle Ages to our time?... Shakespeare, Blake, Rimbaud, Mallarmé, Hölderlin...

Cs : There does seem to be a strikingly close resemblance between you and Blake. Perhaps he fascinates you because he displayed the same duality which some people find in you. On the one hand, the playful poet whom children understand - on the other, the vision-ary prophet addressing a disintegrating world.

W : Yes, I feel exactly the same mentality in Blake's works as my own.

Cs : You are a prolific translator ... of Shakespeare, Burns, Blake, Mallarmé. In what languages do you translate directly from the original?

W : Without a word-for-word rough translation I may try, from time to time, some easier German or French poems. To tell you the truth, before I start I always need a rough translation. I have some knowledge of English, French and German, but it's a great help. It seldom happens that I translate something without knowing the original text.

Cs : The reader never can tell.... Let us see now what did you derive from Eastern philosophy. Does it influence your conception of the Universe?

W : Profoundly, no doubt.

Cs : You mentioned Lao Tse. Did he influence you? Does he attract you? You have translated some of his work.

W : If you can call it translation. I worked from rough translations. I do not understand Chinese - especially the old Chinese which Lao Tse used. In fact I think nobody understands or has ever understood that. Lao-Tse wrote in a highly original and individualistic language of his own which nobody ever spoke.

Cs : What is it in his teachings that particularly interested you?

W : The Knowledge of the Evidence - the knowledge that one may carry this Evidence, possess it, identify oneself with it.

Cs : What is this Evidence? Could you describe it in a few words?

W : Lao-Tse calls it Tao - the Way; and the possibility of identifying ourselves with it: Te, - a sort of elemental force.

Cs : Does that mean that we can, to some degree, rid ourselves of our egotism, become part of others - and of the world?

W : Perhaps, among other things. Socrates called this Evidence Daimonion, - with Kant it became the categorical imperative. In various religions and philosophies the Evidence is expressed in various terms. One concept of it is ethical, the other is mystical. Thus the idea itself becomes more and more complex and obscure.

Cs : You think that Lao-Tse expressed it in the clearest, most convincing, or most attractive manner?

W : Not necessarily. Lao-Tse was the first one I read, around the age of sixteen. Since the same age I have studied extensively Hindu religions, in which there are many approaches to and many concepts of the Evidence. The idea of Atman for example, or Om.

Cs : You've written a poem which seems to have been inspired by historical events. Such inspiration is seldom felt in your work, but there is a gigantic poem, *The Fall of Mahrud* - was it inspired by 20th century events, our historical predicament, - or are the human conditions you were born into completely irrelevant to the poem?

W : Undoubtedly, *The Fall of Mahrud*, mirroring the earthquakes that shook our world, echoes historical events, - not necessarily those of the 20th century.

Cs : The great crises of history....

W : Yes.

Cs : .... of centuries past?

W : Those as well. But what I have experienced personally is, of course, much more immediate for me than the turmoils of the past.

Cs : I called *The Fall of Mahrud* a gigantic poem in an aesthetic sense, not only because of its length. There is another poem of yours, *The Ascension of Mary*, dated 1952 - like the *Fall* - which you dedicated to the memory of your mother. What was the inspiration behind that one?

W : I wrote the greater part of the poem before my mother's death. But somehow it did not stick together, it lacked cohesion. It was only after her death that I could mould it into shape, - in her memory, as it were. In spite of the fact that more than half of the poem had existed, in a shapeless form, for more than ten years.

Cs : A more recent poem of yours - *Salve Regina* - seems to be related to the Ascension of Mary. Is it just an acoustic illusion - or is there in fact some spiritual affinity between the two poems.?

W : The two poems are very closely interrelated. The thematic resemblance is, of course, obvious: both are addressed to Mary, mother of Jesus.

Cs : Recently you have been writing a great number of sonnets. Any particular reason for that?

W : It's Mallarmé's influence, the influence of his sonnets. With him, the structure of the sonnet remains unchanged, but the content has a great fluidity, much greater than in *vers libre*.

Cs : So it seems to the reader far more complex than the traditional sonnet in which form and content alike are determined, restricted.

W : Quite. The type of sonnet Mallarmé wrote is a fascinating concoction. Its sentences are complicated, as pregnant as Latin, branching off in different directions. Its content, however, becomes, at the same time, more and more elusive and ethereal, - a mixture full of contrast between self-imposed restrictions and total fluidity. The polarities are extreme; this type of sonnet incorporates qualities which seem incompatible. I wanted to explore all the possibilities it offers - hence the sonnets *á la* Mallarmé. They are not sonnets at all in their essence, only in their structure.

Cs : Some people - and I among them - feel they are particularly difficult poems to follow. Do you think the poet should experiment on the one hand with all known, and, on the other, with all as yet unknown forms and possibilities of writing? Even with those which will gain acceptance or approval only in some distant future?

W : Yes, I think one should explore everything. Including those things which will never be accepted, not even in the distant future. We can never know, at the start of an experiment, where it will lead. Perhaps it will be an abortive, still-born enterprise, perhaps it will be a necessary and useful experiment - only we cannot know that, not even after we have completed it. It may take decades or centuries to prove whether it was a useful experiment of a useless one. It may never be proved at all.

Cs : In other words you accept the risk of failure and it does not worry you that posterity may decide that in some of your poems you were side-tracked up a dead end?

W : The possibility that this poem or that one led nowhere does not worry me in the least. I never think about it.

Cs : Permit me to ask a very naive question. Do you understand all your poems?

W : No. I don't believe that a poem can be completely understood - digested, as it were, to the last crumbs. If we took the simplest, most primitive poem, for example: "*Kutya, kutya, tarka, Se füle se farka*" ("Dog, dog, piebald dog, - It has neither ear nor tail") and put it under a microscope in order to find out whether or not we understand every bit of it, - we would discover that it is full of imponderables.

Cs : But can a poem pass the test of time if it is not quite understood even by posterity - can it survive if it remains obscure forever? Are there any such masterpieces?

W : At any rate there are a great many lines in Pindar's hymns, in The Divine Comedy and in a lot of other works which are very obscure indeed. Of course, in many cases the obscurity is caused simply by linguistic development. The obscurities of the Chinese Shiking or the Hungarian Plaint to Mary* are mainly due to changes in the language.

* First extant poem in Hungarian, manuscript at the University of Louvain.

Cs : Do you think those who claim to have derived much pleasure from, say Dante's *Il Para-diso*, yet profess themselves unable to appreciate modern poetry, are merely being snobbish - or do they simply delude themselves?

W : I can imagine people who profoundly understand and love some poet of the past and are, at the same time, genuinely limited in their appreciation of modern poetry. Or romantic poetry, or 18th century poetry... One has one's blind spots.

Cs : You have translated some of T. S. Eliot's poems, met him personally, in Rome. Could you tell us what made you interested in his poetry - and which poems of his do you prefer: the earlier or the later?

W : He has published extraordinarily few poems. But those published - whether belonging to the earlier or the later period - are, all of them, very mature, highly polished, definitive works. So I could not draw a line, I could not say which is the more valuable, his earlier or his later poetry. Each has something solid, rock-like, almost unavoidably final about it. That suffices for me.

Cs : Something solid, rock-like... It almost sounds as if you were talking about Anglo-Saxon poetry. Do you in fact feel any affinity between the poetry of Eliot - and, to some extent, that of Auden - on the one hand, and Anglo-Saxon poetry on the other? Is there a connec-tion, a continuity... can one establish when the ancient attributes of poetry re-emerged and began to permeate the modern poet's work?

W : Oh yes. I think they first became obvious in Hopkins, but one can discover them, in different forms, in the works of Chatterton, for example, or of Coleridge, Wordsworth, Walter Scott... In fact, all periods of English poetry can be related to Saxon or Celtic poetry.

Cs : So, in your view, the Celts and the Saxons still survive - at least in English poetry. Have I interpreted your remark correctly?

W : Yes. I would even go so far as to say that the Celts and Anglo-Saxons are very much alive, - whereas among modern English poets only those will survive who have retained their roots in this fecund humus of archetypal material.

Cs : In your more ambitious poems one could always feel - I hope it does not sound too pre-tentious - a kind of universal presence. At the same time you do not give the impression of one who seeks to redeem our finite world. I mean: you are acutely conscious of the contrast between your own mortality - and the infinity of the cosmos; without being passed by a sense of mission. You are the most purely poetic Hungarian poet. And to turn to the rôle of the poet: do you feel he has a priestly vocation, does he fulfill a priestly function, is he chosen, predestined? Or is he like other men?

W : I think the poet is like any other man. Of course, everyone has a sense of mission and in the same way as William Blake I have it too. In fact I have attempted to do something in this field as well: in my sketch-book, Towards Completeness, I have tried to communi-cate my conception of what I called "Evidence" a few minutes ago.

Cs : About this sense of mission: when you want to communicate, to give something to your fellow-men, are you guided by the same considerations as was Stefan George, for example, who regarded the poet as an appointed priest - or by different considerations?

W : By different ones. My whole mental structure, determined at birth or before, is such that its basis contains some sort of message. Blake had the same conviction, he himself said.

Cs : I would like to recall the name of another predecessor: Montaigne. In your poems I somehow sense the same humility towards your fellowmen as Montagine felt towards the illiterate gardener. Am I right?

W : Yes.

Cs : And can I therefore call your poetic credo a profoundly humanist one?

W : Humanism can be defined in many different ways, which has caused many misunder-standings. I would rather avoid this label. It seems to mean everything and means noth-ing. It causes misunderstanding end confusion.

Cs : What other term would you use instead? Humane, charitable, selfless, - how would you de-fine your ars poetica?

W : I could hardly express it in a single word. For me the complete man - and I am not thinking of poets alone - is he who can make full use of his inborn qualities, fulfill his potential. He who, if born with the gift of poetry, will use this gift well; or if he has the making of a good craftsman or sportsman or farmer, will profit by his talent as best he can. He who meets and fulfills his destiny.

Cs : Can I put it this way: that in the final analysis you, called obscure by some and a pessimist by others, have a very humane and heartlifting influence on your readers and those who understand you - because you have retained the child's ability to wonder.

W : Perhaps. In any case it is fundamentally important for all of us to retain the childhood, embryonic or perhaps even pre-conception quintessence of our being. The term 'Evidence' implies solid substance as well.

Cs : A final question which has long since intrigued me. Reading your poems I have come to the conclusion that you, as all true poets, would like to speak to the multitude. Is that so? Do you wish to address yourself to the largest possible audience - or only to the select few.

W : For me only one man exists: Jesus. All other men live or neglect to live in that they are one with Jesus - or not. Of course, I am not thinking of the Christian religion as such; - you pour a bit of holy water or what-not on somebody's head and then he is supposed to be one with Jesus. I am not thinking of that. For me PEOPLE - don't exist.

Cs : Who, then, does exist for you?

W : Jesus exists and He exists in all who exist in Him, through Him, by Him. I write because I want to expose better, approach nearer this identity with Jesus, in myself and in others. I couldn't care less how many read my poems and how many don't. To bring the sensitive reader of good will a step nearer to this sameness, one-ness with Jesus: that is my only aim.

Cs : In other words what matters is not whether or not your work is published today or tomorrow;* what matters is that the poem, written to him who is one with Jesus, should BE.

* Between 1947 and 1955 Weöres was only occasionally allowed to publish his poems - and never in a volume. At the time of this unrehearsed interview (4th of September 1963) the publication of his latest work had been held up for considerable time.

LÁSZLÓ CS. SZABÓ is a Hungarian writer and essayist living in London. He works in the Hungarian section of the BBC. His publications include an introduction to László Gara's *Anthologie de la Poésie Hongroise*.

translated by Henry Hiż

Jesus Christ
prophet and reformer

LESZEK KOLAKOWSKI

W HEN A HISTORIAN speaks about Jesus, he asks, above all, what do we really know, reliably, about this man? He also asks, what, in the Jewish culture, are the antecedents of his teachings and what way was the image of the Jewish god changing from the Pentateuch to the late prophets; he wants to find out whether Jesus the prophet can be taken as a continuation of or as the crowning of those changes; he is interested in the results which, on this topic, were brought out by the research on the Quarman manuscripts. Only people who are very highly qualified specialists can speak reasonably about these topics. Nor do I consider these topics here.

A historian of ideas may, moreover, try to place Jesus within that totality of history which goes under his name and try to search through his inexhaustible topic, exploring the immeasurable region of events and thoughts which grew around the myth of Christ. Indeed, when we speak about him, about him as a person, it is difficult to free ourselves from the twenty centuries of events through which we see him. The figure of Jesus lies in the shadow of theology and of the theological controversies with which every word of the Gospel is barbed. How can we forget the monstrous ambiguities, some apparent, some real, with which the history of Christianity weighted the teachings of its founder? Yet this point of view does not concern me here.

Again, a historian of religion may treat Jesus Christ as an element in a methodological structure. He may compare it with other structures in order to reveal the similarities and the differences of cultures. He may try— although it does not come easily—to forget about the extent to which this figure lies in the shadow of the contemporary situation and about the pre-

LESZEK KOLAKOWSKI, a Polish philosopher whose work has exerted great influence on a whole generation of young Marxist 'Revisionists', is at present a Professor of Philosophy at Warsaw University. After a speech in which he criticized the Gomulka regime, Kolakowski was recently expelled from the Polish United Workers' Party; his expulsion was followed by voluntary resignations from the Party by many writers and journalists. This essay was first given as a public lecture in Warsaw on October 22, 1965, and subsequently in the Warsaw Atheist journal *Argumenty* (Dec. 1965). Kolakowski's work includes a book on Spinoza, *The Individual and Infinity*, (1958) and *Religious Thought and Church Affiliation,* a study of Eighteenth Century religious thought, primarily in Holland. HENRY HIŻ, a linguist and a logician, originally from Warsaw, is now a professor at the University of Pennsylvania.

sence of Christianity in the world of today. He might attempt to reach the same kind of comparative attitude or esthetic distance which we can afford toward Egyptian or Greek myths.

Finally, a biographer may try to decipher the psychological profile of Jesus and to give to it a unified meaning—if he can succeed in liberating himself from any apologetic intention, be it Christian or blasphemous, underlined with anti-Christian ardour. This is not the point of view that I have in mind either.

I do have in mind the purely philosophical point of view. And this means, exactly, neither historical nor psychological nor that of comparative religion. I am attempting to have such a degree of freedom as to read the canonical and the apocryphal texts of the Gospel without recalling the commentaries or even Paul's letter. I am attempting not to read into the simple words any head-spinning theological or philosophical speculations. I would like to summarize what, in the figure and in the teaching of Jesus, can be discovered by a layman who does not admit to any variety of Christian faith, to any dogma or to any church community but who does accept the tradition of which Buddha, Socrates, Kant and Marx are elements. I do not want to reconstruct the psychological profile of Jesus. I am attempting to ask about his place not only within the Christian tradition but within the totality of European tradition. I ask in what way the mission which he ascribed to himself became a component of the complicated weaving which forms our inherited cultural treasure and exactly what part of the mission entered it. And I ask about this tradition independently of "Christological" dogmas around which the Christians have formed their own religious consciousness.

Philosophers and Jesus

As we know, Jesus Christ was not a philosopher, and one does not read about him in textbooks on religious philosophy, not even in Christian textbooks. Contemporary philosophers rarely deal with him. However, some philosophers did deal with him and it is worthwhile to consider this, in order to outline possible stereotypes of philosophical interest toward that surprising figure. Among the great, Pascal, Kierkegaard, Hegel, Nietzsche and Jaspers spoke about Jesus.

In Hegel's understanding, Jesus Christ was a certain phase of the historical self-knowledge of humanity. He was a visual, sensory manifestation of that idea of god to which man has access when he conceives of god as that of which he himself is another being. The personality of Jesus is, thus, reduced almost to a certain stage of human consciousness in its relation to the absolute. This does not mean that Hegel makes Jesus unreal, parting him of personality and humanity. Indeed, he says that he, Jesus, is far more of a man than the Greek anthropomorphic gods. But he deprived his personality of that peculiar, eternal, and enduring uniqueness. He denied to it that extra-historical exceptionality, that quality which founded Christianity and which is based on the belief that there entered, in history, a supra-natural call from outside of history.

Kierkegaard opposed Hegel in this respect just as in others. He developed a picture of Christ as constantly contemporary and by this contemporaneousness as true for Christians. He explained that Christ is, for us, a sterile historical information if we do not treat him as a carrier of the past revelation. On the contrary, for each individual existence the real Christian life is only when each existence knows how to make him literally contemporary, hence to understand his invitation, "Come all ye who labor and are oppressed and I will comfort thee," as addressed to him personally and as spoken to him anew every moment. For a Christian, Jesus is not just a messiah who at a certain historical moment came to teach the dogmas in the name of God and to preach the commandments. He is the personal continuity of Christianity in each Christian separately. He is like a counter-element permanently alive in every existence, and each will find in his presence the answer to its own weakness and misery.

In principle, in spite of all differences, we find in the efforts of Pascal, in his attacks on deism and on "the God of philosophers," the same attitude to Jesus. For Pascal, the entire world shows to us neither the complete absence of a deity nor any obvious presence of it. The world is not abandoned completely nor is it evidently under God's protection but manifests "the presence of God who is hidden." This ambiguity of God's habitation in the world is the ambiguity of our fate; the fate of those who are able to know God but who are permanently stained by sin. Jesus Christ is that by which our knowledge of God becomes for us the knowledge of our own misery. This conjoined knowledge is greatly needed by man. Each of these two truths—that God exists and that we are miserable—we can learn without the other. But only the apprehension of Jesus, the person, contains, with necessity, both of these truths amalgamated. The knowledge, alone, of our disability is a source of dispair. And the net knowledge of God remains a speculative theorem without a value for life. We reach both the apprehension of our bare fall and the hope of a possible cure in the apprehension of Jesus. This and only this constitutes Christian faith. Philosophical Christianity is therefore impossible. Neither a Christianity which would rely on the validity of speculative proofs, nor a purely historical Christianity nor a Christianity which is based on a holy history is possible. Jesus Christ appears to us, aside from his dogmatic and his historical aspects, as the existence of the real redeemer. In the presence of this existence, which is neither a simple fact nor a simple doctrine, we have a feeling of the obscurity in which we live and a presentiment of the way which would lead us from this obscurity.

Among the "great" philosophical interpretations of the figure of Christ there is also the doctrine of Nietzsche. He is the greatest of those very few who have dared to proclaim themselves not only the enemies of Christianity but the enemies of Christ. Jesus, for Nietzsche, was that one who tried to annihilate all essential values of life, who glorified his own inability to resist and who raised this weakness to the rank of virtue. He made all values unreal by transfering them to the spiritual "interior" of man and he codified the morality of the people who are unable to defend their own rights and who search for comfort in their own passivity, making their passivity a cause of pride.

These are, in a summary characterization, three different attitudes of philosophers to the person of Jesus. Nietzsche addresses him as a prophet to a false prophet—that is an authentic prophet to a false prophet. Hegel's attitude toward Jesus is that of a historian of Spirit toward one of the studied historical phases. Pascal and Kierkegaard's attitude is that of Christians who search for, in the most personal values, the supra-natural realities of their faith.

One could think that, in some limited sense, the orientation of Pascal and Kierkegaard is also acceptable to people who are not involved in any of the dogmatic contents of Christianity. Not in the sense, of course, that they would look at Christ as a personal and a historically unique incorporation of the supra-natural world, an incorporation to which one could address oneself with a question or a worry. Only in the sense that Jesus, just as any of the great thinkers, prophets, reformers and philosophers is suitable for that peculiar contemporization in which universal values are tied to a unique source. Indeed, when a philosopher wants to transcend the purely historical or the purely factual point of view, he deals with the philosophical or the religious tradition in such a manner as to make the content of that tradition neither a bare fact to be understood nor a bare thought with respect to which one must take an approving or a negative "stand". He treats the cultural tradition neither as if it were a cumulative set of "truths" nor as if it were a sequence of neutralized historical facts. Rather, he treats it so as to show in it the universal values which are, nevertheless, permanently linked to the person of their author and which can not be freed from their personal source. This duality belongs to those difficult components of a genuine philosophical intention toward tradition. When Jesus is placed in that perspective he is neither reducible to a set of events (among which were also, as events, the contents of his teachings) nor to a set of abstract values about which one can reflect quite independently of the circumstances of their coming into being. We treat his teachings as, using an ugly expression, "essentialized fact" or as a universal value linked in its content with its own factual derivation.

The main prophecy of Jesus

From a purely historical perspective, Jesus was a Galilean Jew who believed in the Jewish God and who believed that God entrusted to him a particular teaching mission. Also, it was he about whom his disciples believed, in turn, that he could quiet the winds by his word, walk on the lake with dry feet, draw fish into a net, resurrect the dead, heal the lepers, return vision to the blind, drive out demons from the posessed, talk with Moses and Elias, multiply bread for the poor, turn water into wine and wine into blood. For them he was the one who fulfilled the promises of the Old Testament concerning the Messiah and whose mission was testified to by his resurrection. This Jesus, although he accepted the tributes of his believers, did not consider himself a god. Thus, when he was called good he said that only God is good and he acknowledged that he did not know when the promised day would come and he said, "not what I will, but what thou wilt." In this sense, it is impossible to assert that Jesus made Christianity if the belief in Jesus' deity is to be among the foundations of Christianity. It was, rather, Paul who started the deification process. And Paul finally won in spite of the constant oppositions remaining in the pre-Nicene fathers. He won and established the dominant understanding of Christianity in spite of numerous "arian" returns. This Jesus, as we may suppose, considered himself a Jewish reformer charged with a supernatural mission as God's annointed, that is, as Christ. He considered himself as the one who, from God—the very same God in whom he and his listeners believed—brought the news about the approaching end of the world and an appeal to all to prepare themselves immediately for the final cataclysm. He was unhesitatingly persuaded that the end of the world was imminent, so imminent that he often told his diciples and his listeners that many of them would still see the coming of God's Kingdom on earth. This was to be preceeded by pestilence, by starvation, by earthquakes, by falling stars and by the eclipse of the sun, and was to be ended by the visual descent of God's son from the heavens, surrounded by angels playing trumphets. The unfulfillment of these prophecies did not diminish the belief of the disciples who explained them differently. But this soon expected cosmic catastrophe imposed quite a new perspective to all things. From that moment, all terrestrial problems disappeared in the shadow of the apocalypse. All earthly realities, the entire plurality of things which serve life, lost all their sense and all their independent value. The corporal world ceased to be important. The world may still be the object of duty but can not be the object of desire because it is fragile and approaching its end.

Jesus the Reformer

In light of all this, the dictates of the new teachings are understandable.

For a long time readers of the Gospel were struck by some traces of inconsistency in the personality of Jesus. He preaches peace, forgiveness, mercy and desistance from opposition to evil. In his own behaviour, however, he is easily made irritable even by a small thing. He announces that even those who, in his name, perform miracles, prophesy, and exorcise demons, will be, by him, told that he never knew them and driven away if they do not fulfill the will of God. He announces fierce vengeance to the cities which will not follow his commandments. He promises that the fate of the Tyrians and the Sodomites will be easier on the Day of Judgement that that of the inhabitants of Chorazin and of Bethsaida who, in spite of his miracles, disregard his teachings. To Peter, when he expresses the hope that his Lord will not be killed, he says, "Get thee behind me, Satan." He curses and condemns to wither away a fig tree on which he found no fruit although the time for figs was not yet there. He drives out, with a scourge, the money changers from the temple. He proclaims that he is bringing the sword not peace, that he will separate families and that because of him, in every house, fathers shall be divided against sons and daughters against mothers. His listeners say "This is a hard saying." When he meets opposition or scepticism he becomes violent. He is unhesitatingly sure of his mission and only at the very last moment, dying in anguish, he seems to burst out with a cry of despair against the God who forsakes him. But even that shout of despair is a quotation from a Psalmist.

It may seem as if the impulsive character of Jesus does not quite fit his teaching, as if in some of his behavior he reveals the angry old Jewish God whose image he changes in his teachings—following anyway, in this respect, the intentions of earlier prophets.

As a matter of fact, it is difficult to characterize in one word the attitude of Jesus toward the Old Testament. This is witnessed by the unending disputes on that question in the history of Christianity. (Did he cancel the Old Testament? Did he complete it? Did he correct it?) Thus, the Sermon on the Mount begins with the statement that he does not want to destroy the law but to fulfill it. But the following content can hardly be reconciled with that passage. The extension of the commandment against killing to the simple anger against one's neighbor and the extension of the commandment against adultery to the very desire of somebody else's wife can be understood as a completion of the laws in the very same spirit which guides the entire teaching of Christ: it's not the gestures which matter but the spirit from which they come, not the behavior but the purity of heart, the love of neighbors without any ulterior motives. But when the principle of an eye for an eye is contrasted with abandoning opposition against evil and turning the other cheek, he does not supplement the Old Testament. Rather, he annuls it. He does it as if he doesn't notice it. Certainly, he does not want to interrupt the continuity of the Jewish creed, he wants to renew it. He wants to give it an "internalized" sense. He does regard the ritual prescription of Mosaic Law, he does not observe the Sabbath nor the ritual ablutions. He does not pay the taxes for the cult; exposing himself to the rage of orthodox men. He represents a continuity with the late prophets though he evokes rigorous prescriptions of the Deuteronomy as if on purpose. He wants to underline the contrast of his teaching to the tradition which was, partly, already archaic. The interruption of the continuity was done by his disciples mainly in the Jewish Diaspora. However, not only do the set of teachings perform it as well, the teachings can easily be formulated in such a way as to make them no more a completion of the faith of Israel but rather its transgression on a very fundamental point. That's exactly how things appear in the encyclicals of St. Paul.

This fundamental point has the following meaning. Indeed, Jesus does not simply replace some laws by others, he does not simply complete them or correct them. Rather, he teaches that no regulation is necessary. For, love itself includes the command, so to speak, makes it unneeded, being spontaneously entangled with it. And only love is of importance. In other words; the contractual relation between man and God is not altered by the change in the content of the contract. The contract ceased to exist in favor of the relation of love. In this way, Paul understood Christ's teachings and so did Augustine and so did Luther. Only that has real values which comes from love. But whatever grows from the root of love can not be judged by law nor measured by a section of an ordinance. Nothing matters which is just a gesture and does not come from the desire to fulfill God's will. All of us have duties towards the world but none of us has any rights. None can have claims on the world nor can expect anything from it. With a great force—and for the first time, so radically, in the Mediterranian culture—the rule of the fundamental dichotomy was stated; the soul and the rest of the world, good will and the totality of the existence of things. Only the soul matters. In view of the approaching total catastrophe, only a blind man relies on temporal successes. The heavenly kingdom is a praiseworthy pearl for which we have to give everything we possess. "For what shall it profit a man, if he shall gain the whole world, and lose his own soul?"

The mission of Jesus Christ is to reveal the misery of the temporal world. "Freely ye have received, freely give. Provide neither gold nor silver, nor brass in your purses. Nor scrip for your journey, neither two coats, neither shoes, nor yet staves." All the temporal connections, all that links us to the physical world diminishes to nothingness in view of that single important truth—the connection with God. The rest is secondary—either neutral or hostile. Jesus renounces his mother and his brothers, saying that the disciples are his family. He demands that his followers abandon fathers and mothers, wives and children, sisters and brothers. According to Luke he even demands that they would hate their fathers, mothers, brothers, sisters and children.

In the perspective of the world which Jesus reveals there is no graduation between the good and the bad. The world is divided into the chosen and the rejected, into sheep and goats, into the beneficiaries of life and the victims of eternal fire, into the sons of the kingdom and the sons of evil, and into good seeds and weeds. Who has, it will be given unto him, who does not, it will be taken away. There is nothing in between. This division corresponds exactly to the division between the spirit of love and the spirit of lust. To be sure, Jesus addresses himself to all. He says that he came to free the sinners, not the just men. He continuously asks to forgive all faults seventy-seven times. He believes that the tender heart will wash sin away. At the same time he knows very well that he can not break obdurate pride. He hates the proud, important, sure of themselves, satisfied in the feeling of str ngth and law, the rich and the misers. To those he does not promise the kingdom. He embraces the disposed and the miserable, the prostitutes and the tax collectors. Those believe in him because they know that the temporal life is misery and suffering. And this is what one must believe to accept in one's conscience Jesus' teachings.

The dichotomy of the world and of God's Kingdom is a radical one. It constitutes, also, an absolute reversal of all values. The despised are raised to glory. The proud are cast away with disdain. This division is the second point in which the traditional Mosaic view of the world is changed. It is a universal division and the only important one. And it is not linked with the division into the chosen people and the rest. Perhaps, just as before, Jesus wanted to be, in this respect, the renovator (rather than the destroyer) of the Judaic tradition. Just as before, he continued the shoots grafted by the prophets. But he set himself up in opposition to the tradition when he chose to confront the older and more radical form of the tradition, when he showed the conflicts between himself and the classical Mosaic tradition, and when he abolished the idea of the chosen people and introduced, instead, the universal principle of division.

All these novelties were generalized by the disciples, above all by Paul. In his writings,. law and faith are opposed to each other. Generally, universalism became formulated unequivocably. (For God there is no Greek or no Jew.) The misery of temporal life is changed to the command of asceticism. At the same time, however, in the very same letters, a new division was established as a dogma. The condemnation of heretics appeared. The death of Jesus cemented a group of reformists into a separatist community. Christianity, as a community, was not formed because of the belief of the disciples in the truth of Jesus' teachings. Rather, it grew out of the belief in his resurrection and, later on, out of the belief in the deity of the teacher. Many times in the later history of Christianity, the deification of Christ was questioned; it is not confirmed by the Gospel. However, even those deniers acknowledge that the only common dogma of Christianity, of Christianity in general, without further specification, is exactly the faith that Jesus is the Christ. The historical man born in Galilee and crucified in Jerusalem is God's annointed. This dogma was the most constructive for Christianity and even for Christianity of the most "lax" variety.

Nevertheless, Jesus remained in our culture, not only for those who believe in his deity or in his supranatural mission. He is present in our culture, not through the dogmas of this or that religious community but through the values of some precepts which were the real novelty and which are—and this is to be stressed—alive not in the form of abstract norms but are alive in a permanent link with his name and his life, as they are transmitted by tradition and independently of how much historical accuracy is in that transmission.

Jesus for Us

Let us summarize, in five points, these new rules which we can free from the apocalyptic prophecies of Jesus, from the belief in the imminent end of the world, although we know that in his teachings the rules were the function exactly of those prophecies.

1. *Abolishing law in favor of love.* Let me repeat, abolishing and not supplementing. This thought entered European culture as a persuasion that the relations between people based on confidence make impossible the relations of contract. When mutual confidence and love organize living together in a harmonious way, a contract is unnecessary and the relations of claims and duties are superfluous. The God of the Pentateuch was revengeful and desirous of obedience, sometimes cruel obedience. This god broke the covenant with Abraham for the price of absolute readiness to submit, for the readiness even to sacrifice one's only child. This god was transformed into the God of Mercy and with him the possibilities of a new look at interhuman life were opened. The opposition between the link of a contract and the link of love remained in our culture in a manner of existence which was not necessarily connected (though generically joined) with Christian beliefs and which is alive today in innumerable varieties. What else is the contrast between existential communication and objective communication in contemporary philosophy if not a successive re-creation of the same differentiation? For, indeed, not only Christian philosophies were bringing again and anew this same contrast. The philosophy of Rousseau, of Kierkegaard and of Jaspers each re-creates it anew. Also, when Marx contrasts the links of interest in the society of the exchange of goods with the link of free association of people with voluntary solidarity, he picks up, following the old socialists, the very same motif which grew out of the roots of Jesus and which is present in modern Christianity, most often in heresies and most rarely in the Church. Even that Nietzsche, when he says that what comes from love is outside of good and evil, repeats the thoughts of the enemy although he is not aware of it. All the utopias which want to abolish the order of contracts, and the legal linkage, in favor of the order of voluntary solidarity truly experienced, in a word, all the utopias of universal brotherhood, are bearing fruit on the same graft, though often they are indifferent to their own remote beginnings.

2. *The hope of eliminating violence from the relations among people.* This hope, indeed, often seems to us peculiarly utopian and peculiarly naïve. Everybody can, as a matter of fact, easily assert that he never in his life saw a Christian who would take his own Christianity literally, thus turning the other cheek when he already was slapped. However, this command, taken

literally, is something else than its limited version which demands the abolition of the sources of violence. Nobody expects from Christians that they would apply the commandments of the Gospel in their own lives. One, rather, expects that they would take seriously modest and elementary rules of tolerance, that they would refrain from violence. But even that demand is often considered fantastic. It seems to people who like to pride themselves on their realism—as if that word would mean anything or if from its acceptance would follow any concrete directive—that the idea of abolition of violence deserves only a hearty laugh. But who is here näive? Those who think that, in spite of all the evidence from human history, it is possible to diminish the part of violence in the relations among people and that much has been already won and even more can be won without strife? Or those who imagine that nothing can be accomplished without the use of force and, in particular, that with its use everything can be accomplished? No opponent of Christianity could deny that Christianity, without the use of brutal force, gained the position in which it itself could practice violence and could use the name of Jesus as the instrument of torture. It is also true that some forms of practical action based on the principle of persuasion without violence (for instance, the action of Gandhi) were not all unsuccessful. The principle of abandoning violence in international relations is verbally accepted almost universally. This is just the point—somebody will say—verbal acceptance, not much follows from verbal acceptance. Well, I would reply that much follows from it. The values which are verbally accepted and which are violated in practice are verbally accepted only because there is a pressure of universal opinion which forces agreement. Let us not despair about hypocrisy, rather let us accept that hypocrisy is the testimony of the factual social power of those values with which it camouflages itself—following the famous aphorism of La Rochefoucauld. It was not a long time ago when the leaders of states did not hesitate to proclaim that they conducted the politics of expansion by war and conquest. Such announcements have become a rarity. The idea of a world without violence is accepted and by this the hope for a world without violence is not a silly daydream. Näive are not those who think that the degree of the use of force can decline and who fight for its decline, but näive are those who believe that force resolves everything. Such a believer seems to have some kind of infantile fixation. The application of force toward children, up to a certain age, is unavoidable. Normally, however, it gradually decreases with age. Sometimes, parents extend the use of force beyond need. An individual brought up in that way usually acquires the persuasion that it is impossible that anything except force would order the relations among people. From his own infantile experiences he builds an infantile view of the world, promoting it to the rank of a primitive philosophy of history. He is proud of that philosophy and he says that it is "realistic" or "deprived of dreams," etc. But, the belief in the omnipotence of violence is not only näive but also, in the long run, self-defeating. Thus, it is known that the forms of common life which do not use anything but force meet defeat just because they are helpless in a situation in which force is useless. To the contrary, people who are persistent and resolute often achieve their aims without the use of force, rather by courage joined with intelligence. Renouncing force is not necessarily passivity nor readiness for a cowardly obedience. Christ renounced force and fought infinitely for his own point of view. He broke the resistance of those who commanded force when he perished. The idea of life without force is neither stupid or utopian. However, it calls for courage of which those who worship violence as a universal means are most deprived. They are ready to fight only when they command force against those who are weaker and never otherwise.

3. *Man lives not by bread alone.* This sentence Christ quotes from Deuteronomy, from the texts which he contradicts so often. But he gives to it an enlarged meaning. As lilies and ravens, we should not worry about life and food. Is this also a product of god-fearing naïveté? No. In the entire European culture the effort for the acceptance of values which are not reducible to physical needs or to the satisfactions of vegetative functions persists. All the time, the attempt is made to agree that there are values which are true and independent of the others. Such an agreement must seem trivial. It does not strike us as a novelty. But all that Jesus preached, if it remains later on in the culture, is a banality after centuries. It is because of that it became a banality. Nothing is more banal than that man not only clothes himself and eats. But it appeared, sometimes, that a long fight was necessary to accept this banality. It was necessary to argue persistently, for instance, that human spiritual creation cannot be measured according to the doubtful advantage which it was to bring to material productivity: Let us keep, therefore, the thankfulness to the one who did remind us that we live not by bread alone, even when we realize that the precept that we should live as lilies and ravens can not be taken literally.

4. *The abolition of the idea of the chosen people.* Jesus has opened God for all. Or, simply, he fulfulled the opening which was started before him by the Jewish prophets. His God does not demand from his people to not marry the daughters of the infidel or to fight other nations. He says that all just people are his people. He promises that many will come from the east and the west, from the north and the south to seek God's Kingdom, together with Abraham, Isaac and Jacob. The God to whom Jesus turns fell in love with the world and fell in love with it to such an extent that, according to the words of John the Apostle, he gave it his own son for its salvation. To him there is no Greek nor Jew. We bring up, again, a triviality about which it is almost embarrassing to speak but which entered European culture as a great cause, as an irrevocable problem, once it appeared, and as a value drenched in the blood of the many who fought for its acceptance. There is nothing

more modest in the realm of theoretical reflection and more provoking of dramatic clashes than the thought, if one takes this thought quite seriously, that there are no people chosen by God or by history, chosen above others and beloved, and by that authorized to impose its leadership over other people in the name of whatever reasons. Thanks to the teachings of Jesus, the idea that fundamental human values are the property of all and that humanity forms one people became an inextricable part of our spiritual world.

5. *The essential misery of all that is temporal.* It is not important now to what degree this picture of the human world as incurably ill is "correct." What is important is only that it became an unaltered fragment of the spiritual development of Europe. It is a thing consistently recurring in all sorts of philosophic reflection, not only in Christian thought or in the thought directly inspired by Christianity. Jesus explained to people that they are miserable, that they hide from themselves their own misery. Pascal, when he accepted this belief, made out of it the center of spiritual life. All are right who say that this thought sometimes was used to disarm people of their desire to improve the temporal existence, that it justified the spirit of resignation to fate, that it forced acceptance of previous conditions. The doctrine was used to extinguish the protests against exploitation of the communities which were oppressed and deprived. It was given the sense which made a virtue out of the disbelief in any real improvement in the world. It is also true that the choir of well-fed and satisfied was decorating itself with this belief and that they explained to the hungry and deprived that earthly goods are of little importance and that one should not worry about the temporal fate. Those interpretations swarm in the history of Christianity to such an extent that we are no longer moved by their hideousness.

Contrary to all that, there is another way of understanding this, a way which does not necessarily imply an approval of those people satisfied in their privilege. The baseness of that approval was disclosed a long time ago and, as we see, Christianity has slowly renounced it. However, in the persuasion that there is an essential weakness of human existence, there remains something that can be, and really sometime is, the topic of philosophical reflection, independently of the use of that persuasion for those other means. There is in it something which always was important as a subject for philosophers and, moreover, which may be considered without regard to the belief of or disbelief in the hereafter. Nor does it lead at all to the conclusion that, in view of the structural disability of our existence, all effort to repair what can be repaired is vain and sterile. One can try intensely, and one can fight without end, to change in the conditions of human existence all that which can be changed. Still we can know that the absolute is unobtainable, that human existence will always be essentially crippled without repair and that a fundamental disability is present in us and linked with the very human finiteness. This topic will not cease to intrigue philosophers.

This is an incomplete and selective—but not arbitrarily selective—set of values that, thanks to the teaching of Jesus, permanently entered the spiritual substance of Europe, and of the world, and is not essentially connected with Christian dogma. However, this abstraction of values in a non-Christian form, from their personal roots, is a sort of cultural impoverishment. This is connected with the monopolizing of Jesus within the dogmatic Christian communities and with the decay of his personality in other regions of the spiritual world. The danger seems to be that all the symptoms of the decadence of Christianity will result in an unavoidable disintegration of the histo ical meaning of the existence of Jesus. This is what we want to avoid.

One can say about many of the above mentioned points that "it's nothing new." One can, justly, find similar points in the religions of Asia. However, in the circle of the Mediterranean culture, to which we belong by birth, these values are connected with the teachings of Jesus and with his name. It is the spiritual supply which he introduced and to which he gave an impetus. Hence, any attempt to "invalidate Jesus," to eliminate him from our culture on the basis that we don't believe in the God in which he believed, is ridiculous and fruitless. Such an attempt is the deed only of unenlightened people who imagine that a crudely formulated atheism can suffice as the view of the world and can, also, justify someone's curtailing the cultural tradition according to his own doctrinaire plan and by that taking away from it the most vital saps.

If, finally, following our uncertain hope, the Christian world will prove able to make an essential improvement and change, then it will pull the strength for self-improvement only from its own source. (Non-Christian critics can weaken Christianity but they themselves cannot repair it.) The Christian world can re-create that ability only by continuous attention to the spiritual supplies which are connected to the name of Jesus. Maybe one day, by that, we can free ourselves from the dark nightmare of the clerical, fanatic and dull catechism, which for the last four centuries has oppressed and sterilized our national culture.

Independently from that hope, however, the person and the teachings of Jesus Christ cannot be relegated from our culture and rendered invalid, if our culture is to continue to exist and to create. The stature of the man, who for centuries was not just a teacher of dogmas but a model of the most illustrious human values, cannot fall into non-existence without an essential disruption of the continuity of spiritual life. For he incarnated, personally, the ability to express his truth in full voice, the ability to defend it to the very end without evasions, and the ability to absolutely resist the established reality which did not accept him. He taught how without an appeal to violence one can confront himself and the world. Hence he was a model of that radical authenticity only in which every human being can give real life to his own values.

Leszek Kolakowski
and the Revision of Marxism

GEORGE L. KLINE

I. *Introduction*

IN 1906, seventy-five years after Hegel's death, Benedetto Croce published a vigorous critical study under the title *What is Living and What is Dead in the Philosophy of Hegel.* The seventy-fifth anniversary of Marx's death came and went in 1958. Now, six years later, it is perhaps time for a similarly comprehensive philosophical study of Marxism. The present essay might even be construed as, in part, a preliminary exploration along these lines. On the question of what is *vivo* and what *morto* in Marxist philosophy, I shall make my own position clear from the outset: What is dead, or at least dying, is an orthodoxy based principally on the writings of Engels and Lenin; what is alive, or at least viable, is that form of "revisionism" inspired partly by the early writings of Marx himself and partly by other, especially Kantian and existentialist, modes of thought.

In social-psychological terms: it is revisionism which attracts the more sensitive and intelligent among contemporary Marxist-Leninists; orthodoxy satisfies the less sensitive and intelligent, or the intellectually conformist and politically ambitious.

This is quite understandable. Compared to the deadness of philosophical orthodoxy, revisionism in general—and Marxist revisionism in particular—is vital and exciting. Nothing is duller than the writings of epigoni, however impressive the thought of the masters whose doctrines they repeat. Orthodox Platonists, Aristotelians, Thomists, Cartesians, Spinozists, Kantians, Hegelians, Marxists, Leninists, Deweyans, Whiteheadians, Husserlians, and Wittgensteinians are dreary

This essay originally appeared in George L. Kline, ed., *European Philosophy Today* (Chicago, 1965). Notes and a bibliography are omitted here.

creatures. But not everyone can be an innovator; hence the importance of revisionism. For it occupies the viable middle ground between two intellectual extremes: the unrealizable extreme of absolute doctrinal innovation and the reliable but deadening extreme of absolute doctrinal reiteration. So long as philosophical and political doctrines are corrigible, they will be subject to revision —in the double sense of *review* and *reform,* of critical scrutiny and theoretical modification.

The *term* "revisionist" has been used in English for at least a century in a technical legal sense, and since the 1870's in the special sense of a scholar who contributed to the "revision" of the "authorized" (King James) version of the Bible. The first widespread use of the term in its contemporary political and philosophical sense came with the attack upon the position of Eduard Bernstein (1850-1932) in the 1890's. German and Russian Marxists, with their predilection for abstract words ending in "ism" (e.g., "pauperism," "economism," "opportunism," "deviationism"), quickly branded Bernstein's views as "revisionism." The name has remained, primarily as a polemical term employed by the critics of revisionist writers.

But the fact and the idea of revisionism in philosophy and politics have very ancient roots. Indeed, the history of Western philosophy may be seen as a series of cumulative revisions, beginning with the Platonic revision of Parmenides and ending with contemporary revisions of Husserl, Heidegger, and Wittgenstein. Of the major philosophers perhaps only Plato and Hegel, and with qualifications Kant and Peirce, are original enough to be considered not only "unorthodox" but also "non-revisionist."

Revision is thus a natural and productive aspect of intellectual life. Yet Leninists and Stalinists have made "revisionism" a term of abuse, denying that Marxism-Leninism can ever be justly or usefully revised, and branding every attempted revision as heresy and betrayal—a product of political reaction or counterrevolution. This strategem is not new. The first wave of German and Russian revisionism, which threatened to dilute the purity of orthodox Marxism in the decade after Engels' death (1895), was stoutly resisted in Germany by Karl Kautsky (1854-1938) and in Russia by G. V. Plekhanov (1856-1918), L. I. Akselrod, Lenin, and others. The second, and more restricted, wave of revisionism which, in the 1920's, splashed against the rigid breakwaters of Leninist orthodoxy was violently beaten off by the ideological spokesmen of Soviet Leninism. The third and largest wave of revisionism, released by Stalin's death in 1953, has been resisted with unprecedented violence—and on an unprecedented scale—by Communist authorities in Eastern Europe and China as well as the Soviet Union.

Revisionism is repeatedly linked to "bourgeois ideology." It is described as "the most dangerous manifestation of bourgeois ideology within the working-class movement." Revisionists are called agents of imperialism and reaction. Index cards in Soviet libraries refer readers from the heading "Revisionism, Philosophical," to the heading "Bourgeois Reaction, Philosophy of, and Revisionism"! There is, of course, a grain of historical truth in this polemical juxtaposition.

Orthodox Marxist-Leninists regard Kantianism, Nietzscheanism, existentialism, and positivism as "philosophies of bourgeois reaction." And, as we shall see, each of these philosophies has in fact influenced one or another of the contemporary philosophical revisions of Marxism.

A recent Chinese Communist critic goes so far as to lump together "modern revisionism," "imperialist reaction," and "natural catastrophes," thus suggesting that revisionism is a kind of "ideological catastrophe"—which from the official Marxist-Leninist viewpoint it may very well be.

The fury of the official onslaught upon Marxist revisionism sometimes seems designed to mask lingering doubts in high places about the purity of what passes for orthodox doctrine. The official "Marxist-Leninist" position is in fact often quite as heterodox as that of the declared, or even self-confessed, revisionists. But when doctrine or policy is modified by political leaders, the result is never referred to as a "revision," but rather as the "creative development of Marxism-Leninism." "Revisionism" in the narrow and pejorative sense in which the term is used by official critics turns out to be a name applied by the politically powerful to modifications of doctrine or policy introduced by the politically powerless, in directions which the former regard as a threat to "ideological purity" and political stability.

This characterization applies, of course, to the relationship between political leaders and intellectuals *within* a given Communist country or bloc; and it relates primarily to *philosophical* revisionism. In the case of *political* revisionism, and of relations *between* Communist countries and even blocs, the situation takes on added complexity. Both before 1929 and after 1948 (the dates which roughly demarcate the period of Stalin's absolute ideological authority in the international Communist movement) there have been, and continue to be, cases in which one Communist-bloc leader accuses another of revisionism. Before 1929 Bukharin, Zinoviev, Trotsky, and Stalin exchanged such charges—mostly in terms of left- and right-wing "deviation." After 1948 Stalin and Tito exchanged similar charges. Since 1961 the Albanians have been calling Tito a revisionist; in 1964 the Chinese joined them in openly branding not only Tito but also Khrushchev as a "modern revisionist." There is, of course, more than a grain of truth in the charge—if Lenin be taken as the standard of orthodoxy on such questions as violent (revolutionary) versus nonviolent (evolutionary) "paths to socialism," or the question of "peaceful coexistence of states with different social systems." On such doctrinal issues Mao and Hoxha are demonstrably closer to Lenin than either Khrushchev or Tito. (They are also more reckless and irresponsible as political leaders; but that is another story.)

Many other examples of specific doctrinal revisions might be mentioned: Lenin's voluntarism and stress on the revolutionary role of the peasantry were widely regarded, before October 1917, as revisions of Marxism, but were universally hailed during the Soviet period as "creative developments of Marxism." Stalin, in the 1920's, proclaiming the revisionist political doctrine and program of "building socialism in one country," and repudiating Marxist-Leninist egalitarianism, branded his relatively orthodox opponents—Trotsky in the first case,

Zinoviev in the second—as "anti-Marxists" and "enemies of Marxism." Khrushchev's Party Program of 1961 implicitly repudiated the doctrine and program of the "withering away" of the family which had been accepted by Marx, Engels, and virtually all of the "old Bolshevik intellectuals," but rejected by Stalin in 1936. The Program stresses the proposition that a new kind of family, the "firm, stable socialist family," has made its appearance on the stage of history, and is here to stay.

To these examples of *political* revisionism, we may add one or two instances of *philosophical* revisionism "from above." Stalin (in the late 1930's) quietly eliminated the dialectical law of the "negation of the negation," placing an un-Leninist emphasis upon "gradual" or "progressive" development (*postepennoye razvitiye*) in nature and history. Under Khrushchev (in the late 1950's), the suppressed law was cautiously reintroduced. Again, Stalin's *Marxism and Questions of Linguistics* (1950) introduced a series of unilateral revisions into Marxist-Leninist theory, including a sudden increase in respect for formal logic and a general de-emphasis of "dialectical logic." This particular revision has largely been preserved and even expanded (with respect to mathematical logic) under Khrushchev and his successors.

II. *Political and Philosophical Revisionism*

I have already introduced a distinction between political (or programmatic) and philosophical (or theoretical) revisions of Marxism. It is now time to define political revisionism in detail sufficient to permit us to distinguish it clearly from philosophical revisionism. (The remainder of this paper will constitute a definition, both implicit and explicit, of philosophical revisionism.)

Political revisionists—who are sometimes referred to by their critics as "deviationists"—reinterpret *facts* and revise *theories* concerning the history and status of "capitalism" and "socialism," modifying their socio-economic and political *programs* accordingly. Political revisionsts may be classified as either "moderate" or "extreme."

"Moderate" political revisionists accept the *fact* that mid-twentieth-century "capitalism," at least in Great Britain and the United States, is significantly "socialized"—in the sense of "planned, equitable, and cooperative"; and that Soviet-style "socialism" is to a considerable degree "capitalistic"—in Marx's sense of "competitive, exploitative, and non-egalitarian." From this *fact* they derive a revisionist *program:* stress on class collaboration rather than class struggle, economic and political cooperation with "capitalist" countries (this applies especially to Yugoslavia and Poland), and the peaceful transformation of capitalism into socialism.

All of this, as Soviet critics have been quick to point out, echoes the 1899 position of Eduard Bernstein, as well as that of European Social Democrats and British Laborites since the turn of the century.

Soviet critics who attack the revisionist doctrine and program of peaceful transformation or growth of capitalism into socialism are forced to make a delicate distinction between this "counterrevolutionary, reactionary theory" and the strikingly similar view put forward by Khrushchev at the Twentieth Congress of the Communist Party of the Soviet Union in February 1956. Khrushchev agrees with the revisionists—versus the Chinese and Albanian "dogmatists"—that the transition can and should be non-violent. But where the revisionists—according to Soviet critics—count on a "spontaneous" (*stikhiiny*), unplanned, and unguided process, Khrushchev sees a "deliberate" (*soznatelny*), planned, and guided one. However, to a dispassionate observer, the revisionists do not appear to rely as heavily on historical "spontaneity" or "drift" as their critics charge. Their disagreement with Khrushchev—and it is a real one—concerns the character and quality of the admitted planning or guidance. Khrushchev insists that all planning be centered in a single monolithic party; the revisionists are prepared to share decision-making and responsibility with other social and political groups.

The "extreme" revisionists go one step further, denying that any political party holds a monopoly on political skill, judgment, or dedication to the public interest. Questioning the principle of one-party rule, such revisionists welcome loyal opposition parties, socialist (but non-Communist) or agrarian in nature. Of course, the very idea of *loyal* political opposition is the sheerest heresy to an orthodox Marxist-Leninist.

Moderate political revisionism has been codified in the 1958 Program of the League of Yugoslav Communists, a document which Soviet critics stigmatize as the "catechism of contemporary revisionism." Extreme political revisionism found some support in Poland in 1956 and 1957; but its most articulate spokesman has been the Yugoslav Milovan Djilas, whose views proved sufficiently offensive to the moderate revisionist leadership of the League of Yugoslav Communists to cost him several years in prison. Perhaps extreme political revisionism, by its very nature, is too subversive of established authority to be acceptable by any group or party. Philosophical revisionism lacks organized support or encouragement for rather different reasons. It remains the creation of isolated and lonely individuals scattered across Eastern Europe, of a few members (now mostly ex-members) of Western European Communist Parties, and of a very few of the less conspicuous among younger Soviet philosophers.

III. *Marxism as Ideology and as Philosophy*

This is not the place for a detailed discussion of the term or the concept "ideology" or of the relationship which ideology bears to philosophy and to the special sciences. However, we may note that the peculiar sense which Lenin gave to "ideology"—a sense still mandatory for Soviet Marxist-Leninists—makes it equivalent to "theory." In Lenin's view, all knowledge, whether true or false, adequate or inadequate, and all theory, whether rational or "rationalizing," is ideological. This means that all knowledge is a super-structural reflection of relations within the socio-economic base, hence, in a "class society," necessarily partisan to the interests of a given class. (This is Lenin's famous notion of *partiinost*.) Pushed to its logical extreme, the Leninist reduction of theory to ideology undercuts any distinction between ideology and science, or between ideology and philosophy. It is the root of a notorious Leninist aporia, which issues in the abortive attempt to carve out some place for genuine (in effect, though not in terminology, "non-ideological" or "supra-ideological") knowledge by interpreting "objective and absolute truth" as a product of the accumulation of partial and relative truths.

Marx's own notion of ideology was much more restrictive. In his characteristic —although by no means wholly consistent—view, ideologies are false theories (or, in his Hegelian terminology, forms of "false consciousness") of a special kind, namely, those which serve to mask or to "rationalize" the harsh realities of a given socio-economic system.

In the present discussion, "ideology" is used in a sense broader than Marx's but narrower than Lenin's. An ideology is understood to be a more or less coherent set of theoretical claims and practical (i.e., social and moral) value judgments which function to organize the commitment and action of social groups. It may serve this function equally well whether the theoretical claims involved are true, false, or indeterminate in truth-value. A philosophy, in contrast, is a coherent set of practical valuations and of theoretical claims of utmost generality, which, to be acceptable, must pass the internal test of self-consistency and the external tests of applicability and adequacy. The special sciences (physics, chemistry, biology, etc.) are sets of theoretical claims of more limited generality and (ideally) free of value judgments. Both philosophy and the special sciences —unlike ideology—make essential truth-claims and stand or fall with the success or failure of these claims.

Philosophies, like the special sciences, are essentially corrigible, hence inherently subject to revision. Philosophers and scientists are "revisionists" both by temperament and by training. But ideologists permit only the kind of pseudo-revisions "from above" which we have already discussed.

Contemporary ("third wave") revisionists of Marxism are more self-conscious and reflective about the nature of, and the need for, philosophical revision than were their "first wave" predecessors around the turn of the century. Leszek Kolakowski (b. 1927) is probably the leading theorist of philosophical revisionism, as well as the most productive philosophical revisionist, of his generation. He points out that not only Marxism but also phenomenology and psychoanalysis, as movements, include an orthodox group "which can do nothing but repeat the original formulae without variation," as well as a more creative and independent revisionist group. Kolakowski considers Bergson's philosophy, in contrast, to be a position which has not advanced beyond its first formulations; today it has (orthodox) "admirers" but no (revisionist) "offspring" or "continuers."

He goes on to say that the "humanist left," for which he considers himself— and is widely considered—a spokesman, is marked by an attitude of "revisionism" in the sense of "permanent criticism." According to Kolakowski, to claim that any doctrine or method is exempt from revision is to abandon "science" in favor of "theology."

Kolakowski puts the distinction between Marxism as ideology and as philosophy as that between "institutional" and "intellectual" Marxism.

Institutional Marxism, in his view, is a set of doctrines and value judgments the content of which is fixed, and on occasion modified, by political authorities. Institutional Marxists do not have to be intellectually convinced of the truth, or even understand the meaning, of the doctrines which they profess. Thus, every institutional Marxist, Kolakowski wrote in 1957,

> "knew" in 1950 that Lysenko's theory of inheritance was correct, that Hegel's philosophy was an "aristocratic reaction to the French Revolution," that Dostoevski was a "rotten decadent" and Babayevski an outstanding writer . . . and that the theory of resonance in chemistry was obsolete nonsense. Every [institutional] Marxist knew this even though he had never heard of chromosomes, did not know what century Hegel lived in, had never read a word of Dostoevski, or worked his way through a secondary-school chemistry text.

Of course, by 1956 institutional Marxists "knew" the contrary of most of these claims—and with equal assurance! Similarly, every institutional Marxist in the Soviet bloc was convinced before February 1956 that socialism could be achieved only through violent revolution—and after February 1956 that the only correct course was a "peaceful transition" from capitalism to socialism. Institutional Marxist scholars reversed themselves even more abruptly on the question of Marr's theories of language following Stalin's statements on linguistics in June 1950.

In contrast, intellectual Marxism—for Kolakowski—is not a set of doctrines, but an attitude, a method, and a set of analytical categories. The attitude is rational, critical, and unsentimental; the method is historical and "deterministic," probing the causal interdependence of social phenomena, and stressing group antagonisms; the categories include "class," "ideology," "consciousness," "relations of production," etc. None of these categories is either crystal-clear or diamond-hard, although institutional Marxists insist that *all* Marxist categories are both.

The conception of "orthodoxy" or "doctrinal purity"—as Kolakowski points out—applies only to institutional or ideological Marxism. But such "purity" masks essential vagueness and ambiguity, required if ideological formulas are to remain fixed while their content changes. Ideology, in Kolakowski's view, can never be eliminated; its social function—organizing the values of social groups, reinforcing belief and commitment for historical action—is vital. But it can be "de-totalized"; its predatory and "imperialistic" grip upon intellectual life can be loosened and perhaps eventually broken.

IV. *Philosophical Reviews of Marxism:*
A Historical Sketch

In terms of the distinction outlined above, "revisionism" may be defined as the label which ideological or institutional Marxists apply to unauthorized changes in the content of philosophical or intellectual Marxism—to the extent that these changes call into question the "purity" of Marxist ideology.

Revisionism was possible in the decade after Engels' death because Marxism had not yet become a required ideology, sanctioned by political power; to use Kolakowski's term, it had not yet been "institutionalized." Following upon the "institutionalization" of Marxism-Leninism in the Soviet Union in the late 1920's, revisionism was effectively excluded from Soviet intellectual life. Its appearances since then, even during the cultural "thaw" of 1956, have been feeble, sporadic, and quickly suppressed. Outside the Soviet Union, however, revisionism was still possible within the Communist parties of Eastern and Western Europe; it flowered briefly after Lenin's death in 1924. The third and greatest flowering, of course, came in the "socialist" countries of Eastern Europe, especially Yugoslavia and Poland, in the decade after Stalin's death. This was possible because the rigidity of institutional Marxism was temporarily relaxed, most fully in 1956-1957.

Philosophical revisions of Marxism, both early and late, have been concentrated in the areas of epistemology and ethics, which are the least-developed portions of classical Marxist theory. Marx himself wrote almost nothing on theory of knowledge; Engels' "theory of reflection"—which Marx allegedly endorsed—has always seemed to most non-Marxist, and to many thoughtful Marxists, both primitive and inadequate.

As for ethics, Marxism, like Hegelianism, is oriented toward the social and "world-historical" and away from the individual and ethical. Hegel wrote no treatise on ethics; indeed—as Kierkegaard pointed out long ago—there is no room in the Hegelian system for an autonomous ethic. The same is true of Marxism, in the sense that it admits no intrinsic or irreducible ethical criteria. In his maturity, Marx, following late Hegel, held, in effect, that whatever is the objective outcome of the immanent dialectic of history is right. Lenin—the "Machiavelli of revolution"—added that whatever serves the cause of revolution and the building of socialism is right. From these two criteria, *historical* and *strategic,* respectively, there is no possibility of appeal to any independent *ethical* criterion. Marxist revisionists in ethics have been concerned—either explicitly or implicitly—to discover or devise precisely such a criterion.

The elements of Marxism which were rejected by revisionists, both early and late, are more closely associated with the work of *Engels* than with that of Marx. This applies not only to the epistemological "theory of reflection," already mentioned, but also to ontological materialism and the generalization of the laws of the Hegelian dialectic from human history to the whole of nature. These three doctrines, taken over by Lenin, form the core of orthodox dialectical materialism. A fourth Engels-Lenin tenet, not emphasized by Marx, is the claim that the history of philosophy from the pre-Socratics to the present day can and should be interpreted as a struggle between two "camps"—that of the "pure" philosophical materialists and that of the "pure" philosophical idealists. Of course, Leninists admit that some major philosophers have been relatively "impure" waverers. But where less partisan historians see complexity and subtlety, Leninists apply their exclusive and exhaustive "either-or" (materialism *or* idealism, and *tertium non datur*). Thus Plato, Hume, and Dewey are "idealists"; Aristotle, Locke, and Spinoza are "materialists." Kolakowski wrote a large book on Spinoza partly to show that the seventeenth-century thinker must be considered "neither-nor." Similarly, half a century earlier, the Russian Machians (Bogdanov, Lunacharski, et al.) has insisted that their own "empiriocriticism" was a "neither-nor" position. The chief philosophical aim of Lenin's *Materialism and Empiriocriticism* (1909) was to reduce the "third" positivistic position of the Russian Machians to a form of idealism. In the end, Lenin argued, there is no essential difference between Mach or Avenarius and Bishop Berkeley!

The revisionists who reject these four Engels-Lenin tenets, however, are virtually unanimous in accepting what they take to be *Marx's* central contributions: his philosophy of history, his theory of social change, and his general critique of capitalism and religion. Some of them appeal to the "young Marx" of the Paris Manuscripts of 1844 for support in their rejection of Engels and Lenin.

Nietzsche once said that there are only a handful of possible philosophical systems—which accounts for the similarity of the great traditions of Indian, Greek, and German thought. Be that as it may, there does seem to be no more than a handful of possible revisionist positions. At least, the pattern of contemporary Marxist revisionism bears a striking resemblance to that of the first wave of Russian revisionism, in which revisions in ethics took three forms, paralleled by three forms of revision in theory of knowledge:

ETHICS	EPISTEMOLOGY
1. Kantian	1. Kantian
2. Nietzschean	2. positivist (Machian or "empiriocritical"
3. "Spinozist"	3. "quasi-Kantian" (Plekhanov's theory of hieroglyphs)

In both ethics and epistemology, group No. 1 was most heterodox, group No. 3 most nearly orthodox; group No. 2 stood between the other two, although somewhat closer to the first than to the third. The members of the first group were: P. B. Struve (1870-1944), S. N. Bulgakov (1871-1944), and N. A. Berdyaev (1874-1948); of the second group: A. A. Bogdanov (real name Malinovski: 1873-1928), V. A. Bazarov (real name Rudnev: 1874-1939), A. V. Lunacharski (1875-1933), and S. Volski (real name Sokolev: 1880-1936?); of the third group: Plekhanov, Akselrod-Ortodoks, and Alexandra Kollontai (1872-1952).

I shall say comparatively little about the epistemological revision of the post-

Engels, post-Lenin, or post-Stalin period, and this for two reasons: (a) Contemporary revisionists have written very little on epistemology, and (b) the epistemological views of the earlier revisionists were for the most part slavishly derivative from Western sources—from Kant and Cohen or from Mach and Avenarius. It is curious that Lenin, who devoted an entire book to criticism of the Machians, paid not the least attention to the Kantian and Nietzschean revisions in ethics, which were not only philosophically more significant, but also represented a more serious threat to the "doctrinal purity" of Marxist-Leninist ideology.

Although a serious Kantian revision developed within the German Marxist movement in the 1890's, the German Marxists felt *no* intellectual sympathy for, or ideological interest in, the philosophy of Nietzsche. Even the Kantian revision in Germany—as seen in the writings of its founder, Eduard Bernstein—was primarily political and only peripherally philosophical. Bernstein's "Kantianism" amounted to the claim that the advent of socialism should not be regarded as the necessary outcome of an immanent historical dialectic, but as the possible (and eminently desirable) realization of a freely chosen ideal. Similarly, Bernstein defined exploitation (in 1901) in ethical rather than economic terms, as "the morally reprehensible utilization" of one man by another or others. But his opposition of *Sollen* and *Sein* was vague and programmatic, not analytical or systematic.

There appear to have been at least two reasons for the exceptional interest in Kant and Nietzsche on the part of early Russian Marxists: (a) the historical circumstance that by the middle of the last decade of the nineteenth century Kant and Nietzsche had become the two commanding figures in Western-European philosophy, displacing the Hegelianism and the anti-Hegelian positivism that had prevailed until then; (b) the doctrinal attractiveness of Kant's *ethical* criterion and Nietzsche's *aesthetic* or *cultural* criterion as supplements to, or substitutes for, the *historical* criterion (for evaluating human acts and institutions) offered by Hegel and Marx.

The Kantian Marxists attempted to defend the autonomous individual against the historical "heteronomy" of classical Marxism by providing a theoretical *justification* of "proletarian morality." They placed positive emphasis on the dignity and responsibility of the individual moral agent. The Nietzschean Marxists undertook to free the creative individual from the restricting confines of normative ethics by a *repudiation* of every kind of "ought." On this point Nietzsche and Marx concurred: both the proletariat as a class and the *Übermensch* may be said to stand "beyond (bourgeois-Christian) good and evil." The Nietzscheans placed positive emphasis on the freedom and spontaneity of the individual artistic creator. It is probably no accident that several of the Nietzschean Marxists were productive writers and literary critics, or that Maxim Gorky was for a time closely associated with this group.

Kant's ethics includes at least four distinct, and partially independent, strands: (1) its "formalist" stress on the *a priori* nature of moral judgment; (2) its "normative" emphasis upon duty and the right; (3) its "individualist" insistence that the human person must always be treated as an end-in-himself and never as a means only; (4) its "libertarian" claim that men's actions, although "phenomenally" determined, are "noumenally" free. It was the third point—ethical individualism—which was accepted by all of the Russian Kantian Marxists, but especially by Berdyaev, who disliked Kantian "formalism" and "normativism," the points in which Kant is most sharply opposed to Nietzsche. Thus, while emphasizing the dignity and autonomy of the individual, Berdyaev rejected "abstract obligation" in favor of ethical creativity and passion. Indeed, it might be more accurate to describe Berdyaev at the turn of the century as a "Nietzchean-Kantian" Marxist. Such a position goes beyond revisionism, bordering on eclecticism, if not syncretism. It is not surprising that within a decade Berdyaev had largely abandoned Kant in favor of Nietzsche and was beginning to develop his own form of religious existentialism.

The theoretical difficulties which faced the Russian Kantian Marxists—as exemplified by Berdyaev—cluster around the related notions of *progress, freedom,* and *individuality:*

(1) Berdyaev's "postulate" of an objective ethical *progress* in the historical (hence phenomenal) realm, coupled with a denial of the noumenal as "otherworldly," is open to the criticism which Kant himself leveled at "uncritical" or "pre-critical" philosophies, namely, that the *empirical* evidence which would establish the reality of such progress is not, and in principle cannot be, conclusive.

(2) The Kantian stress on individual moral *freedom* and responsibility proved incompatible with the Hegelian-Marxian stress on the determined collectivity of the "world-historical." Sensing this, Berdyaev moved from historical determinism to a "semi-positivist" mitigation of determinism and ultimately to an assertion of the central existential reality of human freedom.

(3) Kant's dictum that the *individual person* must be treated as an end, never as a means only, is left in the Kantian-Marxist formulation without serious philosophical support. Berdyaev's non-Kantian comrades could justifiably claim that, from a Marxist point of view, such a principle remained theoretically ungrounded and in no way binding upon revolutionary practice.

The Nietzschean Marxists were unanimous in welcoming Nietzsche's repudiation of the ethics of duty and his celebration of the ethics of volition and creativity. But they disagreed sharply on the question of whether volition and creativity should take individual or collective forms. The more individualistic, and thus more orthodoxly Nietzschean, among them were Volski and Lunacharski; the more collectivistic, hence more orthodoxly Marxist, Bogdanov and Bazarov. However, the "collectivism" of the last-named—as opposed to the normative collectivism of later Leninists and Stalinists—was meant to be voluntary and non-normative. The Nietzschean collectivists maintained that under socialism individuals would freely desire to subordinate their interests to those of the social whole. The Leninists and Stalinists declared that individuals were dutybound to do so.

Ranged on a spectrum from most to least individualistic, the Nietzschean Marxists would stand: Volski, Lunacharski, Bogdanov, Bazarov. Their views cannot be examined further here; instead I offer three brief summary comments on the Nietzschean revision of Marxism in Russia:

(1) Nietzsche is closer to Marx than is Kant. Kant's approach to individual morality is "pre-Hegelian" and non-historical, Nietzsche's is "post-Hegelian"—theoretically as well as chronologically—and "culture-historical." To be sure, Nietzsche regards the "dead" weight of past history as an obstacle to present creativity. But for him this creativity is not an end in itself; rather it serves *future* history, enriching the cumulative culture which is in process of becoming.

(2) The theoretical tension between the ethical positions of Marx and Nietzsche reaches its peak in the position of egalitarian versus élitist ethics. Who is to shape and reshape cultural values? According to Nietzsche, the solitary few; according to Marx, the solidary many. The Nietzschean Marxists tried to have it both ways. Their disagreement on the matter of individual versus collective creativity was symptomatic of the deeper difficulty attendant upon any attempt at a synthesis of the ethics of Nietzsche and Marx. Once again, revisionism merges into eclecticism, coming dangerously close to syncretism.

(3) The Nietzschean Marxists followed Nietzsche in rejecting traditional theism while accepting a "new" immanentistic and humanistic religion. Gorky and Lunacharski declared that "God-building" (*bogostroitelstvo*) should be the "religion of the proletariat," whose god would be mankind itself as the collective creator of historical culture. Such a view is more compatible with Nietzsche's position than with Marx's; it was impatiently repudiated by Lenin and his followers.

The "revisions" which cropped up here and there in the Communist parties of Eastern and Western Europe during the 1920's were too meager and sporadic to permit ready classification. There seem to have been brief flirtations with Nietzschean Marxism among the Czechs. A form of positivism (officially labeled "mechanism") flourished in Moscow and Leningrad until it was "liquidated" by Soviet authorities in 1930. The most serious philosophic contributions were those of Georg Lukács, then living in Vienna, and of Ernst Bloch (both born in 1885).

The "neo-Hegelianism" of Lukács' *Geschichte und Klassenbewusstsein* (1923) was promptly attacked by the Soviet guardians of Marxist-Leninist orthodoxy. Lukács himself was not slow in repudiating the "revisionist tendencies" of his own work. After the Second World War, and his return to Budapest, following a long stay in Moscow, he heaped abuse upon Western "neo-Hegelians" such as Maurice Merleau-Ponty (1908-1961) who persisted in regarding *Geschichte und Klassenbewusstsein* as Lukács' major contribution to Marxist theory. In essays written in 1946-47 and published in 1951 under the title *Existentialismus oder Marxismus* Lukács sharply attacked the kind of Kantian-existentialist ethics later to be defended by Kolakowski (see below, Sec. V). His attack is focused upon Sartre, Simone de Beauvoir, and Merleau-Ponty.

Bloch, in a series of works which began to appear in 1918 and continued into the 1950's, offended Marxist-Leninists by distinguishing a "warm stream" and a "cold stream" in Marxist thought—the former characterized as the impulse to freedom and revolutionary action, the latter as the impulse to realistic and deterministic analysis of social situations. In opting for the former, Bloch undercut Marxist determinism, stressing the openness of the historical process and the efficacy of human hope. In 1954 he listed Plato, Aristotle, Leibniz, Kant and Hegel—idealists all—among the intellectual forerunners of his own "principle of hope," conspicuously omitting the materialists from whom Marxist-Leninists are expected to trace their philosophical lineage. Such heresies have long given Bloch a place apart among both revisionists and anti-revisionists in the Soviet bloc. It is not surprising that within a month of the erection of the Berlin wall in August 1961 he should have sought political asylum in Western Germany —becoming the only major Marxist philosopher to do so. He is now (1964) a professor of philosophy at the University of Tübingen.

The third wave of Marxist revisionism, touched off by Khrushchev's denunciation of Stalin (and, more guardedly, of "Stalin*ism*") at the Twentieth Party Congress in February 1956, was much more massive and potentially destructive of orthodoxy than either of its predecessors. In many ways it presents a magnified image of the first wave of German and Russian revisionism: the Kantian and Nietzschean revisions in ethics have been replaced by a single "Kantian-existentialist" or "anthropological" revision (whose most articulate spokesman is Kolakowski). Corresponding to the early and relatively orthodox "Spinozistic" revision in ethics is a relatively orthodox "Hegelian" revision. In epistemology the early Kantians and Machians have been succeeded by neo-positivist or "analytical" Marxists. This is not strange in view of the historical continuity in theory of knowledge which runs from Kant through Avenarius and Mach to the Vienna Circle and beyond.

The forms of contemporary philosophical revisionism may be represented schematically as follows:

ETHICS		EPISTEMOLOGY	
1.	Kantian-existentialist	1.	———
2.	———	2.	neo-positivist or "analytical"
3.	"Hegelian"	3.	———

Spaces left blank indicate lack of interest or failure to develop clear positions. This applies to the "Kantian-existentialists" and "Hegelians" with respect to epistemology; to the "positivists" with respect to ethics.

As in first-wave revisionism, group No. 1 is most heterodox, No. 3 most nearly orthodox. A majority of contemporary revisionists began as Leninist-Stalinists, shifting intellectual position rapidly between 1954 and 1957, in the wake of such political and ideological traumas as Khrushchev's de-Stalinization drive (February 1956), and the Polish and Hungarian "Octobers" (October-November 1956). Russian revisionists of the first wave had passed through a similarly rapid intellectual evolution during the late 1890's and early 1900's;

but all of them had *begun* as revisionists, if moderate ones. They were confronted with no ideological or "institutional" Marxism from which to break away.

Contemporary "Kantian-existentialist" revisionists make very few explicit references either to Kant or to existentialist thinkers. However, their *critics* have been quick to note, and deplore, the "marriage of Kantianism and existentialism" entailed by their ethical position—as an official Polish critic expressed it in 1958. Many of them seek a ground for ethical individualism in "der junge Marx," especially the eloquent if not always coherent critique of "alienation" and "reification" of the Paris Manuscripts of 1844. In fact, some revisionists use "early Marx" not only against Engels and Lenin but also against "late Marx." The early Kantian and Nietzschean Marxists might have done the same, except that the Paris Manuscripts were not published until 1932.

The neo-positivists as a group are in retreat from speculative philosophy, whether Hegelian or Marxist-Leninist; they express their contempt for "fuzzy dialectical thinking" by calling it "Hegelianism" (Russian *gegelyanstvo*). They include some of the younger logicians and philosophers of science, in the Soviet Union as well as Poland and Czechoslovakia, who are professionally concerned with questions of mathematical logic, axiomatization, information theory, cybernetics, and even computer-programming. Some of the relevant names are L. Tondl (Czechoslovakia), Helena Eilstein (Poland), and A. A. Zinoviev (Soviet Union). The last named is the author of an interesting monograph on *Philosophical Problems of Many-Valued Logic,* published in English translation in 1963.

The "Hegelians" have also withdrawn from speculative philosophy—into history and commentary. They have been active in translating and commenting upon Hegel's *Phenomenology* and certain other works, and in tracing the influence of Hegel upon Marx. This group includes Tadeusz Kronski (Poland), who died young in 1958; Milan Sobotka and Ivan Dubsky (Czechoslovakia); Lukács (Hungary); and, to a lesser extent, E. V. Ilyenkov (Soviet Union).

Philosophically, the Kantian-existentialists may be said to be oriented toward the individual human *future,* the Hegelians toward the collective "culture-historical" *past,* and the positivists toward *neither.* The latter are non-temporally oriented—as befits thinkers whose noetic models are to be found in mathematics and formal logic.

V. *The Individual, the Collective, and the March of World History*

The remainder of this essay will be devoted to an analysis of the Kantian-existentialist attempt to reconcile individual moral responsibility with the objective march of world history. I shall try to bring out the parallel between the position developed around the turn of the century by one of the most sensitive and intelligent of young Russian Marxists of that period, Nicholas Berdyaev, and the position elaborated in the late 1950's by one of the most sensitive and intelligent of young Polish Marxists of our own day, Leszek Kolakowski.

The first Kantian revision in ethics took its origin in the efforts of several gifted and erudite young Marxists (notably Berdyaev and Struve) to answer the central question of Marxist ethics, namely: How can *one* of the competing class-moralities be *proven* objectively superior to the other(s)? What is the *justification* for the Marxist commitment to proletarian, rather than bourgeois or feudal-aristocratic, morality?

The classical Marxist answer to these questions, according to Berdyaev, takes two forms, one *logical*—not, of course, in the sense of formal logic but in the Hegelian sense of a "logic of history"—the other *psychological*. (It might be more precise to say that the Marxist answer appeals to two kinds of *criteria,* one historical, the other psychological.) The first states that proletarian morality *will* in fact triumph, as the necessary outcome of the "immanent conformity to law of the historical process." The second states that because of its class-interests the proletariat as a class necessarily *desires* the triumph of this morality.

Berdyaev finds these answers true but inadequate. To establish that proletarian morality *will* triumph or that the proletariat *desires* its triumph is not to prove that it *deserves* to triumph. One might consistently—though falsely—assume that history is realizing an *immoral* ideal, e.g., increasingly efficient exploitation. The march of history, Berdyaev admits, might be a moral retreat rather than an advance.

To speak of the historical realization of an *immoral* idea is, of course, to make at least implicit appeal to an independent ethical criterion reducible neither to "class psychology" nor to the "logic of history." Berdyaev himself makes this appeal explicit when he proposes a third answer, an "objectively *ethical*" grounding of proletarian morality, which is essentially Kantian. Proletarian morality, Berdyaev asserts, must be proven *worthy* to triumph by being shown to correspond more closely than any competing class-morality to the principle that individuality is an end in itself "giving moral sanction to all else and needing no sanction for itself." (Any proffered psychological or historical sanction— Berdyaev seems to recognize—would entail a vicious circularity.) In asserting, with Kant, that the formal distinction between good and evil precedes all sense experience and hence all historical determinations, Berdyaev adopts a position which is not only un-Marxian but also un-Hegelian.

Kolakowski, in 1957, sharply qualifies Berdyaev's "postulate of historical progress," placing clearer emphasis upon the moral autonomy of the existing individual than Berdyaev was prepared to do in 1901. His ethical revision of Marxism, although independent of Berdyaev's, is parallel to it in many ways and encounters many of the same theoretical difficulties.

Kolakowski stands at the turbulent confluence not only of Marxist and non-Marxist intellectual currents but also of the disparate streams of recent Polish positivism, contemporary Anglo-American analysis, and Continental existentialism. His terminology and rhetoric reflect a hospitable cosmopolitanism which sometimes verges on the eclectic—a danger, as we have seen, in all revisionism.

Thus, he stresses the "mutual exclusiveness" of values and loyalties and admits the "permanent possibility of tragedy." He sees an "incurable antinomy" in the realm of human values, an antinomy which no possible social change could alleviate. He speaks of "anguish," "absurdity," "authenticity," "risk," "decision," "commitment." Yet in the same breath he can refer to "pseudo-questions," "many-valued logics," the distinction between "normative" and "descriptive" judgments, the need for empirical enquiry. Only occasionally does he use purely Marxist terminology, as in discussing the "contradiction" between the "façade" and the "content" of a social system. Compared to his fellow-Marxists in the Soviet Union and elsewhere in Eastern Europe, most of whom still speak in the accents of the nineteenth century, Kolakowski's idiom is modern indeed.

The ethics of Kierkegaard is close in many essential respects to that of Kant. Kolakowski, an avowed atheist and anti-cleric, seems to have derived a great deal from both thinkers—although his public acknowledgments are to Sartre and (usually in a peripheral or illustrative way) to the nineteenth-century Russian thinkers Belinski and Herzen. Of the four strands in Kantian ethics, Kolakowski seems most firmly committed (like Berdyaev) to ethical individualism but also (unlike Berdyaev) to normativism. He hedges on the question of freedom, attempting to combine an assertion of individual free choice with an acceptance of social determinism. He implicitly rejects Kant's formalism, insisting that "'duty is only the voice [glos] of a social need." Thus for him morality is not *a priori* but, in Kantian terms, *a posteriori* and "heteronomous." That is, as a Marxist he sees the ground of moral obligation not in the individual moral agent but rather in a historically conditioned social structure ("stratum" or "class").

Yet Kolakowski's "Responsibility and History" is an impassioned defense of individual moral autonomy against the heteronomy of history, or, as he puts it, an affirmation of the "total responsibility of the individual for his own deeds, and the amorality of the historical process."

Like Belinski, whom he mentions here, and Herzen, whom he does not, Kolakowski condemns every sacrifice of the existing individual to an abstract historical future. "What right do I have," asks the Intellectual (interlocutor of the Revolutionary in the brief dialogue with which "Responsibility and History" opens), "in the name of that speculative dialectic of the future to renounce at present the supreme values of human existence?" And the Intellectual continues: It is immoral to sacrifice the present for the future; and to give up truth, self-respect, and moral values is to sacrifice the future itself.

Kolakowski characterizes the Hegelian-Marxist philosophy of history as a "historiosophy," using a nineteenth-century term still more or less current in Polish—and to some extent German and Italian—philosophical discourse, but strange to English and American usage. In a general way, Kolakowski's use of the term "historiosophical" parallels Berdyaev's earlier use of "logical" (see above, p. 96), although it is pejorative, whereas Berdyaev's references to the "logic of history" were not. Historiosophy, which is an expression of the "cunning of the *Weltgeist,*" is for Kolakowski a nightmare of abstractions.

In the world of historiosophy, he writes,

there are no more individuals: they appear only as instances of [general] ideas, bearing the mark of their species upon their foreheads. In that world we do not eat bread and butter; we restore our labor power, which is consciously organized for the purposes of socialist construction. We do not sleep; we regenerate cerebral tissue for creative work in realizing the *Weltgeist;* we talk not to men but to carriers of ideas, which are themselves only representatives of certain conflicting social forces in the gigantic march of history . . . [Thus] we move from the swamp of everyday life to the madness of abstract life, as if we were passing from a brothel to a monastery.

In Kolakowski's view, the historiosophical assurance that "we can read the future of the world as reliably as a railroad timetable" is an "insane illusion." He derides the "poverty of prophetic historiosophy" and urges "historiosophers" to confine themselves to a study of the historical necessities of the *past*.

But Kolakowski's principal objection to historiosophy is not so much theoretical as moral. It is not merely that we cannot be as sure of the future as we can of the past, but that "the greater the degree of certainty we have concerning the intentions of the demiurge [of history], the greater the threat" to our moral sanity, the greater the danger that we will substitute criteria of historical effectiveness for ethical criteria.

In more theoretical and general terms, Kolakowski characterizes the reduction of ethical to historical (or "historiosophical") criteria as "ethical Hegelianism" or "pseudo-Hegelianism." Its extreme form is *Stalinism,* a position which entails the claim that whatever serves socio-economic "progress" is morally obligatory, thus erasing the distinction between the "historically progressive" and the "morally right." But since it is difficult, if not impossible, to know just which present acts or policies will contribute to future historical progress, Stalinists (or "institutional Marxists") permit others to make this decision for them.

Kolakowski sharply rejects the value-dogmatism (he calls it "axiological absolutism") of the "normative interpretation of historiosophy," i.e., the deduction of *Sollen* from *Sein* (an explicitly Kantian polarity), of duty from historical necessity. Such dogmatism is closely related to the judging of present acts in terms of their anticipated consequences for world history.

Putting the point in theoretical terms (in a section of his essay entitled "Conscience and Social Progress") Kolakowski writes: "Practical choice in life is made in a world defined by '*Sollen*' and not by '*Sein.*' . . . It is not true that historiosophy determines our main choices in life. Our moral sensitivity [*poczucie*] does this." This sensitivity, he adds, must not be dulled or smothered by the "opiate of the *Weltgeist.*" Putting the point in personal and political terms, he declares: "We are not Communists because we have recognized communism as a historical necessity; we are Communists because we have joined the side of the oppressed against the oppressors. . . ." ,

Generalizing his tormented reflections on the "historical crimes of Stalinism," Kolakowski asks—unconsciously echoing Berdyaev: "If crime is the law of history, does knowledge of this law justify one in becoming a criminal?" His answer is unequivocal:

No one is absolved from the moral responsibility for supporting a crime merely because he is convinced of its inevitable victory. No one is exempted from the moral duty to oppose a political system, a doctrine, or a social order which he considers to be base and inhuman on the ground that he also believes them to be historically necessary.

Kolakowski in 1957 had experienced more of the "horrors of world history" than Berdyaev in 1901 could imagine. And he was painfully aware that many of the worst of them had been perpetrated by professed Marxist-Leninists:

> Between obedience to history and obedience to the moral imperative yawns an abyss on whose brink the great historical tragedies have been played: the tragedies of conspiracies and insurrections doomed to disaster, and the opposed trage-dies of collaboration with crime based on a belief in its inevitability. On both of these brinks the moral drama of the revolutionary movement in recent years has also been played out.

To avoid vicious circularity, Kolakowski says, we must acknowledge the logical priority of social progress *or* of moral values, but not both. To define social progress in terms of moral values violates the principles of historical materialism; to accept any value as absolute violates the principles of the dialectical method. This strikes me as a succinct and accurate formulation of the dilemma of Kantian Marxism.

As we have seen, Kolakowski wishes to remain a Marxist, even at the risk of undermining his Kantian commitment to "moral values" and individual moral responsibility. As a Marxist he accepts one form of the doctrine of "historical inevitability"—a social determinism which reduces men's moral convictions to reflections of their social circumstances. He repeatedly insists that such deter-minism is compatible with individual moral responsibility. But in at least one place he sensibly suggests that the determinism in question may be "statistical" rather than "strict."

> The fate of an individual cannot be determined by the generalized laws of the class struggle, any more than the behavior of an individual particle of a gaseous substance [i.e, a gas molecule] can be predicted from the general laws governing the mechanics of gases [i.e., statistical mechanics], although the latter remain valid with respect to aggregates.

There may be a very high probability, even a "statistical quasi-certainty," that at least one of the thousand people standing by a river bank will leap into the water to save a drowning child, but anyone who actually *does* so must have made his own (free) decision. And no one who fails to do so has any right to appeal to historical, social, or even biological necessity as an excuse for his inaction. In Kolakowski's words:

> Neither our own supposedly irresistible passions ("I was unable to resist the impulse"), nor anyone's command ("I was a soldier"), nor conformity to social custom ("Everyone did that"), nor the theoretically deduced law of the Great Demiurge [of history] ("I thought I was acting for the sake of progress")—can be regarded as justification.

None of these kinds of determination "relieves the individual of moral responsibility, because none of them eliminates the freedom of individual choice."

In explicitly Kantian terms, Kolakowski asserts that certain human actions are ends-in-themselves, hence obligatory, and others are "counter-ends-in-themselves," hence absolutely forbidden. If moral values are subordinated to the realization of historical necessity, then nothing in contemporary life can be considered an end in itself, and moral values in the strict sense lose their validity.

For Kolakowski the free individual faces not a historical but a personal or "existential" future. Men who permit their own moral choices to be "historiosophically" determined are like

> tourists who scratch their names on the walls of dead cities. Everyone can . . . interpret himself historically and discover the determinisms to which he was subject while he was becoming what he now is, that is, in his past. But he cannot do this with respect to the person he has not yet become. He cannot infer his own future from historiosophical predictions.

In order to do this, says Kolakowski, one would have to treat oneself as wholly in the past, in other words, as dead.

Such a claim sounds not merely "existentialist," but specifically Kierkegaardian. It suggests that Kolakowski may tacitly recognize the inconsistency of his attempt to combine moral autonomy with socio-historical heteronomy. When he sums up his position as involving: (1) ethical individualism ("only individuals and their actions are subject to moral evaluation"), (2) social determinism ("moral judgments are socially conditioned"), and (3) the right to moral judgment of political decisions and institutions—he gives the impression of being most deeply committed to the first and third of his "theses," and quite possibly —like Berdyaev half a century earlier—on the way to abandoning, or at least drastically modifying, the second of them as inconsistent with the other two. Whether or not this is the case, Kolakowski's attempt to combine individual moral autonomy with a form of socio-historical heteronomy—although it is marked by moral passion as well as intellectual vigor—comes dangerously close to syncretism.

VI. *Conclusion*

Soviet critics explain the striking renaissance of both political and philosophical revisionism in the 1950's as "a manifestation of bourgeois ideology in the working class." They attempt to account for its influence in Poland, Yugoslavia, Czechoslovakia, and East Germany, and its lack of influence in the Soviet Union, in terms of the relative newness of "socialism" in the first four countries and its relative maturity and stability in the last. The same reasoning, however, would lead one to expect serious revisionist tendencies in Rumania, Bulgaria, and Albania, where—in the post-Stalin decade—there has in fact been no evidence whatever of revisionism, either political or philosophical. A more plausible explanation is the greater rigidity and tighter ideological monopoly of institutional Marxism in Rumania, Bulgaria, Albania, and the Soviet Union. Whatever revisionist currents exist in those countries have long since been forced beneath the official surface into the "cultural underground"—along with (to use Soviet examples) non-representational painting, religious and erotic poetry, novels like Pasternak's *Dr. Zhivago* and Abram Tertz's *The Trial Begins,* and plays like I. Ivanov's *Is There Life on Mars?*

Similarly, the more plausible explanation for the flourishing of revisionism in the freer milieu of Poland and Yugoslavia, and to a lesser extent and for a shorter time in Czechoslovakia and East Germany, would seem to be, as a Bulgarian critic admitted in 1957, that it is "a reaction to dogmatic Marxism." To be sure, the same critic added the qualification, "in its *form*" (presumably as opposed to its *content*). This qualification was omitted by Lukács, who recently characterized revisionism as a "reaction to Stalinism," but insisted that he himself was *not* a revisionist, and indeed that revisionism must be resisted—though with persuasion rather than force.

It is difficult to predict the further development of philosophic revisionism among contemporary Marxists. The major revisionist writings date from 1956-1957; since 1958 very little of philosophical significance has been published by Eastern European Marxists. This is probably due less to failing interest or slackened intellectual vitality than to the increasing pressure of institutional Marxism; and such pressure shows little sign of abating. As a Soviet spokesman put it in 1958: "Either we destroy revisionism, or revisionism will destroy us; there is no third way." The official campaign to root out revisionism has been unparalleled in scope and violence; it is hardly surprising that this campaign should have succeeded in driving most of the revisionists underground.

A Soviet critic has described the "logic of the revisionists" as moving from "rejection of Stalin in the name of Lenin" to "rejection of Lenin in the name of Marx," and finally to "rejection of Marxism generally." This particular sequence applies more directly to political than to philosophical revisionism. The parallel sequence in philosophy would be: rejection of Engels and Lenin in the name of Marx, rejection of late Marx in the name of early Marx (and of Kant and Sartre or Wittgenstein and Carnap), and, finally, rejection of Marxism generally.

No contemporary revisionist has publicly taken this last step. But it seems likely that philosophical revisionists like Kolakowski might, if given the opportunity, move further away from Marxism—as Berdyaev and the other Kantian Marxists did after 1903—in the direction of existentialism, neo-Kantianism, or perhaps some new man-centered philosophy of their own. Such a move would represent a doctrinal loss to intellectual Marxism, and an ideological blow to institutional Marxism. But it would be a distinct gain for philosophy.

GEORGE L. KLINE is Associate Professor of Philosophy and Russian at Bryn Mawr College. He is the author of *Spinoza in Soviet Philosophy* (1952), translator of Zenkovsky's *History of Russian Philosophy* (1953), and editor of *Alfred North Whitehead: Essays on His Philosophy* (1963). He has published numerous articles on Russian philosophy and intellectual history and on Spinoza, Hegel, Marx, and Whitehead.

translated by Czeslaw Milosz
JULIAN PRZYBOŚ

Equation of the heart

They strangled the air with banners.
Under all the triumphal arches
the rebels put dynamite.

Who am I? An exile of birds.

The table under my pen, having swollen up to its edges
exceeds itself
like a tank about to attack.
Already today the house burns with tomorrow's fire,
faster my heart assaults me.

Shrapnel bursts from poles of street lights:
The lamps were lit in the streets all at once.
The day passes in an armed song of soldiers and gives its last rattle.

From the rusty grass the ribs of the fallen ruffled the sod.

Alive, I walk in this present and yet bygone city.

Who am I? An exile of birds.

The gardens—the new moon like a thorn rising from the boughs—
The world without me fulfills itself, motionless and free,
and only the laurel of autumn leaves falls on my head.

. . . so that I never keep silent.

Gentle,
I would turn my every pocket into nests for swallows
flying away from people.

JULIAN PRZYBOŚ (b. 1901) is a poet of the Polish Avantgarde and an influential art-theo-
retician, known for his highly intellectual and 'constructivistic' poetry. He lives in Cracow.

translated by Marcus Wheeler

Tabu

JACEK BOCHEŃSKI

Reverend Fathers, now I will tell you all.

Yes, I admit it, it was arranged.

No, Reverend Fathers, I don't know why.

The place was arranged—past the toll-gate, in the copse to the left of the bridge; and the time was arranged—immediately after sunrise; and the donkey.

Yes, and the disguise.

Why, Reverend Fathers? I don't know.

I was not thinking anything, except that it was a beautiful morning—because that day the sun had begun to shine after a long period of rain and the sky had cleared; I was not afraid of anything, except whether Diego had come and would be there waiting, nothing else; there was a ringing in my head, because I had hardly slept that night, and I had risen at daybreak; so I was walking along without a thought, in the sun; the road was deserted—I walked past the toll-gate and none stopped me, and past the toll-gate it was still brighter and at that hour there was no one about, so I almost ran, and I was looking at the sky and the cloudless Pyrenees.

No, Reverend Fathers. Diego didn't know either.

Diego was there already, by the river. I turned off to the left of the bridge into the copse. I moved quietly, there was not a sound; I could see the bank of the stream behind the trees and I thought—it's here; but Diego had not noticed me yet; two donkeys were cropping the grass, one grey, the other mouse-coloured—the grey one saw me; I came nearer, my heart standing still, but Diego still didn't see me; he was sitting by the stream, the water was gurgling and Diego was looking at the water. "Diego", I said, just whispering the name. "Dolores". He trembled suddenly and turned away. "Sister Dolorosa", he said, and looked at me, and I looked at him, and saw how gay he looked; he was smiling—radiant all over—and said again: "Dolores". The water gurgled and the donkeys cropped the grass. "We must hurry, Sister Dolorosa", he said. "All right", I said. "What a beautiful day". "We need to get as far as we can from the town". "I'll ride the grey one", I said. And we went to the donkey. But no. "We can't go like this", he said, "you meet all sorts on the road, I have a disguise here for you". He rummaged in his bag and brought out a groom's clothing, trousers—I said nothing—so be it, I thought—trousers, I thought, or a millstone about my neck or into fire, so be it—I stopped short, something strange came over me, as if I had lost all sensation. "Diego", I said, "Diego, I am not afraid at all". "Carissima", he said, but then darkened and looked sad. Suddenly breaking away, he mounted his donkey and left the grey one for me, to catch him up presently—meanwhile he would survey the road and wait by the bridge. I stood there feeling nothing, there was a kind of cold dryness inside me; even with a millstone about my neck, I thought; no, that's wrong, I wasn't thinking anything; I threw off all my clothes and delved into the bag.

And on with the trousers, Reverend Fathers.

I did it quickly.

Then up on the donkey.

I was a little afraid, but the sun was shining, it was quiet everywhere and the way was clear, there was no one on the bridge, Diego would be waiting, that's where I was going. When he saw me, his mouth moved but he said nothing. Such big eyes he had! And he kept them fixed on me. Coming quickly towards me, he took my hand, held it for a while and whispered: "Dolores!" I was hot. "Where is your habit?", asked Diego. "In the bag". "Good. Let's go".

We went at a trot. Diego did not spare his donkey, because it had been agreed that on the first day we should make haste and get as fast as possible to the mountains. So we clattered along and stones flew in all directions from beneath the donkey's feet. And Diego's hair streamed. We kept looking at one another, laughing and amazed that we were actually on our way. Perhaps I am dreaming, I thought. But Diego was as real as broad daylight and those jolly little donkeys.

I will tell you quite honestly, Reverend Fathers: he only kissed me once on the road, when we were watering the donkeys.

I was cross about it.

I did not try to stop him, but I was cross.

I said nothing. He said: "Once we're over there ..." I took him to mean, over the mountains. He seemed to want to, go on, but said no more—just looked. I thought he was talking about the French frontier. Then he said again several times: "Dolores, when you and I get over there ..." And closed his eyes. Or: "Sister Dolorosa, you have no idea what it will be like over there". "What will it be like?", I asked. "Beautiful". I felt that this referred not to the kingdom of France but to something Diego wanted to do with me. He did not explain, but asked whether I knew the word 'Eden'. Of course I did. "Eden begins over there", he said. "Or Gehenna", he added after a pause.

Reverend Fathers, you will please remember that Diego is a poet and a madman.

"I present this castle to you", he would say, as we passed some derelict peasant hut; the clouds in the sky, too, he would offer me; but what I liked best were the stories he told about Centaurs and Pegasuses and suchlike. "Dolores, my white lily", he would cry. Or: "To me you are sweeter than the honey of Hymettus". Thus we passed the journey till evening; how and for how long we rode, I do not know, because it was like a dream journey and as if we were Adam and Eve, only that day created by God and marvelling at the trees and flowers and various creatures. So it continued, that journey, for many hours—how many, I don't know. Finally Diego said: "I'm hungry. I know an inn about half a mile from here, we can put up there for the night". I was frightened, but the donkeys were exhausted, night was upon us and there was no shelter in the open, unless we were to make for the forest. "The inn is in a secluded spot", said Diego encouragingly. "No one will recognise you". "What does it matter?", I said peevishly, although I was trembling all over. "The prioress won't come after us on a donkey. Let's stop for the night". Diego laughed. And now, when we had reached the inn, I went in first. In the courtyard a black dog barked furiously. There were a lot of people sitting on benches, drinking and making a tremendous noise. The inn-keeper was a tall man with fish-like eyes. "We wish to stay the night here", I said. "Who is 'we'?", he asked. "My master and I". "Where is this master of yours?" At that moment Diego came in. "Ah", I said, pointing to him, "here's my master!" I know I blushed; the man with fish-like eyes was saying something and I was covered in confusion and made some reply that was completely beside the point. He smacked his tongue, looked me up and down with a foolish expression and chuckled. But Diego rattled his purse and gave him some money. "Very well, Senor", said the inn-keeper. "Stay the night here. But I have many guests and I shall have to put you together in one hut. At that Diego said that he could perhaps ... "No, no", the inn-keeper interrupted him and asked: "What do you want to eat and drink—lamb or capon, wine or cider?" Diego chose lamb and wine, and I asked for salad and cider, and lamb too, because Diego was hungry. Our meal was served. "What is to become of us?", I said. "Do you know, Diego?" "No". "What are we about, Diego?" His eyes misted over. "Have we gone mad? Tell me, Diego". "We are still over here", he whispered. The black dog looked through the door, came in, sniffed under the tables and lay down in the corner where our bag was. Then it got up and sniffed all round the bag until the inn-keeper shouted at it to be off. Diego laughed again and said the lamb was good. Yes, not bad, I thought—and now in my convent refectory they will be saying grace and the sisters will be sitting down to their supper: only I am missing, the prioress is looking pale and whatever can have been going on all day there...

"Listen, Diego, what is to become of us?" - I spoke quietly, very quietly, so that no one should hear—"What do you suppose is happening at the convent, Diego?" "Probably the sisters are weeping for you". "I don't know whether they are weeping—maybe some of them are. But, do you know what, Diego, I'm frightened of that black dog".

He was quite ordinary, Reverend Fathers, like any other dog. Only he was black. Sometimes a person gets an idea into his head, but I noticed nothing else special about him.

Later he appeared again in a dream.

He and the inn-keeper.

The details? I see. Well, then, Diego said: "Come on, Dolores, let's have a look at the stars, then to sleep!".

There were no stars, but the moon was leaning out from behind a mountain, so we stood for a while, then took a candle to the hut in which the inn-keeper had bidden us spend the night. Everywhere men, strangers to us, were already lying and there were only two sleeping-places in the corner unoccupied. But no one was asleep yet. They were saying something in hushed tones in the Basque language. None addressed us. They stopped talking when we entered and asked us nothing, neither where we came from, nor the object of our journey, nor who we were. Nor did we know who they were. "So much the better", muttered Diego, then whispered: "You sleep by the wall, further away from them, and I will take this place at the end". I did not want to be right by the wall, because it suddenly struck me that, if anything happened, I should have no way of escape from there. "No, Diego", I said, and I thought that, by the wall, I should have no freedom of action and would only be in Diego's power. "No, Diego, I prefer the place at the end". "You take *that* bed", he repeated; "what's the matter with you, Carissima, lie down, I'm going to blow out the candle". "No, Diego, I'll blow out the candle". "Whatever is the matter with you?" "I'm afraid". "What of?" "Those Basques and the dog". I said. But it was a lie, because it was Diego I was afraid of. Or was it? Was it not perhaps the night, or eternal damnation, and what I had done. Although, St. Mary Magdalene be my witness, I had done nothing yet, but I was afraid that I might do something that night or the next, and that that would be final—and what would follow, I was afraid of that, too. Diego at once went quiet, as if he had lost patience, and took the place by the wall without a word. I put out the candle, lay down carefully on the bed and, lying completely still, I could for a while hear murmurings and Diego's breathing. The Basques began to snore and make whistling noises in their sleep, and I closed my eyes. In my mind's eye various sights were floating before me, then Diego sighed and I felt his hand reach out to me. I shuddered. "Are you asleep?", asked Diego. "I shall be presently". He found my hand in the dark, squeezed it gently and held it thus. When I tried to free it from his grasp, he would not let go. Suddenly one of the Basques who was lying close to us moved violently. This scared me and I tugged with all my might to get my hand free, but Diego held it still harder, and I gradually weakened and lay back, making no further effort to break away. Then he released his grip, but I no longer tried to withdraw and was even happy to have him stroking my hand in the dark, until finally he grasped it harder again, so strangely somehow and with such a shudder that it went right through my whole body. Then at last he let go himself and withdrew, as if in flight, and I at once fell asleep. I know nothing, remember nothing, except hearing a noise and someone moving about, but I dreamed about a fish—a great, long fish with an enormous snout—and this fish was on top of me, I'm not sure what he was doing, but probably swimming. It had the inn-keeper's eyes and grinned senselessly, fish-like, with its whole snout, and pressed upon me. I could not move and I could feel it touching me on my legs, thighs and points higher; it was all slippery and what it did to me hurt. No, it was not a fish, but that dog—it scratched me with its claws; that black dog was leaping upon me and I was naked; no, it was not the dog but the inn-keeper—he was saying something but I couldn't understand, and he kept on with those paws just like an animal; there were voices nearby, and people. I know now that it was a dream, only I didn't know where I was. I opened my eyes and it was light, the dawn must have come, and someone was embracing me and kissing me. Diego! "Do you know, Dolores, the Basques have just gone", he said. "I was waiting till they went, but I thought I would burn up from love for you. I lay awake half the night, then it got light and I looked at your mouth ..." He kept kissing me as he spoke, but at first I did not move but remained, half-conscious, lodged in his arms, so bewildered was I, until finally I said: "Listen, Diego, leave me now, I don't want you to touch me, you must go". He suddenly went numb and presently got up. At the time I felt disgusted by him. We spoke little to one another before midday.

Yes, that then was the second day.

We set out, of course, along the same track.

Please believe me, Reverend Fathers when I say that I did not know the way. It was only then that Diego.

On the donkeys again, along the bottom of the valley, in between the hillocks—again, the heat.

We were travelling rather more slowly, because the track was uphill and since morning the sun had been beating down. The sky was like crystal. And there was no one anywhere about—we were alone under that sky. Diego did not look at me. We pushed on in silence up the valley, oppressed by the quiet, the heat of the sun and that something between us which had dragged on since the night at the inn. I don't know why or how it was, but Diego appealed to me now as he rode along looking somehow sad and hard; and I thought that I was in love with him—that there was no doubt about it now—and that perhaps I would do *it*, as wished, here somewhere in the mountains; let him take me to France, I thought; after all I have run away from the convent, and we agreed to beforehand; it's a bad sin, but probably I shall do *it*. Then, about noon, when we had reached a wide ridge from which we could see a shepherds' hut not far off in a clearing, and Diego suggested that we should give the donkeys a rest and that we could perhaps get some fresh milk from the shepherds, I begged him not to take me down there, because it was so nice and so lovely on the ridge, and there were fir-trees all round. "Let's lie down here in the shade instead and rest", I said. And when Diego lay down and did not touch me but only asked why I was so cruel, and suddenly burst into tears, saying that I had punished him that morning unjustly; I put my arms round him and said: "Don't cry, it will be all right now". He began kissing my arms and looked at me as if these words of comfort had been uttered by an angel. "Dolores", he said, "you know, I ..." He could not finish the sentence and began crying again. "You know, I ...", he repeated. I hugged him, from love and pity, from pride, and also in fear, because he was crying. I no longer knew whether this was a man or a child, and I was afraid. Then through his tears he said: "Dolores, Dolorosa, my little white dove, I did not want to hurt you in any way; I wanted nothing that you did not desire yourself; I did not want to offend your innocence; but you know how it was, I wanted it to be quite pure, Dolores, but you ..." He was crying, and I held him as tenderly as I could and thought: he loves me. "Calm yourself, Diego, it will be all right, you'll see". Suddenly he shuddered and cried: "Now look what you've done to me! Whatever am I doing? Who am I?"

I have said already, Reverend Fathers, that he was in a way like a child. Not because he cried, but because after that promise I had made, when I hugged him and comforted him, he was at once happy. And also because he really did not know, I think, why we were escaping to the kingdom of France or whether indeed we were going there or how we should live when we were there. He dreamed rather than thought about it, seeming to expect some miracle to happen, and he would only talk about "over there". But "over there" was not France, it could have begun in Spain, because he thought of it for the most part as *it*—what we had to do and I had been thinking about on the ridge, but which he could never call by any other name, as if he were afraid of it. France and *it* were for him all the time confused.

He is a very strange man, Reverend Fathers.

Imagine the scene, Reverend Fathers. We are on our way and there is France before us—we have only to cross the Pyrenees. What would it be like, when we had crossed? Diego said: "We shall hear the music of the spheres". Couldn't I hear it already off and on, playing over there? I felt as if I had indeed heard some such sound. But what *things* would there be over there in the land of France, what sort of houses and animals, that was what I wanted to know. "There will be a great grove of almond-trees, all in blossom—we shall go into that grove and there will be a scent of almonds. Though there will be more than just a grove. There will be rivers flowing with wine and nectar and we shall drink from them. And there will be lambs of many colours—yellow and blue lambs and lambs steeped in Phoenician purple - grazing in the meadows. It will rain golden mead and everywhere water-lillies will bloom. Yes, it will be splendid in the kingdom of France, but who will receive us there when we first arrive? Who? Forest fauns with Pan's pipes". I said: "For God's sake, Diego, there are no such things". But he retorted: "Ah, there is greater freedom there, the Holy Inquisition does not hold sway, that's why we are escaping to France".

All right, I thought, but in trousers or in a dress? Certainly not in my nun's habit. How will it be? Why do I have to wear these trousers? I wanted all those things, true, but not like this, in trousers. Will he marry me? What shall I be in France? "Diego", I asked, "what sort of dress shall I wear?" "A dress of sea-foam and stars". He always talked so beautifully, it made my heart melt, and I could even see myself in a dress of sea-foam and stars and I knew that he could see me like that, and now I did not care whether I wore trousers or not, I would follow him in sin and shame to the kingdom of France. to those almonds and water-lilies. But sometimes he talked in a different way. "No, my child!"—he used to address me as "my child"—"there will be no music of the spheres, no almond grove, no water-lilies; no one knows what will appear over there, or whether there may not be torments, or wormwood, or whether it may not be our fate to eat the forbidden fruit in tears. No one knows its taste until he has savoured it. At times there is more poison in it than sweetness, perversely God has poisoned his own apple, Sister Dolorosa. It is dark over there and crossing over is like closing one's. eyes and leaping from a precipice into the darkness. And you will reach the edge, Sister Dolorosa, and then you will either go back or leap, or else we shall grapple and then who will push off whom? Will I push you off?"

I well remember the occasion when he posed this question, as if to himself, and I can repeat his words quite exactly. Only bear in mind, Reverend Fathers, that this was later, when we were no longer on the ridge of which I was speaking, but in the high mountains, on the third day of our journey.

I remember that, after his question about whether he would push me off, Diego fell silent, as if he expected an answer. I, too, said nothing and then Diego answered himself: no, never! He would not do such a thing. He wanted to go on and suddenly opened his mouth, but for some reason he did not say anything and remained, his mouth open, looking at me, but in such a way that I could not be sure whether he loved me or hated me. If there exists anywhere an abyss of darkness into which one may cast another from a precipice, Diego could with that look have cast me down and killed me. But he did not want to give me a push into the abyss, he preferred that I should fall off of my own accord! I realised then that he preferred it that way and that it was just that he was waiting for with his mouth opened wide. Diego probably guessed that I realised, because he suddenly went pale and said: "Or maybe I shall? Maybe I shall push you off?"

I felt that at any moment tears would stream from my eyes, because already a spasm had gripped by throat. But Diego went on: "Let us leap into the darkness, Sister Dolorosa, after the apple which God cast over there, that it should float in the murk of good and evil. And you shall bite upon it, Sister Dolorosa, and there will be a worm inside it. Thus it may befall, you know, Dolorosa, that an ugly worm appears, and I think it may depend on the first glance which is cast at an apple, before it is ever touched by the lips—it may depend on this glance, as on a spell, whether the worm will hatch out. So, if there is a worm, you will know where you have fallen. And you will crawl along the ground on bloodstained knees; in pain you will call on, the name of God in vain, and in dust and ashes you will curse both me and yourself."

It was the third day when he said this.

And what could I do?

I listened, my throat constricted, with disgust, and thought—why does he torment and terrify me thus? what does he want? perhaps he really does hate me; and how could he go on about that worm? No doubt something like this has happened with other women, otherwise how does he know what it is like over there? He must have been there with whores; maybe this is not the first time and maybe he said the same thing to them, but they had not taken a vow of chastity; well, I don't want it, I've had enough.

That day on the ridge? No, nothing happened on the ridge.

We lay a while longer on the ridge in the shade, Diego calmed down and the donkeys were rested. The tensions were eased and Diego even said: "Oh, look, Dolores, a cloud!" Because the first tiny cloud had appeared above the highest peak. Diego at once asked me: "Whose shall it be, mine or yours?" "Keep it for yourself, it shall be yours", I said. He said "But it's yours". "No, yours". And we laughed and cried: "Yours". "No, yours". Until suddenly something made a loud cry in the forest above us and Diego put his finger to his mouth. We waited awhile and we could hear crashing noises, someone was coming down, and finally we saw that it was a shepherd approaching, bearing a lame sheep. Diego was pleased, because this man would be able to tell us which path to take, the one leading downhill to a stone hut, or the one going up through the forest. "It's up to you, Sir", said the shepherd. "If you want to get to the sea and reach the frontier by the usual route along the coast, go down to the stone hut; but if you prefer the mountain route, then keep straight on through the forest. But no doubt you will prefer the mountain way. Have no fear. There is only God above us, and the eagles. People of sundry conditions have before now passed this way, white-ruffed hidalgos and men who had escaped perhaps from the galleys. You will get through, too. Keep on uphill through the forest and the path will bring you out on to a grassy slope; you will find it easy riding along the grassy slope, and the sun will warm your backs. Then keep steadily ahead and don't look round at anything, just count the becks flowing through the ravines—one, two, three, four—until you see on the left a deep gorge and a fifth beck, a very noisy one, and a little lower down on flat ground a sheep pen and some huts. There you must halt for the night, because by then it will be evening. Tomorrow the people there will show you the way onward. Only you will have to leave those donkeys with them. Well, Godspeed, good Sirs". He was gone. We laughed. "Providence is watching over us", said Diego, "and has sent the shepherd to prevent us going down to the stone hut and adding needlessly to our journey—unless, of course, this Daphnis is simply directing us to a brigand hide-out, into the arms of shaggy bandits who are even now sharpening their knives. Let's first see if he has counted the becks right". But it turned out that everything was just as this helpful fellow had said: there was a long grassy slope, the sun was behind us, there were four becks, and when we came to the fifth, the sound of male voices singing could be heard from afar. Diego said: "In truth, that's Menalcas and Tityrus sitting there, those fellows don't look to me like a band of rascals". Then a woman's voice joined in the song and Diego added: "There's an Amaryllis, too". The huts were in a valley. Presently we could make them out. The descent was not steep, the donkeys went at a trot, the people greeted us courteously, and only a girl, that same Amaryllis, spotted me at first glance for what I was. "You are a maiden", she said.

We spent the night with them.

Smugglers used to pass that way, too, and the shepherds were used to

Diego actually asked whether there were robbers about, but "No, not now", they said, "and guests are sacred".

We were given roe-deer meat, mushrooms and various cheeses to eat to our heart's content, till Diego marvelled at this splendid treat; and we were promised also provisions for the road. "Leave your donkeys here", they said, "because from here on you will be climbing over crags. Donkeys are no use there. And do not be afraid. Even if someone comes in pursuit, we will say nothing".

These were kindly folk. And lively and merry as birds, with songs all the time

Thus it was the whole evening

It was quite dark and time to turn in, our night's lodging was ready, so we said our prayers

That Amaryllis?

Yes, she had found me out. "But perhaps you aren't a maiden", she said. "Maybe you are his woman?" And, turning to Diego, she asked: "Is she a maiden or your wife?" Diego laughed. "My wife, my wife", he cried. "Then go, both of you, and sleep in my hut". And she gave us one bed between us. I no longer had it in me to protest. We said our prayers

It was fear, no doubt, fear. I thought: here we are in this wilderness from which there is no escape and, besides, it can't be done. Doesn't Diego understand that? But how should he? My virtue is all he wants—to take it at the earliest opportunity. That's what he meant this morning at the inn, and now again tonight, and I realised that all men are the same, but he kept repeating: you shall be mine, you shall be mine. "But how, Diego", I said, "how shall I be yours, when it can't be done—never mind whether I should like to or not—but it's contrary to the will of man and God, you know yourself it is ..."

"It's not contrary to the will of man, since that Amaryllis has already detected you ..." "But it's against the will of God, Diego. And He does not need to do any detection. For He knows everything in any case". "Oh, great heavens!", he sighed. "But, Diego, what are you doing?"

He took me in his arms and began kissing my hair and my eyes; he even kissed the jacket I had on and undid it, although I tried to prevent him, and pressed against my body, quivering and burning. "But Diego, Diego ..." But he wouldn't listen and lay with his cheek almost on my breast; he kept saying, like a man in a fever, almost singing: "You shall be mine, you shall be mine ..." "Be quiet Diego, someone may hear". "Let them hear, let them trumpet to the whole world that you shall be mine, let them ring it out in all the churches ..." "There'll be no trumpeting nor ringing—just remember, Diego, we are here in the position of fugitives from justice". "Do you love me, Dolores?" "Yes, I do, only, you know, I feel so dirty, your hands leave marks everywhere and from every kiss something sticky remains which dries and burns me". "Don't talk like that", he whispered.

"No one has ever kissed me before", I said: "perhaps that is the reason, or perhaps it's because of our sin". "Don't talk like that. Do you love me?" "Yes, I love you, Diego". "Then, if you love me, why don't you want our love to be consummated?" "Consummated? Must it be consummated by the body in sin?"

Again, as if in fever, he let his lips roam over my eyes and shoulders and all over, as he whispered: "Yes, yes, Dolores, believe me, it can be consummated only by the body, and in sin". "But why, Diego?" "Because only then is it possible to know whether it is love, whereas otherwise there may not be any love, Dolores; and indeed, perhaps there is none?" My heart was in my mouth. I thought: what if in fact there is no love between us, if it is being put to the test in this way and if it is already apparent that there is none? Could I still return to the convent?

Meanwhile, Diego kept passing his lips over my arms, my neck and the jacket which I was wearing and it seemed as if he did not know what he was doing and had lost control over himself; and this disturbed me more and more, until I cried out: "No, Diego, it is not the body that consummates love - it is the soul, the soul, I tell you, that consummates true love". He became motionless and said: "You child!" "Why do you call me a child, Diego? I'm not a child, I only want to be chaste, do you understand?" "You child!", he repeated, louder. Then for a long time we lay without moving; around us it was quiet, the moon was shining in through chinks in the roof and the noise of the stream outside could be heard. At last I said: "What do you mean? Is love never consummated chastely, but always in sin?" "The consummation of love", he replied, "is like a rock breaking away from that peak there above us and starting to fall into the valley, taking many other rocks with it, and the whole mass tumbling down headlong and in tumult, neither sinfully nor chastely, but simply headlong and in tumult. If you can ever become merely a stream of tumbling rocks and fall like this into the valley, you will see how love is consummated".

I thought: I will do it. First I rose up on the bed, then sat down. Diego did not stir. I thought: I'll do *it* now. I leaned over towards where Diego lay and hovered above him, but he was biding his time. Some thing whispered in my ear: don't do it, Dolorosa. I withdrew, but at once leaned over again. Diego extended his arms and something, as before, whispered in my ear: come to your senses, Dolorosa, don't do it! And yet I approached and again withdrew, and approached, and withdrew; and then Diego seized me like a madman, tore open my jacket and I shouted

I would have killed him if I had been able, I wanted to rend him in pieces and What am I to say?

Here on my breast, I could feel something hot eating into me and tickling me— it was Diego kissing me—it was like hundreds of ants running about all over my body until they bored into my brain, and I thought these ants even had eyes and were shedding tears upon me. "Leave me alone!", I shouted; "I hate you". I hit him as I cried, shouting: "You filthy wretch! Let me go!"—and he let me go. I tore myself away and ran out of the hut. Diego ran after me. "What are you doing?", he shouted. I told him to leave me alone, said I didn't want to see him now, and ran blindly into the dark. The moon was no longer shining and Diego kept shouting somewhere behind me: "Come back at once!" I fell and did not even get up and there was only the water roaring in the gorge. I was afraid of the darkness and the noise. When I returned, Diego said: "I think love is consummated in sacrifice. There is no love without sacrifice". I did not know what he meant. We slept throught the rest of the night.

In the morning Amaryllis came to the hut. She was barefoot, sunburned, in a short skirt; her shoulders were uncovered and she had a deep cleavage at her bodice. She exuded a smell of sun, wind and cattle; I became aware of that disagreeable smell the moment she entered. I liked all the shepherds there except Amaryllis. She had brought a jug of milk—she laughed and talked a lot and Diego was looking at her. I remember, she poured the milk into mugs and a few drops spilled on to her fingers. Laughing all the time and twisting on her heel, she licked her hand over. It was then that I noticed that Diego was looking at her and that his glance stayed fixed for a while on that deep cleavage. And Amaryllis came near him to fill up his mug.

That morning Diego was very restless; that morning, when he was packing his things, I could see that he was all thumbs and could not get the knots tied; he let his mouth hang open and his lip was trembling. That third day—for this was now the third day that had begun—it was hotter than ever and it was as if there were incandescent pins in the air, stabbing and flashing, and one could feel those stabs with one's skin and one's eyes; it seemed as if the sky was a looking-glass that had been shattered into thousands of burning-glasses, and we went uphill along the stony gorge amid the winking of looking-glass fragments.

The shepherds showed us the way. They said: over there, across the ridge, you will find the pass. And they said: over there you will be able to rest, because beyond the ridge there is a good cave for a night's rest; it's easy to find it, the path has been trampled down.

The donkeys remained with them—the gray one, on which I had ridden so far, and the other one, the mouse-coloured one.

Diego carried his bag.

I could not keep pace with him, he took such great strides from the moment we left the valley where we had spent the night. He hardly looked back at all, but marched ahead, irritable and flushed with anger, as I could see, pressing on as if in self-defiance; he was cross and kept stepping up the pace. The path went uphill, at first gently, then more steeply. The sun burned down and the heat was growing ever more intense. My mouth was dry and red circles were flitting before my eyes. I had never been in wild mountains like these where there was nothing but rocks and the way led straight to the sky. Again and again something shook loose underfoot; the boulders were unstable and some of them tumbled down below with a crash. In these conditions, I thought, I shall hardly make it. Diego was forging on, step by step, up and up, without pausing for rest. But it was apparent that he was having difficulty and even he was slowing down now; yet that mood of pig-headed obstinacy with which he had set out in the morning pushed him upwards. Once maybe he turned round and looked back at me; and that look contained something of a wounded animal—a fury, powerlessness and fear, as if he would like to fall upon me and throttle me but was unable either to throttle me or to run away—and as if he were afraid that I might inflict on him another such wound. Sweat poured all over him. He adjusted the bag on his shoulders and strode ahead.

I was carrying the other bag. It contained my nun's habit.

What for?

Well

I cannot answer that, Reverend Fathers.

Even at the time I did not know why I was carrying my habit or indeed why I was going at all, but I was beginning to think I had no goal. If Diego was going to be like that, what was I about with him.

Pray to God? Should I have asked God to free me from the fear of sin?

That was all I could have asked Him, since it was only sin I desired.

Ah, but we are talking now! *Now*, as I stand before you, Reverend Fathers, now I feel that I should have begged Him not to lead me into temptation and to restore my innocence and freedom from all temptation; but then, in that gorge, it was something else I wanted—I wanted to be led into temptation and brought to sin and I wanted *it* to happen, though I was losing hope and thinking it would never happen because Diego looked as if

I asked him myself. I began it. I said: "Listen, Diego". At that point it seemed as if we were just about to come out on to the ridge. "Diego", I said, "stop! What do you want of me? Tell me why you are looking like that". But he said nothing. "Diego!", I cried, "is there no God?" This time he responded. "Yes, there is", he said. "Then, don't you see, Diego, it is not I, but God who imposes prohibitions on us. So whom do you hate, on whom do you want to take vengeance, who are you looking at like that—at God?"

He screwed up his eyes and his whole face was contorted in an agonised spasm. "Yes, yes", he repeated in a lower key. "There is a God". After that he only panted from irritation and effort, because, despite the scorching heat, we had started really climbing and still more rapidly, thinking that any minute now we should reach the ridge and that these were the last few steps. But no. We reached the point where the ridge should have been and there was no ridge: we had been deceived by a sort of threshold, a sort of broad escarpment projecting above the gorge. We looked and saw crags towering up in the sun and only up there, between them, gleamed the ridge. Diego cast his eye blankly over those mountaintops. "There is a God", he repeated, half to me, half to himself.

Again I said: "But don't you see, don't you see?" "Yes, I see", he said. "And what must I do?", I asked. "Yes, I see", he remarked, by now somewhat irrelevantly. "But, Diego", I repeated, "what must I do?" "Go back to your convent, maybe", he whispered. "To the convent—from here?" "We are still over here", he said, just as he had the first day, in the inn. "Have you gone mad, Diego?" "Yes", he said—and wept. He wept amid those scorched rocks; he set down his bag, lay down on it and wept unrestrainedly, as he had done that time on the pass, on the second day. "You have broken me", he shouted; "you have destroyed everything; there will be nothing now—this is the end; I fear you and it is not God who has done this, but you. I am shattered and my willpower is gone; I am a handful of jetsam scattered by the wind". "No, Diego", I cried, "this cannot be the end, I love you, it can't be the end, do you hear?" "Go away, Dolores, go back to your convent, the way is still open". "Diego", I said, "be sensible, how can I go away? Nor will you stay here either, lying like that in this wilderness of rocks".

Gradually he recovered his self-possession. But when he did so and took his bag and moved off, I thought to myself that maybe after all this was the end. And it was only now that I was truly frightened. The red circles which I had before my eyes from the heat and fatigue suddenly went dark and began to drop in black pieces. I felt thirsty and craved for water, while my legs, which had before weighed like two blocks of wood, became light and weak. I staggered and sought shade, shade—so as not to faint. I caught sight of a patch of shade far off in a crevice beneath a cliff and turned aside from the path. I don't know how I managed to crawl to the bottom of the crevice, but there was snow there and it was cold, and below it there was nothing, just a steep slope and a precipice. I gathered up some snow in my hand and began eating it. At first Diego did not notice where I was; it was some time before he saw me. He unfastened his bag, took out a water skin and came down with it. It was my endeavour that he should not find anything the matter with me, and indeed the snow and the shade had already made me feel better. I took the water skin and filled it with a congealed, dirty, clotted mass of snow. "We shall have it for the journey", I said. Diego too was by now refreshed: he had sucked some ice and washed his face. I looked up to the ridge. It was bright up there. And there was not a cloud in sight. "Diego", I asked, "what lies beyond that ridge? Does the kingdom of France begin at once?" "I don't know", he sighed. "Who can say what will appear over there".

Then he started on about how there would be no music of the spheres; that there might be bitter wormwood, that God had poisoned the apple, and so on— all the things I have already recounted to you, Reverend Fathers—and about the precipice, and who would push off whom. "Do you remember", he added, "what I said to you last night, when you came back to the hut? Love is consummated in sacrifice. So get that into your head. You will come to the edge and stand on the precipice, but I shall not push you off nor pull you down to the bottom, although I could and would like to and according to the laws of nature even should do so— even though I would be as it were hanging over the abyss, clinging to the bank by a finger. I shall not push you off. I tell you: go back to the convent. This is my sacrifice, while ..." At this point, as I have already told you, he broke off in midsentence and, his mouth still open, waited for something. For what, I could guess —I realized that he was waiting for *my* sacrifice, but I also realised how hypocritically this coward

Because it was he who was afraid of sinning and wanted me to take the first leap into the darkness, so that his sin should be the lesser—the liar

Then he was scared, because I knew why he had turned pale.

And he began about the worm and in his confusion became mixed up and was contradicting himself, then suddenly he said: "Where's your bag?"

Or perhaps he already sensed what would happen to him on the fourth day and perhaps he feared that more than sinning. I think now that he must have had a premonition of something, but at the time I thought only: this *is* the end; and I could hear his words "you will come to the edge, you will come to the edge"—I bit my lip and finally said: "It's back there in the gorge". He said: "I'll fetch it, because it might slip down". He went and I got up at once. It was only a few paces to the precipice. I leaned over and looked down: to fall down there would be certain death. I got down on my knees and began slowly lowering myself to the edge of the slope, whispering a prayer: O God, absolve my sins, even if I pluck up courage to commit this last sin

God saw that I no longer had any other alternative.

I did not want to leap over the precipice, but I might at any moment have slipped from those tufts of dried-up grass; I knew that and was tempting fate as I went on hands and knees, inch by inch, with a prayer on my lips

Yes, Reverend Fathers, with a blasphemous prayer on my lips I went inch by inch, lower and lower, and one tuft of grass broke off and I slithered. A shudder of panic went through me, I dug my nails into the ground and into the grass roots, and they too broke off. Beneath me I could see the bottom of the precipice and thus upon my knees, in mortal fear lest I lose my foothold, I remained there—then Diego returned. I could hear his footsteps. The thought still flashed through my mind for a moment: I will jump! But I could not. And the footsteps suddenly went silent. Diego said nothing, evidently realising what I was doing. That silence lasted quite a long time and I dared not turn round to look. I had fixed my gaze upon the precipice and had frozen there above it, until something suddenly tugged at me. It was Diego who approaching from behind, had grasped me by the shoulders and proceeded to pull me violently. Then he dragged me forcibly to a mossy hollow and threw me down there. Now that I was lying in a safe place, he shouted: "Dolores, what did you intend to do?" I said quietly: "Nothing, nothing at all, Diego; I wouldn't have killed myself, there was still a stretch remaining to the edge, I was watching out". He bent over me and surveyed me a little uncertainly, with a mixture of alarm and hope, in bewilderment and as if trying to hazard a guess. But I felt great relief, joy even, that it had ended thus. I closed my eyes and desired one thing only: that he would start making love to me as he had done before in the night—and let him strip me naked!—and that everything would be accomplished, right now and in despite of God

I was not afraid of condemnation; I was quite faint and my senses were ebbing away.

Yes, Reverend Fathers, I confess that it would have been sin committed with the deliberate intention of offending God, and thereby mortal sin.

My senses then were ebbing away and I retained only the wish that Diego would start doing that which he had always desired; that I should learn what *it* was and how it was consummated; and that Diego would thereafter have to remain attached to me, since we should be united in both body and soul—and he did not believe in any other kind of love, and I had realised that his soul would only be united with mine when our bodies were united. And, as I lay there on the moss lacking the instinct of self-control and without a thought in the world, Diego sensed what I was waiting for. "Carissima!", he said, and again: "Carissima! Carissima!" He whispered very tenderly. Then he covered my face with his hands and with his palms caressed my eyelids, my lashes and my mouth; next, he transferred his hands to my breasts and touched me on the hips and thighs, then finally he embraced my whole body, and this embrace was the pinnacle of happiness and delight—but he did no more, no more, saying only: "Dolores, we have to cross the mountains before nightfall". "All right, Diego", I said. I looked at him and he was once again as radiant and beaming as he had been the first day by the stream, when we were beginning our escape. Meanwhile the sun had moved across the sky and lit upon the crevice. I do not know how many hours had passed while we were there. A fair number probably, because the shadows were now falling differently, slantwise.

I got up. We took our bags and set off by the crags towards the ridge. But it was no joke. It was not possible to walk, but only to clutch at the rocks with one's hands and drag oneself along on all fours. We laughed. "Diego", I said, "when you go like that, you are like a cat". "And you are like a mouse—I shall eat you up in a minute", he replied. Then added: "What have you got in your bag? Only your nun's habit? You'd do better to chuck it over the precipice, you'll find it easier". I thought: yes, I'll chuck it away and tonight, over there, I will submit to him. But Diego had fastened his bag cleverly on his shoulders. I fastened mine in the same way and did not throw away my habit. Then we had our arms completely free and it was more convenient for climbing. The rest of the way up to the ridge, although it was hard going and steep, passed happily. Diego had to help me several times, because I could not take long strides. We laughed again like children and finally, before we could see that we had reached the ridge, a view opened out on to the far side.

Over there stretched a long mountain chain.

"Where is France?", I asked. Diego pointed to the chain. "Shall we be going there?", I asked again. "Yes", he replied, "we shall".

But that would be tomorrow. For tonight I wanted only to be with Diego and I was delighted when the moon rose like a huge head. "Look, Diego!", I shouted, because I had never before seen such a blazing red ball and it seemed to me to be a sign from heaven. It was already dark and we had only the light of the moon when we discovered the way down to the cave. There was indeed a well-marked path and the cave was almost like a dwelling. People must often have been there, for we found some utensils, a knife and a couch made of branches still not very withered. Diego immediately cut fresh branches from the dwarf pines—there were many growing nearby. And we lit a fire. I held Diego's hand and snuggled up to him. The flames were reflected in his eyes as in a looking-glass and lent a colour to his face, over which light and shade played alternately. Meanwhile the moon had risen high in the sky and had become smaller and paler; and from all this—the light, the warmth and the smell of the pine burning—a very special kind of spell descended upon me. The effect it had was to make me grip Diego's hand more and more tightly, because I still remembered our journey and how it had been above that precipice; but now Diego was near and something drew me to him more and more violently, more and more restlessly, more and more—I don't know how to describe it. Now it will be hard, I thought. Then Diego stripped there in the cave and I could see his bare back—his skin was quite white (well, he's a man, I thought)—and his legs. Then he turned at once to me and lay down and we both lay there on the pine branches, whispering "Do you love me?"—"Yes, I do", then he began to remove my garments

But how am I to describe *it* to you, Reverend Fathers

He had stripped me to the waist and immediately he ceased to hear or understand. He was shouting something, just one word—'camellia'. I shielded myself from his gaze and he kept on crying 'camellia'—it obsessed him. I could feel him breathing rapidly. He pressed his whole body against me, twined his arms about me and caught me up in that impatient breathing of his. It was then I became afraid of what might shortly happen, since he seemed unable to understand, but like a madman, gloating over the sight of my nakedness, kept repeating 'camellia'. I had nowhere to take refuge from him and despite myself lay up against him, so that he embraced me still more importunately. I became afraid of that power, and he was now reaching out for the rest of my clothing in order to tear it off. Then it was that something hit me and I thought I must say it to him while there was yet time, so I whispered: "Diego, I don't want to take off anything else—remember—don't do *it* to me". But he appeared not to hear. "Yes, yes", he cried, and then again: "Camellia!" "Do you hear me, Diego?" "All right, all right", he replied, as if choked or stunned by something. By me, I knew it was, and I was amazed that my body should be the cause of such insanity. I was pleased and so, from vanity, Reverend Fathers, I proceeded to ask whether I was really so attractive to him—because I did not think I could be—and Diego started shouting: "You're beautiful!" From then on he kept repeating the word 'beautiful', as before 'camellia', with blind obstinacy, like someone half-delirious

I swear, Reverend Fathers, I am trying to hide nothing from you—it is just that I am gagged by bashfulness and by human nature.

Because after that he went all tense and fell upon my belly and tried to uncover it completely, tugging and tugging as he shouted "You're beautiful, beautiful!" It was as if he had touched me with red-hot iron. "No!", I cried. "You're beautiful!", he shouted. "No!" "Now, oh now, you must be mine!" But now, in a paroxysm of despair which seized me from the knees and went right through me to my throat, I was defending myself with my teeth alone. He kept shouting: "You're beautiful!" and: "What are you doing, Dolores?" But I didn't know what I was doing and from fury that he had touched me as if with red-hot iron and that I felt I had to resist, whereas before I had wanted to submit; from fury that it had all turned out like that, I bit him—until I drew blood. Diego kept shouting something in that faraway, monotonous voice, then suddenly went motionless. It was only then that I realised that he was saying something different and I made out that he was groaning: "Why, Dolores? Why, why this, Dolores?" He kept repeating this, as just now the words 'camellia' and 'beautiful'. I did not reply.

Water

Please may I have a drink of water, Reverend Fathers.

I did not manage to reply to his question. I just thought: let God answer him. Precisely those words, that God should answer him, Diego had once before had occasion to hear from me, much earlier, before I ran away from the convent. They should have stuck in his memory. I said them one time in the Church of the Holy Cross. We had not met by arrangement that time. We usually saw each other elsewhere: at the theatre, in the players' bivouac. We used to fix our rendezvous for the mornings, when the players and musicians would be roaming about the town while Diego was in one of the tents, minding their costumes and doing some writing. I was able to call in at the theatre without being noticed. It was on my way from Miguel the baker's. So it was there we usually arranged to meet. But, on the day of which I want to speak, Diego had come to Holy Cross Church. I encountered him in the side chapel by the altar dedicated to the Blessed Virgin Mary. We at once knelt down, as if to pray. I asked: "Did you know I should be here?" "Yes, Sister", he said. I already had a premonition that something was wrong. He said: "I have spent a whole night communing with my conscience. In a day or two the players are going to Burgos, and I have decided to leave with them". Consternation took my breath away. "What?", I said. "Do you mean to tell me that you intend to leave for good?" "Yes, for good, Sister". "Is it because of me?" "Yes", he replied, and added: "I am afraid that soon it would be too late, because, human nature being what it is, there is nothing a person might not do in a moment of frailty. We are nearing the gates of hell, Sister, and we are being tempted to knock; and he who knocks at the gates of hell, to him will they surely open".

Meanwhile a priest had come out of the vestry and, passing us, knelt before the altar. Diego fell silent. We could not talk freely, because many people were moving about the church. "What?", I whispered again, when it emptied; "did you decide to leave just because of what we did yesterday?" For on the previous day I had been with him in the players' tent and there we had kissed for the first time. "Yes, just for that it took me a long time to settle accounts with my conscience", he said. "I said to myself: you are a blind man groping your way in the dark and leading by the hand a child who does not know what is in store for her at the end of the road. You have no right to make trial of her innocence. So let us say good-bye, Sister, and let our meeting at this altar of the Most Blessed Virgin be the last in our earthly life".

I knew that what he was saying was right and proper, but I could feel only one thing: I must stop him. We were kneeling with heads bowed and hands piously folded, not daring to look at one another. Again and again someone passed by the altar. In an undertone, as if deep in prayer, I said the only words I could summon up from my throat: "Don't go away". He replied: "I must Sister". "If you do, simply by so doing you will destroy me". "No, if I go, I shall save you".

I wanted to restrain him from going, if only for a while. It would be easier for me to bear the parting if he went, not of his own accord, but as a result of a decision by me, at a time of my choosing; and I thought that I should then manage to overcome this wicked love and do so in good time. But the time and place were not appropriate for lengthy talk. "I don't know what will happen if you go", I said. "Stay, I beseech you. No appeal probably could be more desperate than that which I am now making here. For, don't you see, it is not to the Mother of God, but to you I am praying!'

It was as if, after my words, he had yielded, as if he had given way beneath them; as he bent low, his head touched the altar step. "Dolores", he said after a while, "is there no salvation?" "Let God answer you", I whispered then, exactly as I wanted to now in the cave, when, naked, he kept repeating in that faraway voice the single question: "Why this?" But I could not say it a second time, because he should have remembered it from the Church of the Holy Cross. That time, in the church, I added in conclusion: "Don't pass sentence on me". And he stayed, and did not leave with the players; but now in the cave, after everything that had happened, I wanted nothing, just nothing; I was empty, and said nothing.

And morning came, the morning of the fourth day.

At first, Reverend Fathers, I did not realise what was in the offing. That day began normally. Perhaps Diego too was not completely aware of what he was doing. Anyway, we did not talk about *it* and we behaved as if everything was to go on as before. Diego rose and went to the stream which flowed nearby to fetch water. I busied myself preparing a meal. Diego returned, sat down on a rock and was patching up a shoe. It was a fine morning, only I noticed that very dark clouds were gathering over the peaks on the French side. I said: "There'll probably be a storm. Not a drop of rain has fallen since we set out". "There won't be a storm", Diego contradicted me. For breakfast we had cheese—that Amaryllis had given us two large hunks of cheese two days ago. We felt tired after the night and the climb; my legs ached and Diego had shadows under his eyes. Before we moved off, he lay for a long while on the grass looking up at the sky. Meanwhile the wind had indeed dispersed the clouds on the French side. Over there it had become fine and beyond the mountain chain distant hazy landscapes showed up in the rays of the sun. I cried: "Look, Diego, now we can see the lands of the kingdom of France". We both turned our eyes in that direction. It was impossible to make out very much, fields and hills vanished in the silvery streaks of light and fused at the horizon with the blue of the sky. I thought it looked lovely and that I should not be surprised if in the kingdom of France there actually were almond groves, showers of golden rain and water-lilies blossoming. Diego finally rose and unhurriedly fastened his bag. "We must go now", he said.

We set off. I still failed to understand what was happening. It was only after a while that I observed that we were following again the very path down which on the previous day we had run from the ridge to the cave, only now we were going in the opposite direction—uphill. I enquired anxiously whether Diego had lost his way. "No", he replied tartly, "I have not lost my way". I was beginning slowly to piece everything together. Obviously, he was leading me up to the ridge, but why? Did he mean to go back to Spain? I preferred now not to ask. I had grasped, as it were with my heart, not with my mind, the whole truth about him and about myself. It seemed to me that I was to blame. I felt very sorry for Diego.

It was only at first that I had feared the possibility of having to go back. But it was rather a kind of sadness—that profound kind from which a person would most gladly lie down and beat his head against the ground—that had descended upon me then. And I had only at first been afraid, because almost from the outset I had ceased to believe it possible that we should go back and I knew that, if I wanted, I could still halt him; I could stop and say "Here, Diego, I am at your disposal and shall be yours" and indeed give myself to him forthwith in the sun, on any patch of grass, and by that sacrifice—to use his word—turn him aside from the road to Spain.

I had to, Reverend Fathers—I had to think like that and act accordingly. Nothing else could save me from the return, and the millstone about my neck

Oh, Reverend Fathers, pitch darkness now descended on my wits. I shrink even from disclosing it, but since I am now so humbly confessing all my sins, I must tell you that I did indeed feel contrition and the need for penance, only in my blindness everything was topsy-turvy; it was towards Diego I felt contrite and it seemed to me that I had to expiate my guilt not before God but before him.

Because it was like this: after our meeting in the Holy Cross Church I had tried for several days to stifle that cancer which was gnawing at me. I spent much time in prayer and I did not go once to the tent. Until one time I happened to be talking to Sister Modesta—the subject of our conversation I do not now remember—and Sister Modesta said: "The players are leaving today". It was as if I had been struck by a thunderbolt. But would Diego be going with the players? Without a second thought I ran to the theatre-ground. I do not know myself how I managed to get through the convent gate and then to creep between those horse-cloths spread out on frames to the tent where Diego was sitting. I do not know myself how I plucked up the courage not to run away when I saw strangers in the tent. Diego, covered in confusion, at once leaped up and in rather forced tones muttered:"*In saecula saeculorum:* who are you looking for, Sister?" "I must have a word with you", I said. Then all the players who were there cast glances at one another. One of them whistled. I had the impression that this whistling conveyed mockery or had some crude significance. Then suddenly they all trooped out, on the pretext of having to load up the carts—they were, of course, leaving that day. But before they went out, the one who had been whistling grinned and said: "Don't stop to say more than three paternosters, Diego, or you'll have to follow us to Burgos on Shanks's pony". With that he disappeared out of the tent. "For God's sake", whispered Diego, "what are you doing, Sister? Now the cat will be out of the bag. You can't stay here". "What are you worried about?", I asked. "What do you mean?", he said. "What should I be worried about, if not your peace and quiet and your innocence?" "My innocence or your own?" "What do you mean?", he repeated. "I have done nothing to merit suspicion ..." "Quite so, you just want to cast me on one side to preserve a clean conscience; you are an angel without blemish". "Dolores, what is the matter with you?", he shouted. "Here I am, and I am no longer afraid of anything, that's what's the matter".

He fell on his knees before me. "There is only one thing we can do", he said. "We can both run away while the going is good". But he kept looking round nervously and listening out for sounds outside the tent. "So be it", I said. He embraced me. "Carissima, do you know what you are doing?" "Yes, Diego". And we agreed that we would try to cross the Pyrenees in secret to the kingdom of France and that he would buy some donkeys, and we fixed the day and the place in the copse by the bridge

I was to blame, Reverend Fathers. He was blameless.

As we approached the ridge again, I knew that it could not end like this. I wanted something to impede us on our way, so that we should be forced to go back and stay another day and night in the cave. I prayed for a storm. But there was no storm. Before midday the clouds had vanished without trace in the blue of that sky, clear as ever. Meanwhile we had crossed the ridge and I had looked for the last time at France; and beyond the ridge, as we descended from it towards the huts, the unbearable heat beat down once more, and once more the air winked and there was a burning and stabbing in the eyes. All in all everything was repeating itself for the second time. Diego said: "So you see, Dolores, it's not Eden, only Gehenna—we are doomed". But I said: "No, Diego, it can't end like this". However, I intended to say no more, or he might think I was deceiving him and myself again. I was afraid to torment him with promises and was waiting only for the opportunity to fulfil them, and I really felt like that stream of rocks of which Diego had spoken to me earlier.

And so to the huts

The shepherds were amazed and that Amaryllis rushed up at once. They asked what had happened and Diego said: "We are going back, that's all. Where are our donkeys?" "The donkeys are here, but you won't get far before nightfall. We have never seen people like you here, did you lose your way or something?"

From the start I expected that we should have to spend the night with the shepards and I wanted it to turn out thus, for I thought: tomorrow we shall be going across the ridge again over there. But Diego was watching me and divined my wish. He even smiled, but differently from the previous evening, differently from two days earlier when we were with these same shepherds, differently from that time on the pass under the fir-trees when he cried "it's your cloud, yours", differently from the first day, when he had said "you are sweeter to me than honey of Hymettus"—it was a rather bitter and suspicious smile. Perhaps he foresaw everything.

After supper Amaryllis once again made ready for us the bed in her hut. Diego was thinking about something and kept moving his mouth indecipherably. This was his habit: when he was deep in thought his mouth moved slightly, as if he was biting on those hidden thoughts. So I asked him: "Don't you trust me, Diego?" "Yes", he said, "I trust you". But I felt that he was afraid of the night which was drawing on, or did not want it to come, only he did not say so, Still, we went to the hut and it was only then he kissed me, but again differently from before, rather cautiously and hesitantly, as if now he had less desire for those kisses and as if he were preoccupied by something else. I again asked: "Diego, do you still want us to do *it*?" "Yes", he said. Then came the one time, the one brief moment, when for the last time I could have drawn back

That time, Reverend Fathers, came when I was throwing off my clothes. Because Diego did not even come near me; he did not watch, he did not move a muscle; but neither did he remove himself, he was just there alongside me; and this caused me the greatest annoyance and for the space of a moment I wanted to sink beneath the earth or run away; I had doubts about everything; but I had to persuade Diego to trust me, so I took hold on myself and pulled him myself to me. I could no longer afford to be cowardly and I pulled him violently and pressed myself against his body importunately and in haste. I wanted to forget what I was doing, and he was right, that, before taking the leap, one closes ones eyes; I closed mine and waited, but not for a fall into darkness, rather for something like lightning, a light and a roar. Diego seemed a trifle startled and unsure of himself; I could hear him hold his breath as I embraced him and then he said something in an unnatural tone of voice. I did not even try to understand, I was trying to imagine that which was to happen shortly, that storm and the thunderbolt which would strike within me; I imagined *it* as something like that and I was afraid only of the pain, not of the sin.

I remember Diego suddenly shaking himself free of his impotence and feeling within him an internal frothing; he was embracing me like something foaming and pulsating; I remember the warmth, the weight and something like the wingbeat of a large bird, and the kisses, as if a bird of prey were boring with its beak. I felt bad and now it was hurting too, but I did not try to defend myself, only pressed my eyelids still tighter; while through Diego currents were passing continually—I could feel them distinctly; and then, at the same time wanting and not wanting it, I opened myself to him completely, so that he might do *it* and have me as he desired. I was expecting a kind of blow, a sharp tearing, a shock, torment maybe, but no, nothing happened

All right, Reverend Fathers, I will tell you everything.

I could feel only the pressure and a kind of short, nagging burning sensation. "Diego!", I cried—and that was the end, Diego again sank down impotently and breathed out heavily. I thought: there's no pleasure in this sin. But I said to him: "Diego, it's consummated, you have had me as you desired". But Diego whispered: "No, Dolores, we are not yet over there, that wasn't *it*". Why wasn't that *it*, I wondered. What now? What was it he wanted? But after a while I thought, perhaps indeed it was not yet *it*. And again he began searching for something else which had not been accomplished before, but he did so as before, only more impatiently, as if disillusioned, tormenting himself, while I waited again, ready for pain and for everything, if only we might now come to know the mystery of good and evil—as he had once put it—and be released from that throat-constricting grief that it had not been *it*. I remembered nothing then, Reverend Fathers, neither God, nor Hell, nor you, nothing save that one thing. I asked whether it was my fault that we had not managed to get over there, as he called *it*, but Diego did not answer distinctly; he began shouting something incoherently—"I told you so! I told you so!"—he seemed to be not with me, or to be ill; he was trembling and kept pressing upon me till I lost my breath; I thought he must be ill; I could hear his heart beating violently and I was suddenly terrified, because he went limp in my embrace and became flushed and damp; and I realised that he was losing his strength, as if defeated, when he came near me, and that he could not do *it* as he had wanted.

"I told you so!", he cried. "The worm! I said there would be a worm". "Calm down, Diego", I said. "What has got into you about this worm? Besides, we don't have to do anything, if our very bodies rebel, don't you see?" "Yes", he said. "The worm! It gives it such pleasure". I only wanted to know whether there was something in me that was freezing him and causing his impotence, or whether it was something in himself, but he would not answer me and insisted that he had a worm; it was only next day

That night he remained completely dead like that, right up to daybreak. He tossed and swore; probably he was tormenting himself with shame and fear, because he had been impotent. In sympathy I said: "Why do you torment yourself thus, Diego?" But he only became still more angry, then, when he fell silent, I could hear the sound of the stream in the gorge; I remembered the sound, now everything was as before; and that, Reverend Fathers, is all.

On the fifth day at sunrise Amaryllis once more came running to the hut, bringing, as she had the first time, a jug of milk; but in reality she came to flash her teeth, and what do you think she did, the shameless wretch! She deliberately rubbed herself up against Diego, and he said to her: "Amaryllis!"— calling her by that name, just like that.

On the fifth day it became evident that Diego did indeed intend to take me back down to Spain. After that unhappy night he did not even seem to care whether I should be able to go back to the convent. He was acting hatefully and seemed beside himself with rage and misery. He kept pointing up at the sky and saying "It's Him!", as if he were threatening God himself, but he preferred not to look me in the eyes, he was afraid. Without any word or explanation, without asking me how I felt about it, he simply took the donkeys from the shepherds and shouted: "Up! up! let's go!" I mounted, for what else could I do. He would not listen to anything, so carried away was he by his fury and his blind determination to return.

But I do remember the look he gave *her*.

For all his fury and despair, for all that he seemed quite mad and a lurching, pathetic shadow of his real self, he looked at Amaryllis. At the last moment before our departure, when the donkeys were already moving off and she ran up to hand him some unwanted oddments which had been left in the hut, he gave her a look just like he gave me during our first meeting.

We did not know one another then. I was crossing the road, returning from Miguel the baker's. Diego was standing in front of a tavern. And he looked. Nothing more. He opened his mouth slightly, but it seemed as if simultaneously he had ceased to breathe out and had just thought of many things. But in that look, in the half-open mouth and in the holding of his breath there was something which reminded one of someone who, being thirsty, had suddenly, somewhere before him in the distance, beheld a lake. And it seemed also that, if the tavern and all the houses about Diego had suddenly collapsed and sunk beneath the earth, he would not have noticed it, but have remained rooted to the spot, continually looking.

Exactly thus did he look at Amaryllis before our departure.

And I saw it.

Then we went back across the grassy slope to the pass with the fir-trees, and we went very fast and I thought Diego would drive the poor little donkeys to death.

I did not think about anything else. By then there was in truth a complete emptiness inside me.

That extraordinary heat, which is rarely encountered in our mountains, continued, but that last day the air became still denser from the scorching and the stuffiness. Not a cloud appeared in the sky, but the whole sky went white and from that whiteness there descended a kind of hot gum which caused a blackness in ones eyes.

Diego did not speak until we reached the pass. First, before he uttered, he was for a long time mulling over his thought. I could see that he was chewing something, something he could not chew through; his mouth was moving, but he was twisting about, going green and pale and choking something down, choking down some monster which was eating into him. At last he said: "It is not inside me". "What isn't?" "The impotence". But he said it in such a way as if he wanted to trample me underfoot; his tone was malevolent and half exulting, as if to convey that, of course, it was definitely not in him, though it might be in me, and that it was for me to do the worrying. He watched, waiting to see the effect on me. "So it is in me, then?", I asked. "It is in neither one of us", he replied. "But God exists!"

"What has God to do with it?", I enquired. "God created the worm", he said.

Then with a whistle he lashed his donkey and went off full tilt from the pass. Only as we came down into the valley, he burst out: "Do you know, Dolores, what I have come to see? There is no running away from God. And do you know, Dolores, from what God comes into being? From fear. Even if He did not exist, He would come into being from someone's fear. And in this case He came into being from your fear, and afflicted me with impotence, and showed that there is no running away from Him over the Pyrenees"—Diego was shouting thus, as he bounced absurdly up and down on the donkey, the mouse-coloured one, for it was that one he was riding—"so that's what I have come to see, that one may try to run away from Him, but He will come into being from fear and manifest Himself by afflicting one with impotence, and therefore we are always in God's hand". "Diego", I cried, "be sensible, why blaspheme like this?" "Let's pray!", he said. But I simply begged him: "Be sensible!"

At last he was silent, when we were by now at the bottom of the valley, somewhere near the inn at which, five days earlier, we had spent the first night. I even felt a ray of hope that perhaps he would really come to his senses and that this turbulent mood would pass. It was only midday, such was the pace at which we had covered the whole way from the shepherds' huts. Then suddenly a frightening thing happened. In the silence a sound rang out. It was carried by the wind to the mountains from the lowlands of the Basque country: in some far-off church they were ringing the Angelus. The sound was barely audible, since it came from afar, but I knew what it proclaimed. "Pull yourself together, Diego", I said, "for this is the last chance. Where are you taking me, to whom do you mean to hand me over?" "To God", he whispered.

We parted, Reverend Fathers, towards nightfall. I had not bargained for Diego's final action. After a whole day spent thus madly careening, we had still about an hour's ride to the toll-gate, and the sun was sinking. I do not know how the little donkeys had borne it all, but now the towers of the Holy Cross Church were already gleaming on the horizon. Then Diego said that he would not enter the town. "What?", I asked. "So where are you going to go?" "Anywhere—it doesn't matter", he replied. Before I could recover, he had hastily bid farewell, turned his donkey round and was setting off again in the direction from which we had just come, leaving me on the road just like that. I did not try to stop him. I felt completely numb. At first I did not even think about what I should do, only where he was going.

There was a wood nearby. When Diego had disappeared in the opposite direction, it occurred to me to hide in the wood. I led my donkey there and sat down under a tree. The donkey sniffed the grass and began to feed. I delved into my bag. I took off my trousers and put on my nun's habit. That was all. I did not cry, I did not pray, I just sat there. Then fear seized me: what next? For night was upon me. So I came out of the wood and rode away again on to the road.

Some strange force bore me up to the toll-gate. It happened without my volition, as it were automatically. Not until I was approaching the entry into the town did I realise where I was, and then I quailed. There were guards standing at the toll-gate. I did not have the courage to approach. But they had already seen me. And when they moved and started coming with torches and halberds, I thought: how could Diego do what he had done, why had he gone

off, and

I don't know, Reverend Fathers.

Sometimes I think perhaps he is not in Spain at all. Then again I wonder whether he did not go back to the mountains to that Amaryllis.

They came from the toll-gate. And it turned out that they knew who I was, and seemed to be expecting me, and that I was not free to go another step, but must be conveyed beneath the halberds and handed over to the Holy Inquisition. The rest, Reverend Fathers, you know—what happened and what they did to me before I took my stand here before you to make my statement.

CEMETERY WALL, Endre Bálint, 1960

JACEK BOCHEŃSKI was born in 1926 and made his debut as a writer in 1944 in the first number of the journal *Odrodzenie*. He subsequently had collections of short stories published in 1949 and 1952. A novel—*Goodbye to Miss Syngilu, or the Elephant and the Polish Question* —appeared in 1960, but Bocheński owes his reputation principally to his historical novel *Julius the God*, published in 1961. In addition to novels and stories, Bocheński has had published numerous journalistic *reportages*, also translations from German and Latin. *Tabu*, part I of which appears here, was published by Czytelnik, Warsaw, in 1965. MARCUS WHEELER is a Slavic scholar and translator. After taking a degree in Oxford, he went into the Foreign Service and worked at the British Embassy in Moscow. At present he is doing research at the Royal Institute of International Affairs, in London.

MIECZYSLAW JASTRUN

translated by Lydia Pasternak Slater
Franz Kafka

Franz Kafka, who once was stabbed by black angels,
Sensed it all long before his three sisters' death.
Running fast on the ladder of Auschwitz' smoke,
By their long ago shorn off plaits they were taken to heaven.
He held in his hand the one, single thread of
The black unwinding clue, the thread which could either
Lead him out of the terrible maze,
Or else to the gas chamber take him.
Here under the lofty vaults of the attic, high in the Castle
(About which no-one is sure whether or not it is real,
Although in the telephone book the name and number are listed)
The Trial goes on each day, to the blaze of summoning trumpets
Of the town's fire brigade, or else - the Last Judgement's angels.
Each day here the gathering twilight sprinkles our hair with the ashes
Of those who were killed. Up above the sky is materialistic
(Not Raphael's courtly heavens). And here, too, is the gaping
Black—crimson abyss of hell, into which we all will
Presently jump on the light parachutes of our souls.

translated by Czeslaw Milosz
A beginning

I looked at the veins of a leaf,
Jars of jam and the knots of a table
And the way a green caterpillar crawled
And the way a tendril of bindweed curled.
I looked at the features of a stone,
A lump of sandstone and clay
And I drove the rustling of a stream
Through the throat of one hour.
I looked at the reflection of a crystal
In the glass surface of my desk.
I sharpened my pencil slowly
And so passed that six-year-long instant.
The rest was a vigil
In a dark room behind the locked door.
Dawn has not yet appeared in the cracks.
Scarcely the first graying
Against dark backgrounds—
Before a key is found which will open.

MIECZYSLAW JASTRUN (b. 1903) is a Polish poet and historian of literature. He is the author of a popular biography of Mickiewicz and a translator of Rilke. Since 1956 Jastrun's poetry has undergone profound change and gained in metaphysical undertone.

translated by Peter Hay

Attila's Nights

the first act of a
tragedy in five acts by

JULIUS HÁY

CHARACTERS

ATTILA

REKA

GUDRUNA } his wives

ILLEK

DENGESIK } his sons

ERNAK

AETIUS, Roman chief commander

LAUDERIC, Gothic prince

MIKOLDA, his sister

EDEKO

ORESTES } Attila's chieftains

LEO, Bishop of Rome

TRIGETIUS

AVIENUS } leading Romans

A ROMAN CITIZEN

Hun and Goth soldiery, servants; Romans with their wives and children.

*Set on the plain of Catalaunum,
in Attila's capital, and
in Rome's neighbourhood
during the years 451-453*

Lauderic's tent.
Old Edeko and the young Lauderic. A few servants.

EDEKO: Ah, these nights, ah what nights...

LAUDERIC: Is this place to your liking, my lord - my princely tent?

EDEKO: These dark, blind nights...

LAUDERIC: Excuse me, my lord... Hold that torch higher, boy!

EDEKO: Nights here, on the banks of the Seine, by strange and foreign waters, or nights at home by the Danube and Tisa—they are the same nights, everywhere the same hay-scented, cricket-chattering nights... Nights that neigh and bark and hoot ... Whooping, whispering, sighing nights...

LAUDERIC: My lord Edeko, will these chairs be enough? I don't know who's coming, how many that is, there'll be.. If you'd tell me, my lord, the rank of the people you are expecting, then I could... Excuse me...

EDEKO: Nights come clothed in black, in silver too... and at times in flame-red gowns ... And, it's all fancy dress. Young prince, the nights are not what they would appear.

LAUDERIC: These guests you don't name might like something to eat or drink...Or even you yourself, my lord Edeko, while you are waiting...

EDEKO: I am old now, Prince, and spend as long in my tent as in the saddle. I've taken to history. I've got one of those brainy Greeks, and a few books. He reads to me when I can't get to sleep.

LAUDERIC: I swear by my princely crown, my lord, I would be greatly ashamed if I didn't find out everything you might want...

EDEKO: The bits in Latin and Greek that I can't follow, he translates into good, clear Hunnish, so that I can.

LAUDERIC: ...if things were not as you wanted them...

EDEKO: "I'm not satisfied with the history books of the world!"—that's what the Great Lord once said to me. And now you see, I too find them wanting. Because they only talk about the day. But what about the nights...?

LAUDERIC: Lord Edeko, shouldn't there really be decorations here, insignia, or standards...?

EDEKO: I am not thinking now of the nights when gossip shuffles round in bedroom slippers. They're remembered well enough in the scandal sheets of both imperial cities. No, I mean nights when on the sudden history sears the sky, when unwarned the instant in a lightning flash reveals: Man, this future could be yours... And then the flash is snuffed, swallowed in the hollow thunder... Only the chosen have seen, only they know what the human race had lost... Why can't history be written about this?

LAUDERIC: I didn't quite catch you, my lord. Do you think there will be a storm?

EDEKO: About the nights of vast opportunity men let slip... Nights of "it could be, but won't"... Nights of great dreams and of miscarried plans... When in seven-league boots we might stride over the filthy horrors of years and centuries, when with a single leap we could skip beyond the endless maze of history...

LAUDERIC: My lord...

EDEKO: But the first cockcrow sounds, the first grey stain shimmers on the horizon - and all's finished... The stride has been missed, and lost, we drag on through the blood-soaked dust...

LAUDERIC: My lord, this is the most beautiful chair I've got: almost a throne. My lord, my father, had it from king Alaric's Roman loot. Should I set it in the middle? In case... someone like that happens to come... And more torches all round ...?

EDEKO: The day's eyes have sobered and see nothing now of the night just passed

... But it was here, do not doubt, it was here... And secretly it burnt its brand in the flank of our days...

The last servant has now left the tent.

EDEKO: So, there we are! (In changed tone): Well, forgive me, young prince, I'm old and at times my mind wanders... But I heard all you said—The tent will do very well, the furniture can stay where it is, no more torches are needed, no food or drink, no standards. As for the number and rank of those who are coming - that isn't your concern.

LAUDERIC: My princely tent is very simple, my lord...

EDEKO: Have you seen the Great Lord's tent? Not the one in which he receives ambassadors or tributary allies like yourself: - his field tent. You won't beat that for simplicity. So don't try.

LAUDERIC: But if you should have any other orders, lord Edeko...

EDEKO: Prince, I cannot give you orders. Don't let me hear that word again! You are your royal father's subject, and your father is the Great Lord's subject. You are not the subject of a subject. You are lord of your own forces and the Great Lord is your lord.—Myself, I am a drop in the ocean of his Hunnish people, born in the tent of simple shepherdfolk, even though I am today one of the twelve supreme chiefs, and as it happens, in charge of the forces which guard the empire's internal peace...

LAUDERIC: Yes, my lord.

EDEKO: Even when crowned heads come under the Hun high command, I can only beg favours, act pleading speeches, fawn on them. And they? They are allowed only to grant what we want without a squeak.—Lord Lauderic! I have entreated you with all humility due to your princely crown, not to allow a soul to remain in your tent or around, within hearing distance. Your guards towards the direction of the Great Lord's camp and over towards the enemy have been replaced by my own soldiers.

LAUDERIC: So they have.

EDEKO: If by chance someone were still to witness... something which should not be witnessed... he must not survive the cock's crow. In a minute or two you too must leave with your servants, prince.—And yet I know, that here, here in your tent...

LAUDERIC: My sister's here! My little sister, Mikolda. I had her brought here at your word, my lord, by a strenuous, dangerous and costly route. I could not help her arriving at this hour.

EDEKO: You have summoned the princess Mikolda on the Great Lord's orders. If everything works out according to expectation... the Great Lord will marry the princess to one of the royal princes... Haven't you been told?

LAUDERIC: I dared not believe it. The royal daughter of one of the smallest Gothic kingdoms, and the Great Lord's ancient line...

EDEKO: The Great Lord holds your little country in high esteem for its valiant people, noble rulers and—mountain passes which, in the eyes of a general count for much.

LAUDERIC: High praise, I know!

EDEKO: Ask for the young lady.

LAUDERIC: At once. (Calls out): The princess Mikolda!

EDEKO: Quickly take your leave of her. She will pass the battle tomorrow in the Great Lord's camp, and then I shall conduct her myself, at the head of a glittering company, on her long journey to the splendid court of the Great Queen Reka.

LAUDERIC: That's where she'll wait for...?

EDEKO: There or elsewhere. There's no shortage of places. The court of Gud-runa, the Literate Queen, couldn't be called poverty-stricken, nor those of the other Great Queens. And a princess bride could do worse than pass her time waiting in the palace shared by the lesser queens.

Mikolda has entered: she is very young, very beautiful,
wearing convent dress.

MIKOLDA (to Edeko): Stranger:...

LAUDERIC: Mikolda...

MIKOLDA: If you are my keeper, I beg you let me return to my convent!

LAUDERIC: My little sister, you must know who you are speaking to...

EDEKO: Sublime princess, let old Edeko be your friend. I am to be your travel-ling companion and guide on a long journey.

MIKOLDA: Let me back to my convent. For me everywhere else is bad, I'm happy only there... I am Jesus's bride.

EDEKO: I can't tell whose bride you are, young lady. Who can foresee the Great Lord's will?—But tomorrow there will be a battle, young prince! A great battle. For all my grey hairs, maybe it'll be the greatest I have seen. And it depends on you, on your valour and on your steadfast loyalty to the Great Lord, whether or not your little sister becomes a Hun princess. And if she does, which wife of which royal son. It has been known for a bride to be returned as she came.

MIKOLDA: Yes, please let me go back.

LAUDERIC: By my scutcheon, lord Edeko, I swear: my knights and I will give no cause for complaint!

EDEKO: The choice is considerable. The Great Lord has more than forty adult sons.

MIKOLDA: Grey old man, I beg you, though you are a pagan... though you may never taste the divine mercy... even if damnation, certain and eternal, awaits you...

LAUDERIC: Sister, for the love of Christ...

EDEKO: Let me hear.

MIKOLDA: Though you are a barbarian, a savage, senseless barbarian...

LAUDERIC: Shut up!—My sister isn't a consecrated nun... no. She has only learnt their habits.

EDEKO: The Great Lord dislikes unfinished speeches. So do I. Speak on.

MIKOLDA: Let me go from here. The Lord will guide me alone on foot back to my dear, distant convent... And there I shall pray for you too... Perhaps for this single act, when I ask my bridegroom, my Saviour in his goodness will free you from hell-fire...?

EDEKO: Mikolda, you are a beautiful girl, believe an old man who has seen much: it's in you, in you the hell-fire is blazing, though clearly it has not scorched you yet. To me eyes speak volumes, and your eyes are eloquent, maid. Beware of that fire; and it's from that... yes... from that a tough, brawny and pagan Hun prince could shield you in his embrace.

MIKOLDA (falls before the crucifix): My sweetest Jesus, who for my salva-tion did suffer and die on the sacred tree of the cross... protect your handmaid ... succour her... or grant me a sweet martyrdom that I may the sooner behold the glorious footstool at your throne...

LAUDERIC (suddenly): By my helm... Girl, hold your tongue! (To Edeko): I'd al-most forgotten... You haven't told me what their creed is—those coming here to-night. (Pointing to the crucifix): Shall I have it taken out? Have it veiled?

MIKOLDA: Don't touch it with your defiling hands!

EDEKO: Our empire has a thousand races and ten thousand gods. Who cares? Let them be, let them hang or stand where they please, it's no concern of ours. Unless you want us to feel sorry that you've been landed only with a scraggy, strung-up god like yours, convulsed on a blood-stained tree. You chose him.

MIKOLDA: Let the remorseless wrath of the Lamb strike down the blasphemer! Amen! Amen! Amen!

EDEKO: We've run out of time, take your leave. I'll marshall the escort and then we start, lady. Till then, give her a talking to, Prince. She should make her fortune smiling, not whimpering.

Edeko goes.

LAUDERIC (after a pause): Have you been blubbering, girl? Have you been blubbering? Aren't we barbarians as well, even if we are a different sort? Go and ask in Rome! Not just the court, not even the child-brained emperor, Valentinianus. But anybody! Ask the least baggage-carrier, as long as he knows Roman blood flows through his knotted veins. Just ask him what we are. Barbarians! Bloody barbarians! Hairy barbarians! Senseless barbarians! Beer-swilling barbarians!

MIKOLDA: I am the slave of God. I am the Lamb's bride. Brother, let me return to my convent!

LAUDERIC: Stupid goose! Don't let our brothers hear of this! Or father! He would have you strangled with your heavenly bridal veil! By my pearl-studded saddle, those damned nuns ought to be whipped for bringing you up this way. —I gallop here over hill and dale with the flower of my chivalry to shed my blood for our royal house, and you would grudge your father and brothers your skinny body's tiresome virginity, when you could make the lord of half the world... what... lord-to-be of the whole world our kinsman?

MIKOLDA: In the convent they didn't tell me about this...

LAUDERIC: There will be a battle here tomorrow, understand that. Man has never fought greater. The two war-lords of the world—for there are only two who deserve the name: Aetius and Attila - are about to lead the hemispheres to slaughter.

MIKOLDA: In my convent we prayed every day: may heaven grant victory to the Christian general.

LAUDERIC: Don't...! Beg your prayer back! Pray again! Would you pray for your brother's ruin? You'd beg God's help against your father's throne?—Our uncle and cousins are gathering over there in alliance with the Romans. If Aetius wins tomorrow, our kinsmen will devour our little kingdom, chase our father and brothers out into the world, unless, as is more likely, they hang them quartered on the gates of our palace. Is that what you want?

MIKOLDA: No, no...

LAUDERIC: But if Attila wins, we will trample our uncle in the mire, and our cousins and the whole bunch of Gothic relatives, arming in the other camp... you see? we shall trample them in the mire... haha! in blood and mire...

MIKOLDA: Mother Superior said: Attila is Antichrist!

LAUDERIC: Hush! Stone walls have ears, let alone tent canvas.—Once everyone was pagan: why the fuss? Father was born as one. Our uncle to this day believes in Odin and hopes for Valhalla.

MIKOLDA: My uncle? Heaven have mercy! The one who...

LAUDERIC: Who over there in the dark is whetting his sword, as Rome's ally, against us. But let Attila win...!

MIKOLDA (to herself): Antichrist! Antichrist! Antichrist!

LAUDERIC: Let Attila win! I'll have thousands, tens of thousands of infidel Goths driven to the water! Up to the waist! Up to the neck! Lord God, which shall flow to your greater glory: blood or christening water?

MIKOLDA: And they shall be saved from hell-fire!

LAUDERIC: Haha! Won't they? Even if... (crossing himself, whispering)... even if it's at the cost of the Antichrist's victory tomorrow...

MIKOLDA (has stood up): Genoveva... Genoveva!... Genoveva...! - that was the name of the virgin who bid the people of Paris hold out when Attila's host rolled upon them... Bishop Lupus... For half a year Bishop Lupus was Attila's companion, and day by day dropped the word of Truth in his ears. Bishop Anianus in Orleans...

LAUDERIC: Schoolgirl.

MIKOLDA: Bishop Nicasius and his sister Eutropia of the holy life, in the rich city of Rheims, in the very presence and sight of Satan himself, opposed Attila and died in sweet martyrdom... Bishop John of the holy life, when Attila besieged the citadel of Ravenna...

LAUDERIC: Attila never besieged the citadel of Ravenna.

MIKOLDA: The virgin Ursula and her eleven thousand virgin companions who died martyrs...

LAUDERIC: Eleven thousand! Haha! By my spurred boots, eleven thousand virgins ...

MIKOLDA (to the crucifix): My beloved bridegroom, grant that one day the Mother Superior may call together the young virgins in the convent, and say to them...

LAUDERIC: What?

MIKOLDA: "Who has converted pagan Goths by the thousands?—Lauderic, the Christian prince."

LAUDERIC: Aha!

MIKOLDA: "And who has converted the pagan Huns by their millions?"

LAUDERIC: Who?

MIKOLDA: "The virgin princess, nurtured in this convent to sanctity... Mikolda ..."

LAUDERIC: By my golden robe...!

MIKOLDA: Have me swear! (Kneels.)

LAUDERIC: What for?

MIKOLDA: I want to swear! Have me swear!

LAUDERIC: Say then: I swear...

MIKOLDA: I swear, O divine Goodness...

LAUDERIC: I swear...

MIKOLDA: I swear by your sacred wounds... by your agonized face... by your holy body convulsed in pain...

LAUDERIC: Little sister, you won't be alone, have no fear... Only let me survive tomorrow's battle! You will see, I shall come and go in Attila's court... And our relative will be there, our great kinswoman, the second Great Queen: Gudruna the Literate, who understands even the language of birds...

MIKOLDA: ...I swear, that following in the footsteps of your virgin martyrs... by shedding of my tears... by spilling my blood...

EDEKO (returning): Take your leave!

MIKOLDA: I have sworn, I have sworn.

LAUDERIC: What have you sworn?

MIKOLDA: Jesus will know.

EDEKO: Your women are already on their mules, princess. Say goodbye.

MIKOLDA: Let's part!

EDEKO: You go that way, Prince. Take a good night's sleep in my lieutenant's tent. I'll have you called before dawn.

LAUDERIC: My sister... Will we see each other again...? Tomorrow's battle...

MIKOLDA: Let's part!

The two part after a brief, passionate embrace.

Long pause. Edeko, left alone, pushes two armchairs to face
each other, sets the torches in order. He prepares drink and
two chalices,
He steps to the entrance, because he hears the guest approaching.
After a further pause, enter Aetius. The Hun officers who had
led him this far disappear at once.

EDEKO: Greetings, patrician!

AETIUS: Dear old man...

EDEKO: In your person I greet not Rome but the greatest Roman.

AETIUS: Grandiloquent, indeed... Lala! I wish I could prove you liar. But unfortunately among the blind, a man with one eye is king.

EDEKO: With one eye, Aetius, you could be not only their king... you could be their emperor. But since you've got the eye of the old Roman eagle... they are terrified of you. They only give you the sword of high command knowing you'll come back with it dulled.

AETIUS: I fear my ears commit treason if I were to listen further—Lalala. It's long since I've been among you, good lord Edeko. Your hair is white as snow since then. Otherwise, how goes it with you?

EDEKO: I am a grain of sand sinking down the hour which counts Rome's final moments.

AETIUS: While I, you see, turn grey attempting to check the drift of those moments.

EDEKO: One must need great wisdom to know how to delay the inevitable.

AETIUS: You are wrong. Wisdom speeds on the inevitable. Folly checks it.

EDEKO: And with all your wisdom you would serve folly?

AETIUS: What else can I do? I am a Roman in the four hundred and fifty-first year of the Lord... (After slight pause): Have I long to wait, old Edeko? It's not easy for a commander-in chief to vanish for hours on the eve of battle. Had not the only friend I've ever had called me...

EDEKO: To use your way of measuring time, Aetius, you've come a few pater nosters too early.

AETIUS: Your words make sense, old man... A soldier should omit nothing before battle...

Brief pause, during which Aetius prays to the crucifix.

EDEKO (listening at the entrance): You must leave it at that, my lord.

AETIUS: Is he here...?!

Enter Attila. Pause. Attila and Aetius gaze at each
other in motionless silence.

EDEKO: May I go?

ATTILA: Go.

Edeko quickly goes.
Attila and Aetius slowly get closer, then faster and faster,
finally they throw themselves into a passionate embrace.

AETIUS: Brother!

ATTILA: My only friend!

They kiss each other.

ATTILA: I was afraid you might not come.

AETIUS: To you, Attila?

ATTILA: To the enemy's camp.

AETIUS: At your word?

ATTILA: I might have been laying a trap for you. It's a long time since we've seen each other, Aetius. I could have changed for the worse.

AETIUS: If you had, life would be no loss. I am a Roman: my strongest emotion is disgust. It's an effort to shave every day without slashing my throat.

ATTILA: Leave that to the emperor.

AETIUS: Lala. But no one must expect me to live, to live every day another day long, in a world which didn't have you.

ATTILA: See: I've turned my hand to world conquest.

AETIUS: By all means. It makes so little difference who the world belongs to. Maybe you could make something of it, so it could be worth the sun's while to to rise on it every day? Anyway, those who still hope, are hoping in you.

ATTILA: And you have brought here the armies of half the world to the plain of Catalaunum to baulk what millions are hoping for?

AETIUS: What else can I do? One has to spin out a lifetime somehow. And in any case I am not one of those who can hope. I love you, Attila, I love you dearly, I have unswerving faith in your greatness. But I cannot hope even in you.

ATTILA: Pity.

AETIUS: Whereas my emperor—I am drawn to him by the most extraordinary passion. I feel a surpassing loathing for him! Lala... Each time he lands himself in trouble, there he is squirming and craving at my feet... For that spectacle alone it's worth saving him from time to time.

ATTILA: Why won't you be emperor?

AETIUS: Pshaw!

ATTILA: No taste for it?

AETIUS: Nah!

ATTILA: Now you could be. Rather not?

AETIUS: I'd rather expect assassins every day than send them out myself.

ATTILA: I see that. Anyway, now's not the time for this. I called you about something else.

AETIUS: You called me for something specific?

ATTILA: Of course.

AETIUS: Pity. I was hoping you simply couldn't bear our being so close not seeing each other. I thought we'd fool the night away, as when we were kids in Rome and Ravenna, both pageboys in the court of the emperor Honorius. —Is this the famous sword?

ATTILA (lifting it): We call it the Sword of God.

AETIUS: Feeble sort of weapon.

ATTILA: This year I shall replace the blade, next year the hilt. After each victory, a ceremony.

AETIUS: If the all-but-legendary shepherd had found not a sword, but a six-footed calf, then that too you'd have taken as a sign: you must now conquer the world.

ATTILA: (earnestly): And that's what it would have meant.—The two Roman empires aren't masters of the world, yet they won't allow a proper master to put it in order. They are the rotting bodies of two dead giants and the human race can't go on under the same sky for the stench of offal.

AETIUS: I'll put up with them, the little time that remains.

ATTILA (coming to the point): How many do you reckon will die in tomorrow's battle?

AETIUS (after brief, silent reckoning): On my side I count on sacrificing a hundred thousand.

ATTILA: And on my side?

AETIUS: Don't count on less.

ATTILA: Right. And which one of us is going to win?

AETIUS: There's no luck in soothsaying. Let's leave that.

ATTILA: No, no, that's just the point. That's why I called you here. That's what to-night's for. I want to know whether you think you're going to win tomorrow.

AETIUS: Well, in this evening's skirmishes you lost. The Northern crest is mine.

ATTILA: I didn't lose: I arrived too late. We both see this as the greater disgrace. What's your estimate of the dead so far on the Northern slope?

AETIUS: Eight thousand.

ATTILA: How many are yours?

AETIUS: Half. The rest were yours. But the fight's still on, and we can't stop.

ATTILA: Perhaps come the dawn and there won't be a hoof-nail left of my Ala-nian horse. And you'll be lucky if a single patrol survive of your Burgundian infantry.

AETIUS: But those—will be up on the crest.

ATTILA: Yes, I think so. You will send them reinforcements by the morning.

AETIUS: You too. You will be sparing with your Huns and Acacirians. The Quadi and Marcommani you distrust. So you sacrifice the Scyrians.

ATTILA: And you the Batavians and the Bretons. Have I hit it? All right. Except by then the hill will have become completely unimportant. A wound bleeding both armies but mortal to neither.

AETIUS: Because at streak of dawn you will push forward your centre. Your Heruls, I know, will replace your long-knifed Scandinavians. This operation is going on at the moment, in complete silence and pitch darkness, twelve miles from here.

ATTILA: I see you still know about reconnaissance.

AETIUS: We learnt it together.

ATTILA: You want a flanking attack into my left wing. You think it could succeed?

AETIUS: Let's see. (Drawing on the ground with his sword): If this is the Seine here ...

ATTILA (marking with his heel): This is the city of Troyes. I made my rear pretty solid, you must admit. And would you, for this attempt on the right flank, throw across the pick of the little Roman cavalry you still have?... Quiet, don't deny it: you've already fiddled provisions across well in advance (drawing) into this larch-grove here. You don't intend such fine fodder for barbarian horses.

AETIUS: That's why you sent your scaly-armoured Sarmatians there: you thought perhaps you could encircle my advanced cavalry. But perhaps you couldn't?

ATTILA: You'll have to withdraw them nevertheless.

AETIUS: While in wide extended line, in vast numbers, you send your choice Hun-nish bowmen into attack. Exactly (drawing)—here.

ATTILA: Where in the front rank you place Gauls, and behind them draw up your real Roman legions, with those veteran golden eagles that have seen so many battles... - Will you drink?

AETIUS: A drop. (They each take one sip.) You'll want to use Lavinian tactics here.

ATTILA: You're a more resourceful strategist, you could probably think up some-thing better.

AETIUS: Not really: the ground practically cries out for it.

ATTILA: And what does all this decide?

AETIUS: Nothing. The centre meanwhile is destroyed.

ATTILA: On both sides. You throw in the first reserves.

AETIUS: You too.

ATTILA: Late afternoon, and that's gone too.

AETIUS: You throw in the second reserves.

ATTILA: You too. It will be night by the time they bleed to death.

AETIUS: Yes .

ATTILA: And what will that decide?

AETIUS: Nothing.

ATTILA: So we shall fight tomorrow's battle in vain.

AETIUS: In vain.

ATTILA: And twice a hundred thousand will die in vain.

AETIUS: In vain.

ATTILA: Let them not die.

AETIUS: What do you mean?

ATTILA: Let's not have them die. Let there be no battle tomorrow.

AETIUS: Lala...!

Pause

ATTILA: Well, that's what I wanted to talk to you about tonight, my friend. Let's not take twice a hundred thousand times what we can't give back even once. If blood is to flow, every drop should flow with a purpose.

AETIUS: With purpose or without: I can't divide the two so sharply. A drawn battle is loathsome. Afterwards the lies begin on both sides... Brr!

ATTILA: If you remain the Roman emperor's chief commander, we two will still have our combat to fight. But then one of us will win. It will have purpose.

AETIUS: If you win—perhaps. You'll trample the Empire underfoot.

ATTILA: Both empires. But this in itself would be a squalid ambition. I didn't receive God's sword for that.

AETIUS: But?

ATTILA (after brief pause): Have you ever watched the ants, Aetius? They live, work and defend themselves with one will, as they have done since the creation of the world. They say a little black demon taught them to live this way in the third week of the world. Since then they have known for all time, at every moment: this is needed, this way, not that, not some other way.

AETIUS: Beautiful...

ATTILA: Have you seen how the bees live? In the beginning, a goddess urged their lives to motion, and they have had no doubts since; what is wisest orders all.

AETIUS: Lala...

ATTILA: Man is a creature a thousand times more intelligent than bees and ants. He of all should know how to live! Why should man, man alone live in perpetual confusion, in perpetual doubt, perpetual quarrel? Human life today is contemptible! A naked eaglet cast from the nest of the universe: he was born its lord, and all he can do is to die in squalor like a beast! Who will cut out for man at last the eternal pattern of his life? Who will engrave the commandment in never-crumbling bronze: for ever this way, and, no other?

AETIUS: You?

ATTILA: No. (Showing God's sword): This.

Brief pause.

AETIUS: You still love women, Attila?

ATTILA: Very much.

AETIUS: Many, and all of them justified by your immaculate morality?

ATTILA: One or two from time to time for love:—love after all has many shapes, changing with life's phases and with every woman. At other times - since life is long - only for pleasure, and then I need a lot.

AETIUS: Should we happen to love only one, our faith packs on that one love the inexorable weight of original sin and its brimstone menace. Ah, rejoice you have nothing to do with this.

ATTILA: Sin to love women? Laugh, Aetius!

AETIUS: I do laugh!... Except that hell... hell is so foul an idea that at times I can't not believe in it... (Changing tone): So? At crack of dawn the two generals ride out before their troops... yes?... Salute, as is proper, and then: every capable fighter from the Great Wall of China to the Atlantic coast gathered here—about turn! ... Elegant. I like it!

ATTILA: Your hand!

Cheerfully they shake hands and embrace lightly.

AETIUS: And by which road do you intend to march out?

ATTILA: Where from?

AETIUS: Here. From Gaul.

ATTILA: In autumn?

AETIUS: Now.

ATTILA: You are joking?

AETIUS: Merciful heavens, you aren't serious?

Suddenly, brief and shocked silence.

ATTILA: Aetius! We've just fought tomorrow's battle here, in our thoughts. Without doubt, the engagement would be undecisive.

AETIUS: Yes.

ATTILA: After a drawn battle how could you expect your opponent to withdraw as if you had beaten him?

AETIUS: Even after a drawn battle... one must somehow find an end. The two sides have to break apart.

ATTILA: After a drawn battle I would have entrenched myself in my camp. Here by the Seine.—That's what I must do now.

Brief silence.

AETIUS: Our friendship, Attila, wasn't born today. Nor is it an adolescent memory. In the sea of millions of small and great nobodies, we are two who alone fit the measure of history.—I know that when your great predecessor, the grand-king Rua, twice rescued me by armed force from my emperor's fury and restored me to office, both times you had advised him to do so.

ATTILA: I and Prince Mundsuk, my father since dead.

AETIUS: I know that when the revolt was suppressed and I had to flee, it was at your will that I was granted protection in your land.

ATTILA: King Rua gave it, because my father, Prince Mundsuk advised him.

AETIUS: At your word.

ATTILA: Yes.

AETIUS: More than once we have ridden side by side as ally generals.

ATTILA: Those campaigns are my finest memories.

AETIUS: Except the one in which you will conquer me.

ATTILA: Perhaps...

AETIUS: Will you believe then, that it's not meanness prompting me to say...

ATTILA: What?

AETIUS: My brother! If the emperor gets to know that I allow you to be here on the doorstep of Italy without a single arrowshot... do understand... he'll have me murdered. And that's the least trouble: but he will send in my place some prize idiot with whom in the end you'll have to fight your indecisive battle.

ATTILA: I take your point, but do see mine as well... Neither can I slink away from the field, as if I had been scared by Rome and her barbarian allies.

AETIUS: Granted. There's no general who doesn't care what is said behind his back.

ATTILA (passionately): I don't want tomorrow's battle. You don't want it. The gods and demons don't want it. Your three-in-one god, why should he want it?... What's forcing us then... what dares to force us...?

AETIUS: I don't know. But you see, in another few hours inevitably we two'll embark on the biggest and most senseless battle in the history of the world. My brother...

ATTILA: If you are my brother, then you know... then you know... you know... (Pales, falls silent, feels his left shoulder.)

AETIUS: Attila! What's happened! Are you ill?... Answer...!

ATTILA: Nothing... (Gradually makes a great effort to continue):... then you know there is... yes there is just one way out.

AETIUS: I know. There is a single way out. To unite our forces and together march on Rome.

ATTILA (back in his former strength): Yes. In a month you are emperor, my perpetual ally... And we'd have saved not only two hundred thousand lives... We'd have saved the world!

AETIUS (quietly): I don't believe the world's worth saving... And then: who knows how history might prattle about me afterwards... And finally... perhaps eternal damnation does exist...? - Are you recovered? A drop of wine?

ATTILA: The sip I drank is my daily dose. Pour yourself some.

AETIUS: I don't drink either... before battle...

ATTILA (after a pause, in a new tone): Aetius! If we can't save two hundred thousand, at least save one.

AETIUS: Who?

ATTILA: I didn't want to tell you, so you won't think this is why...

AETIUS: Say.

ATTILA: My priests have prophesied. About tomorrow's battle.

AETIUS: What?

ATTILA: That I shan't win... but you... will die.

AETIUS (after brief pause): Lala... Pity it should come in such a good-for-nothing battle... Still, better than one of the emperor's hirelings... What was the prophecy? "Aetius will be killed?"

ATTILA: "The enemy's chief commander will be killed."

AETIUS: "The enemy's chief commander..." (Silence. He pours himself wine, takes one sip, then laughs.)

ATTILA: Don't you believe in pagan prophecy?

AETIUS: A soldier believes every prophecy... But a soldier, while he lives, will be cunning.

Enter Edeko.

EDEKO: My lord, the cockcrow.

Pause. Attila and Aetius look at each other.

AETIUS (sighs): My horse, old friend.

Curtain

JULIUS HÁY (b. 1900) is one of the leading Hungarian playwrights. He left Hungary after the supression of the Hungarian Soviet Republic in 1919. Subsequently he lived in Berlin, Zurich and Moscow, returning to Hungary only in 1945. In 1951 he became Professor at the Academy of Theatrical Art and Cinematography. In 1957 he was imprisoned for alleged 'anti-state activities'. After his release three years later he wrote several new plays *The Horse*, *Mohács*, *Attila's Nights*, none of which has been performed in Hungary. Since 1965 Hay has been living in Switzerland. PETER HÁY is Julius Hay's son and a student in Oxford. He has translated most of his father's plays into English.

Reviews

JAN KOTT

Wyspiański with a very Polish finale

THE LIBERATION has been a success; thanks to the right city, the right theatre, the right producer; above all thanks to the right time. Time has proved here to be an extraordinary and unexpected producer. I am quite sure that a year, even six months, ago *The Liberation* would have been puffed up, artificial and shallow, just like the two latest revivals of *The Wedding,* in Warsaw and Cracow, had been. But now, suddenly, a live and succulent *Liberation;* topical though not made to be so; contemporary, though historical; modern, though *fin-de-siecle;* very Cracovian, but not provincial; clear and precise, though very much in Wyspiański's manner; traditional and yet anti-traditional.

Konrad enters the empty stage. There is nothing more theatrical than an empty stage. But here, the empty stage is in its place, ready made, to play with the entire building. Konrad, too, is in his place; dressed in black, generous romantic coat, but underneath has a black, tight, existentialist pullover. He has just left a university seminar, stuffed with Marxism, and gone to wash it all off in the cellar "Under the Rams". In Cracow even a cellar has to be bound up with tradition. One cannot even put out one's tongue without putting it out on ancient walls and tradition. One cannot simply jeer at life without jeering at literature, because in Cracow life is still more entangled with literature than in any other city. Everything here, in a very natural way, becomes theatre at once. Every gesture, therefore, every bolder move of the hand, every protest becomes, just as naturally, anti-theatre.

The conference of literary scholars, organized in honour of Wyspiański[*] on the fiftieth anniversary of his death, took place in the great hall of Jagiellonian University. Where else could it have taken place? The hall is new, pretends to be Gothic and on the walls hang huge canvesses by Matejko. The hall has grandeur and very poor acoustics; it invites rhetoric, false and pathetic gestures; there is something of a national theatre about that hall. Even today everything is so theat-

---

JAN KOTT (b. 1914) is an essayist and theatre critic, Professor of the History of Polish literature at Warsaw University. Known in the West primarily for his *Shakespeare Our Contemporary*, Kott is presently visiting professor at Yale Drama School. BOLESLAW TABORSKI is a Polish poet and translator living in London where he works for the BBC. He has translated, among other things, Jan Kott's *Shakespeare Our Contemporary*. These essays, in Mr. Taborski's translation, will appear in a collection of Kott's pieces on the theatre, due from Doubleday this year.

*The best-known Polish playwright of the *fin-de-siècle,* he wrote a great number of plays, of which *Wedding* is on the permanent repertory of Polish theatres.

rical in Cracow. In Wyspiański's time the total impossibility of distinguishing literature from life must have been much more stifling. Everything was the national stage, and on that stage Wyspiański placed his anti-theatre. But his anti-theatre, bitter and jeering, was absorbed by Cracow, became pathetic, Matejko-like, and in its turn became a new national stage.

Warsaw defies all literary tradition. The memory of writers does not become legend; it is rather kept in biting anecdotes. Even the literary street names are out of place in Warsaw: they either ring false, or too good. There is a street of Winnie the Pooh in Warsaw. In the street the National Bank of Poland has its headquarters. Just imagine the Bank of England being situated in London in Mickey Mouse street, or Alice in Wonderland street.

Wyspiański's theatre has grown into Cracow to such an extent that one cannot even tell whether the famous "wedding" happened first and the play was written later, or the other way round. Even landscape looks like stage sets here.

No wonder then that the actor Zaczyk appears on the empty stage of Juliusz Slowacki Theatre in a romantic coat and an existentialist pullover. He is Konrad and workers free him from invisible chains. In any other city, in any other theatre the scene would be pathetic, symbolic and in all probability unbearable. Here it looks quite natural. After all, they all wear somewhat funny clothes in this city, and have beards, real or false. That happens even at the University, not to say anything about the literary or theatrical circles! They are disguised as statesmen and scholars, as Marxists and Catholics, as revolutionaries of 1905 and as positivists of 1957. Even birds dress up as Muses sometimes occasionally. Wyspiański's genius consisted in placing the national drama in the theatre's dressing room: there he saw first Cracow, then all Poland.

A theatrical dressing room is not only grotesque but has something lyrical and pathetic about it. Lady Macbeth is holding a blood-stained hankerchief in her hand, but you can offer her a cigarette and make a date with her in the café.

Wyspiański was particularly sensitive to that mixture of fiction and reality, so frequently evoked by the threatre's 'back stage'; to the artistic shock occurring at an unexpected collision of real people with characters in a play. The sensitivity to the perverse beauty of theatre within the theatre and to the poetry of the 'wings' was shared by Wyspiański with other innovators at the beginning of this century. But his sui generis "Pirandellianism" was Shakespearian, Polish and Cracovian, all at the same time; it was very serious, too. Dressing rooms were not only back-stage. Cracow was a theatre dressing room for all Poland. That was why Wyspiański's modernist anti-theatre became the new national drama. If everything was theatre, then anti-theatre of necessity became a struggle for the soul of the nation. Anti-theatre meant in this instance a national puppet show; a very special show which had to measure up to *Forefathers' Eve** and outgrow it; a show which imperceptibly became itself a new *Forefathers' Eve*. In this was Wyspiański's greatness and his misfortune. A political puppet show, performed in the wings of a theatre in the shape of a national drama; a political puppet show turning into a national mystery play. In all the world drama there is nothing

*A drama or "dramatic poem" by Mickiewicz; see Kott's next review.

like it. There is madness and genius here, in equal proportions. But whatever one would say about it, above all it is Theatre.

Time has blurred the literality of the allusions, brushed away the dust of professorial commentaries from *The Liberation*. After the fifty odd years the first act has become clearer and simpler, grown to the dimensions of a national grotesque. It has become - God forgive me and you, o citizens of Cracow! - a monstrous "Green Goose". A chorus of the Poles calls to the smoky stove: "Send us a miracle!", but the stove goes on emitting smoke. Unlike Galczyński's miniatures, however, *The Liberation* is a monumental and monstrous "Green Goose" in which history has blended with literature.

The first act of *Liberation* has always been produced half-ironically. But only now Dabrowski and Stopka have given it the full flavour and clarity of the national puppet show. To my mind this is possible, perhaps, only in Cracow, on the original and authentic stage of *The Liberation,* where the actors do not have to learn traditional gestures but have them in their blood; it is enough for them to show themselves, and the tradition in which they grew up, and they will be funny; they will be authentic, be set by the same problems that Wyspiański had to deal with. The stove goes on emitting smoke and all are waiting; waiting for the romantic Godot. At last he comes. He does not speak, only motions everyone to rise. The stove goes on emitting smoke, the coming of Godot does not change anything.

The second act of *The Liberation* is a struggle with the national stupefaction. It is a great scene of the national hang-over which, all of a sudden, strikes us with its topicality. The late night conversations, the national drunkenness and the slow sobering up. Konrad and his little antagonists called Masks throw all the national ideological clichés at each other: art and mission, nation and lonliness, greatness and love, action and duty, fate and histroy. Until the moment comes when Konrad has enough; when he dreams of one thing only: that he could live like a man in a country like any other; that Poland should stop being the Christ among nations, stop saving herself and the world; that foreigners should stop admiring us how noble, unhappy and proud we are; that things should be like they are elsewhere; that there should be censorship and order; that thieves be thrown out; that conversation should cease to revolve round the ultimate things; that there should be an end put to the maddening national stupefaction. And suddenly, in all this, there is a dazzling explosion of great poetry, the purest poetry written in Polish since Mickiewicz's Lausanne lyrics. "I want, that on a summer's day, on dry, hot summer's day. . ."

The late night conversation is over; only a couple more Masks are hissing in their chairs. The hang-over and the Polish Walpurgis-night are over. Konrad is sobering up. He will never again be an ideologue. And suddenly everything begins all over again. The national stupefaction returns like malaria. Konrad runs out and snatches a burning torch from Hestia's hand. Hestia is standing by a neoclassical tomb, dressed in a half-classical half-modern dress, looking as if cut out of a bad drawing in an illustrated periodical or the early years of our century. She has style, because *art-nouveau* is an established style now; she is ridiculous, because the art-nouveau is still ridiculous. The puppet show becomes a national mystery play now. All symbols all styles are now mixed up. A new madness begins. Shakespeare and *Forefathers' Eve*, theatre and anti-theatre, Kosciuszko's peasant Scythemen and the Erynyses. Mickiewicz and Prospero, everything gets muddled up, Konrad chases the Genius out and throws down the trap the chalice with the romantic poetry of tombs.

Wyspiański was undoubtedly a great precursor. One can find everything in him, from Pirandello to Giraudoux, Garcia Lorca, Camus, and Ionesco. He has theatre in the theatre, statues that talk, personality split, anti-theatre, drama of fate, moderization of Greek myths, antiquity, Shakespeare and puppet-show. That syncretism was certainly part of Wyspiański's artistic novelty. But can a modern Wyspiański be shown today in isolation from fifty years experience accumulated in the European theatre? Artistic means have become more sharp and subtle. Wyspiański was a prescursor but today we look at his theatre through all his conscious and subconscious heirs up to, and including, Galczyński's *Green Goose*. There is nothing to be done about it.

If *The Liberation* still remains intelligible to us, if we still partly find ourselves in it, it has not ceased to be a national drama, the reason is that the stupefaction persists, that we are still poisoned by the fumes. Let us imagine how a French, Czech, or Swiss bourgeois, or a Danish worker, or an Italian peasant girl would look at *The Liberation*. What would an Englishman, or a Dutchman, or a German understand from this play? The answer is: nothing; or at most, they would see in it a document of Polish madness. Perhaps they are right. Unfortunately, it cannot be helped. We are on leave from a lunatic asylum. And that is why the Cracow production of *The Liberation* is, perhaps, the greatest theatre event of the year. Bronislaw Dabrowski can be proud of himself; and so can Cracow. Wyspiański's ghost lives in that city. I do not want to live in Cracow, though that ghost sometimes haunts Warsaw too.

Why don't you want to write about it, gentlemen?

THE PRODUCTION of *Forefathers' Eve* was the most important event to have happened in the Polish theatre in the last ten years. This is what we all felt on the first night in Warsaw; this is what audiences feel every night in the tightly packed auditorium of the Polski Theatre. The greatness of poetry and the presence of poetry are not one and the same thing. Mickiewicz's greatness has been written about by Poles and by foreigners. His greatness is indisputable and has its rightful place in histroy and in history of literature. But there is also such a thing as live presence; a dialogue, going on for a century, with someone who is physically present; like all of us, only greater than any of us.

There are anniversaries imposed by dates. We have had many such anniversaries. I must confess frankly, I had been afraid that the Mickiewicz Year would be another of those calendar anniversaries. But it turned out differently. The anniversary was really experienced by the nation. And on this occasion, those often abused words regained their true and full meaning. Every one of us struggles with Mickiewicz as best he can. But every one of us needs Mickiewicz. Mickiewicz is read as no other poet is read. Without Mickiewicz one cannot imagine Polish literature; not only literature. Without him, we could not imagine ourselves.

Mickiewicz's live presence means the *Sonnets,* the *Lausanne Lyrics, Pan Tadeusz* and *Forefathers' Eve.* There are moments when one needs artistic perfection above all else, if only to match oneself with the highest model. The verse of the *Sonnets* is definitive. One can experience the *Sonnets* emotionally, or they may leave one cold, but it is impossible not to experience their perfection. Nothing in Polish has been written better. They are definitive in the artistic order, just as the *Lausanne Lyrics* are definitive in the moral order. Only they remain in moments of defeat and utter despair, when all other poetry is dead.

Without the *Lausanne Lyrics* things would be harder still. This is the hardest personal meeting with Mickiewicz; so personal that it is difficult to share the experience; happy are those who have not had that meeting.

With *Pan Tadeusz* things are different. One reaches for that book after a few months spent abroad. One simply has to read it and send it to all who have gone abroad. It is the only book that can be a substitute for Poland. Maybe that is why it is best to read *Pan Tadeusz* outside Poland. At any rate, one reads it somehow differently. It is a book about a Poland which does not exist and, perhaps, never did exist. And that is why it is a book about Poland that has always existed; but only in dreams and in longing. *Forefathers' Eve,* on the other hand, is a book about Poland that really exists; about Poland in all its greatness and all its tragedy.

At the first night of *Forefathers' Eve* people cried; in the stalls as well as in the gallery. Government ministers were crying, the hands of the technical crew were shaking, the cloakroom attendants were wiping their eyes. *Forefathers' Eve* moved and shocked and became the subject of discussions long into the night. I know no other drama in the whole of world literature that could move the audience to the core after a hundred and twenty five years the way *Forefathers' Eve* did. *Forefathers' Eve* struck home to our hearts with greater force than any play written since the war; in its historical aspect as well as by its up-to-dateness. Its presence has been confirmed with a vehement force, fitting for Mickiewicz, of whom Zygmunt Krasiński wrote that every talk with him was "a fight with daggers drawn".

Forefathers' Eve is the most modern Polish literary work of the first half of the nineteenth century. There, for the first time the hero of a new era appeared on the stage, without the trappings of a historic costume. He had shed his Byronic mantle and spoke his own truth; shouted rather, and so loud that the shout is echoing still. Time did not consume the play's modern spirit and it still haunts us today. There is dynamite in *Forefathers' Eve* ,and it exploded on the first night.

The main plot of *Forefathers' Eve* is a dramatic biography of young noble revolutionaries, jotted down by Mickiewicz when the events were still fresh, in large chunks, every one of which meant a revolution in poetry and an era in the growing up of a generation. In France the story of the same generation, people born around 1800, was described by Balzac, Stendhal and Musset, in such detail that we know the cut of the heroes' jabot, the colour of waist-coats, the amount of laundress' bills, and the price of conscience. Mickiewicz wrote only the essential things about his generation, but they were enough. *Forefathers' Eve* is a fragmented work which seems to be the opposite of composition and order; which grew spontaneously and its main parts divided by decade, and yet, it falls into chapters, every one of which contains a complete version of the most important experiences and great conflicts of the generation.

Forefathers' Eve meant experience of folklore, at a time when villages where cottages had no chimneys were discovered as well as folk songs; peasant grievances as well as old legends; a living source of new poetic truth, a morality more human than the humanism of the libertines and more earthly than the stoicism of the belated successors to the Enlightenment. The social biography of the generation and the romantic's own life story begins with the encounter with the people.

One had to go through love in order to grow up to face one's time. The romantics did not invent unhappy love; they only experienced it as a struggle with the real world. To them it was the most personal experience of social injustice. In the fire of that love, or rather in its hell, sentimentality melted and turned into vehemence and the true feelings of a free man. A man was free when he had rejected catechism and learned to despise feudal prejudice. Because of that Gustaw talks in a different language than all the previous lovers in our poetry. He is the first portrait of modern man in our literature. In his great lyric fugue Mickiewicz shows the intellectual and emotional coming of age of his entire generation, from the first enthusiasm for the "robber books" to the rebellion against the mighty.

The third great chapter in the history of the generation was the conspiracy. Only a few of the best took part in it. A historian can describe today all the various stages in the development of political and social awareness of youth before 1830: their illusions and dreams, the immaturity of revolutional thought, the naive republicanism and the loneliness of the conspirators. But the great metaphor and the great abbreviation of the history of the generation will still remain that inscription chalked on the wall in the prison of the ex-Basilian convent: *Gustavus Obiit - hic natus est Conradus.*

Mickiewicz's artistic audacity is amazing. He had made his personal experiences into a great chapter of the experience of a generation, and now, through the trial of the philomaths, he showed in a breath-taking condensation, the historical path which led to the conspiracy and to the outbreak of the rising on a November night in 1830. Into his great poem he put in his friends, without changing their names; he did not shrink from the most brutal facts, but took in huge chunks of real life and spat them out like a volcano amidst the hot lava. In all the history of the world literature there is no other drama that could make such a tremendous impression by quoting authentic events. Mickiewicz was grasping history in the raw, as it were, and grappled with its great drama without resorting to fiction.

And so it was: the heroes he had chosen were making history.

Wilno was too small for him as the stage of Mickiewicz's drama. From there he moves his scene to a Warsaw drawing-room and to a country house near Lwów. How far have we departed from the cemetary chapel on the Forefather's eve. All Poland is the great scene of his drama; his actors are the youth, the cadets and writers, the patriots and the traitors; Novosiltsov with his henchmen and spies, and Bestuzhev with an outstretched hand. Carts are taking those condemned by the Tsar up North, but North means also the white December night in Senate Square.

The fourth chapter in the history of the generation consisted of the noble revolutionaries' 'road to Calvary' and their attack on heaven. Here Mickiewicz reached the utmost limits of poetry, enclosing the tragedy and greatness not just of the first generation of revolutionaries but of all generations up to the present. At this point the dynamite of Part III of *Forefathers' Eve* exploded, and we were experiencing the up-to-dateness of the dramatic poem. This must be said clearly: we are still attacking the Communist heaven and in this great attack Mickiewicz is on our side. *Forefathers' Eve* is for revolution and for the vehement champions of justice. In this too consists the greatness of Mickiewicz's 'arch-poem'.

The most living element of *Forefathers' Eve* turned out to be the political drama. It revealed all its vehement force, in spite of traditional interpreters. For Mickiewicz's contemporaries, *Forefathers' Eve* was a book about themselves. Its hero was a living man who loved, rebelled, struggled and despaired; who experienced romanticism and folklore, conspiracy, uprising and its defeat the way the best of people experienced them at the time. That was how Mochnacki understood *Forefathers' Eve,* that was how Norwid interpreted the work. "The hero of *Forefathers' Eve* - he wrote - is a deeply feeling man, regarded as mad by little people for whom everything that cannot be contained under their pocket magnifying glass is not essential".

In *Forefathers' Eve* spirits talk about matters of the earth, and people attack the heavens. Mickiewicz is as necessary for our theatres as air; not only in the order of the theatre, but also in the moral order.

"Ivona" has come of age

GOMBROWICZ's *Ivona* is not unlike those cruel and perverse little plays written by schoolboys in the class room behind other pupils' backs. They are usually grotesque and a kind of caricature, directed against teachers, mocking younger brothers and elder sisters, trying to ridicule literature and history; in essence they are a kind of showdown with the entire world, for at that time of life the world consists only of teachers and parents, brothers and sisters, of history and literature lessons. It happened once or twice that such little plays were written by boys of genius. Such was the case of Alfred Jarry's *Ubu Roi*. It was to be a school skit, a terrific satire on stupid schoolmasters and history classes. It was enough, however, to dress schoolmasters as kings and make them perform a classic historical anecdote for a preposterous situation, the grotesque discrepancy between man and the part he is to perform.

Gombrowicz's *Ivona* was written by a conscious writer, but something of school vindictiveness, of schoolboy obsessions and jokes remained in it. Not only in *Ivona* but in all of Gombrowicz's writings, schoolboy obsessions will reappear. After all, two terms invented by Gombrowicz which have passed into common speech and at the same time have become almost philosophical concepts: "to be fitted with a bum", or a "mug" - have been taken from schoolboy idiom. The school has remained for Gombrowicz the purest mechanism of social life.

We all of us have had, from time to time, a dream about sitting in the school-leaving examination. In the dream we are terribly afraid, even though we may not have been afraid when we were sitting to that exam. We feel ridiculous because we have not ceased to be adults even in that dream. The situation is "fitting us with a mug" we do not want to have, still we are helpless. The "mug" and the "bum" are stronger than us. It so happened that I had to pass a couple of exams as an adult. My examiners were my colleagues and yet it was a nerve-racking experience: I turned into a schoolboy again. That mechanism was one of the discoveries made in *Ferdydurke*.

Life often imitates literature: Gombrowicz would probably be amazed to hear that one of the youngest theatre critics in our country put on shorts and went to school pretending to be a schoolboy. The "ferdydurkism" of this story, however, is much more venomous in fact; it appeared later that the critic had been sent to school by the minister of education himself with the task of writing an article for a literary periodical.

Perhaps Gombrowicz would not have been surprised, after all. He himself willingly practised "ferdydurkism" in life. He adored such situations in real life in which something shameful was suddenly revealed, in which conventions were disturbed and a trial of strength would follow to prove who would dominate whom. Domination was his favourite word. He practiced social provocation as a psychological experiment. When I sat down at his café table, his opening words invariably were: "Mr. Kott, you are being admitted to our company today, although you are of base origin."

In those days Gombrowicz was often in the company of Stefan Otwinowski, the writer, and Andrzej Pleśniewicz, a young, very promising and erudite historian, who was later killed during the war. Gombrowicz began conversation by saying: "When I visited Andrzej yesterday. . ." Pleśniewicz tried to deny this, but that was exactly what Gombrowicz was waiting for: "What do you mean, I didn't visit you. Didn't you offer me bad tea and stale doughnuts. . ." Pleśniewicz again tried to deny this, but Gombrowicz would not relent: "You went out for a while to see your old aunt, and taking advantage of your absence I opened a fat note-book lying on your bed. . ." Pleśniewicz was desperate by now: "I have no aunt and no notebook". But Gombrowicz continued: "Do not try to deny, Andrzej, it was a green notebook, covered by a paperweight. I opened it and under yesterday's date I read: 'I have met Stefan Otwinowski; he is a fool and a hack'. Then he waited calmly to see what would happen.

There is a lot of that Gombrowiczian psychomania in *Ivona*. Ivona herself is anemic, passive, obstinately silent. But she exists. Her very presence, her very existence is a constant challenge. It compels everybody to take care of her. It provokes them too jeer or pity, in any event to adopt an attitude toward her. All conventional feelings, gestures, situations become incongruous in the face of her refusal to take active part. The very presence of Ivona humiliates all. They cease to be self-contained, they are compelled to play ever more stupid parts, get involved in ever more preposterous situations. They have to look at themselves with her eyes and then things shameful, indecent and stupid are revealed and exposed in every one of them.

Everybody has been fitted with a "bum" by Ivona, everybody feels a monstrous mug growing on him. Only Ivona's death can rid them all from nightmare. To kill Ivona, again one has to fit oneself with a mug, leave conventional stereotypes behind and create the situation of murder. But that situation, too, is incongruous, does not fit any convention, is inwardly humiliating. In order to kill Ivona one has to become pathetic. One of Gombrowicz's most brilliant inventions is a scene in which the Queen dishevels her hair and daubs her face with ink in order to encourage herself inwardly to poison Ivona. She enters a Shakespearian role, leaps into a ready made cliché - a literary and a schoolboy cliché at the same time.

There are more such psychological discoveries in *Ivona*. The play is derived from the spirit of *Ubu Roi*, but its philosophical problems are far more mature and up-to-date. *Ivona* waited twenty years for its first production and has now come of age. It is not more dated, it has just become clear. We are becoming more and more sensitive now to exactly this type of intellectual grotesque and perverse wisdom.

Adam Kilian's sets for Boleslaw Leśmian's
THE CURSED STALLION, 1962

translated by George Gomori
JANOS PILINSZKY

The desert of love

A bridge, a scorching asphalt road,
the day is emptying its pockets
laying out in turn its possessions.
You are alone in the catatonic twilight.

Bottom of a creased pit—such is the landscape,
gleaming scars in scintillating dusk.
It's getting dark. A stunning brilliance,
blinding sun. Summer, not to be forgotten.

There is summer and heat of lightning.
Without batting a wing, I know, they stand,
like burning cherubs those winged creatures
in splinter-thorned, boarded-up cages.

Do you remember? First came the wind,
then there was earth; and then the cage.
Fire and dung. And once in a while
a few wing-beats, an empty reflex.

And thirst. And then I asked for water.
Even today I hear the feverish gulps
and I endure them, helpless like a stone,
and I extinguish the dazzle, the delusions.

Years go by, years and hope
is but a tin pot spilled in the straw.

JANOS PILINSZKY (b. 1921) is a Hungarian Catholic poet. The body of his work is slim but his influence is significant. His poems have been translated into many languages, including French and English. For a study on Pilinszky, see: *Hungarian Quarterly*, Vol. 5, No. 1-2.

Attila József

ANDRAS SÁNDOR

IN THE AUTUMN of 1937, Attila József jumped under a freight train and died. He was 32 years old. Although he died young, he did not die prematurely like Shelley, Byron or even Pushkin. We can speak of his late poetry as we can of the poetry of Goethe or Yeats. For his work is not only mature, but also complete. The last poem he wrote is a final poem.

His suicide has been considered by turns an act of protest, despair, mental disorder; and all three interpretations are acceptable. We will probably never learn what his actual motive was—he simply went out for a walk that evening leaving no note behind. The last poem records a final state of mind - a renunciation of life - and at the same time, it records the last stage of his life. Reading his poetry, we can watch his advance, how he lost his grip on the world step by step, and how he reached the state in which he could say, "What I hold no longer holds me."

He felt let down by everything he cherished and needed, and viewing his life as reflected in his poetry, one has the terrible joy of seeing fate at its relentless best—much like watching Oedipus' world collapse. I do not mean to suggest that fate exists as an independent force with a pattern of its own, but that human life has spheres of varying significance. And it can happen that a man is defeated in such a manner that the defeat moves sphere by sphere to the very center of his being. There are men who have been defeated in that very center, but only there. They can continue to be active in other spheres and achieve limited consolation.

This formal requirement, however, does not suffice. A man's destruction needs something more to reach tragic perfection. He must have genuine power, genuine humanity—Macbeth has it. Even a villain like Richard has it. Such a man must be destroyed, not in his yearnings, but in his hope of satisfying them. If he is destroyed only *in* his yearnings, he never really had them, or he is weak, which, after all, amounts to the same thing. One source of greatness in József's late poetry is his invincible humanity. Although he lost everything he valued, he did not lose faith. He was too strong to surrender.

> O mankind whom my broken mother
> increased to suffer and did not understand:

I do not shrink from being born once more in your interest
You two billion coupled loneliness!

Strong men do not linger; they live or are destroyed. And to live means to have living contact with one's yearnings.

The word carrying the greatest momentum in József's basic vocabulary is "order." Order in itself is ambiguous or inane unless it is further qualified. For order, expressing only the formal aspect of a state or situation, can be either good and bad. The Hungarian word has a number of connotations that it rarely has in English. One of them is "régime" or "system" in the sense of political systems. It is a word expressing "the order of the day." József believed that the "order of the day" in Hungary and in the world at large was a wrong order, and to emphasize this he often used the word in both of its contradictory connotations. In the poem, "Enlighten Your Child", his irony is quite clear.

You should perhaps mutter a new fairy tale,
One about Fascist Communism.
For the world needs order,
and order demands
that children are not born at random
and what is good should not be free.

His idea of order is best expressed in a fragment of two lines:

Where freedom is order,
I always feel the infinite.

This is vague enough to sound like *unio mystica,* but his idea becomes a little more tangible if we realize that the paradox expressed in this couplet is linked with the concept of "playing" as defined, for instance, by Schiller and many others after him. When József explains in another poem, "Come freedom, you bear me order," he qualifies the content of his wish by saying, "teach your beautiful serious son with good words, and let him play too." And we can learn still more about his good order from its contrast with the wrong one:

I saw blue, red, yellow
smeared images in my dreams
and felt that this was order -
not a drifting speckle of dust was amiss.
Now my dream hovers in my limbs
like dimness, and the order is the iron world.
A moon rises in me at daytime
and at night a sun shines here within.

The poem suggests—as does the coalescence of freedom, order and the infinite in the former couplet—that this order is dynamic, animated, living. József emphasizes these qualities by contrasting his order with an iron order, with a world made of iron. "Iron" too is one of the key words in József's poetry. It has an utterly negative role; he frequently associates it with rigidity and coldness, winter and ice. The analogies are obvious, as is the symbolism they constitute. But the power and suggestiveness of this symbolism can only be properly recognized when reading given poems, or when thinking of his nearly sacrificial death on cold iron rails and under iron wheels late in November.

The destruction of Attila József began in 1932 when he was expelled from the illegal Communist Party. He came from a working class family (with peasant relatives on his mother's side), and he never turned his back on it. His poems tell us all we need to know about his people. His parents did not teach him political radicalism. After long searching, wading through nihilism and various kinds of radicalism, he became a Marxist in about 1930. It is not impossible that he made contacts with Communists earlier in his Paris years. (He studied at the Sorbonne, financed by a progressive minded aristocrat who recognized his genius, after he had studied Hungarian and French literature four years at Szeged.) He approached Marxism slowly, as did Gorky, whom he resembled in some other respects. In other words, his attachment was not a matter of infatuation; it was not easily won, and therefore, it was neither uncritical nor unconditional. What *was* unconditional was his feeling of identity with the working class and the peasants, and his commitment to the spiritual-ideological quest for the solving of a situation he could well consider desperate.

He joined the underground Communist Party and worked for it, conducting seminars, doing whatever had to be done. In this period, from 1930 to 1933, he wrote a great number of poems in support of the working class movement. They served a propaganda purpose, but they were not "revolutionary posters" like many of Mayakovsky's poems. They pose problems and explain *why* they must be solved, not how. He never writes about the Party. His subject is the workers; he speaks in their name, trying to express their problems. His protest, therefore, is never an individual protest.

> Seething and wild,
> we are poured into the casting die
> of this terrible society
> to stand for mankind on the eternal ground.

But József extends his protest to all the oppressed—peasants, small shopkeepers, office workers—to the bulk of the nation. Considering the international output of this kind of poetry, these are quite exceptional poems. They provide an analysis of social and economic circumstances in a thoroughly poetic way, combining community and personal protest. Bertold Brecht was a bourgeois by origin and refrained from writing personal poems in order to write community protest, but József could say "us, the children of matter," and could say that "peasants, while plowing; have me in mind, and workers are sensing me between two rigid movements."

And yet he was expelled from the Communist Party, apparently for his deviation from the Party line. Admittedly he had some unorthodox views. He read not only Marx, but also Hegel, and did not shrink from reading Freud. He developed the idea expressed later in his essay "Hegel, Marx, Freud," that Marx and Freud, the respective discoverers of unconscious forces in society and the individual, complement one another.

However, his expulsion in 1932 was not an insular and random act; he was favored by fate. The stiffening of the party line originated from Moscow—the notorious stiffening which stopped the German Social Democrats from a coalition with the Communists, helping Hitler reach power. It was the stiffening which later broke the neck of many people and led to the great purges of 1938. József sensed this development—"Fascist Communism"—and its significance for the working class and for the world. But the expulsion affected him in a personal and emotional way, not only in the form of an intellectual experience. The Communist Party worked underground, and expulsion meant that for security reasons it withdrew and vanished, leaving the poet completely alone. He had no party publication to read, no party member to talk to, no party headquarters to walk past.

This happened in 1932. During the next year, his destruction advanced one stage further. The incredible happened. The German Communist Party, the strongest political party in the country, the strongest Communist Party in Europe, collapsed, and the National Socialists came to power. If his expulsion from the Party had raised questions of intransigence and of party policy, this time the problems were deeper. Jozsef presents them in "Hegel, Marx, Freud" with perceptible alarm. "Marx writes that mankind only sets himself tasks that can be achieved with the available prerequisites. How can it then happen that half of a country of sixty million people regards the purity of the race as its historical goal?. . .Where is the error in the calculation? How can it happen that the so called "objective prerequisites" are available, but the subjective ones are missing?" He could not reconcile this with Marx. He found that there were powers at work in the people, independent of the forces of production and of the class struggle. He suggested that the instincts and the subconscious can be suppressed also in a community, in a people. He says Marx has to be corrected with Freud in order to save the people from their inhibitions and the revolt against them. At the same time, he was persuaded that the working class, his own class, was not conscious of itself by definition, but had to achieve this consciousness—a view that he might have read in Georg Lukacs' heretical book, *History and Class-Consciousness*. But if his people and their (Communist) leaders could not be unconditionally trusted, he had to sever his direct ties, to remove himself from them in order to serve their interest. Discipline had to take the place of direct emotional attachment. After the withdrawal of the party, the people "withdrew" as well, and he found himself more lonely than ever before. In 1933 he wrote "Without hope":

> In the end you come to level country:
> wet sands and sadness.

You look around musingly and nod
with knowing head, do not hope.

I too try to look around like that,
without deception and with ease.
Silver stroke of an axe
hovers on the poplar leaves.

My heart perches on the twig of nothing,
its little body shivers without a noise.
Stars gather around it tamely
and look at it, just look at it.

This poem cannot be understood without knowing that József established a symbolic analogy between iron and ice on the one hand, and discipline and thought on the other. He established it about this time and maintained it to the end of his life. "Be disciplined. Summer has flickered out," he begins the poem "Winter Night" in which he also says "The winter night glitters like thought itself." He suggest that in winter time, or in the winter of time (history), one must resemble winter in order to survive. Under opression, be it social-economical or psychological-instinctive, only disipline can give freedom, both to resist the oppression and to get rid of it. And thinking, of course, is the discipline of the spirit. There is an immense regret in József's sigh:

O why must I forge
a weapon of you, golden self-consciousness?

The implication is that if freedom *were* order, it would not be necessary to convert gold into iron. Spirit would not have to present itself so as to defend itself in the form of an intellectual discipline. But the order József faced was not made of "golden" freedom; it was the "iron" world.

The poem "Without Hope" presents this net of symbolism in a unique way. The "knowing head" is that of the intellect and discipline. It perceives without deception and with ease. In harmony with it, the axe of iron swings with ease. Its silver stroke—ice too is silvery—still hovers on the poplar leaves while the poplar itself is felled. This tree, nature, actual reality, is felled by the well-disciplined intellect, and now the heart perches on the twig of nothing and shivers without noise. For this is a poet's heart, a singing bird, in the winter of Time.

At this point (in 1933), József was alone, but he still possessed a heart of one piece which could direct its flight, unconditionally pure and innocent. But soon enough he came to think and feel differently, He had psychic disturbances and turned to psychoanalysis. He turned to it with his trust in Freud, a faith in intellectual disciplines which could cure maladies of the mind. But in his case, Freud proved as unsatisfactory as Marx. He was psychoanalyzed several times, but with no positive result. It has been argued by some that he received inadequate treatment. His doctors, to defend themselves against these accusations, have claimed that his illness was beyond remedy by the time he turned to them. Whatever the actual situation, his illness appeared inevitable, reflecting the human predicament of his time. Some patients were bound to receive mistreatment from bad doctors; some patients were bound to turn to the doctor too late. And some diseases, or diseases in certain cases, were bound to be incurable—not by definition, but in actual fact. And what was true of physical and mental illnesses was also true of social and political ones. Recent history has furnished us with too many examples that man cannot shape his own fate.

József never rejected Freud, as he never rejected Marx. But he had to accept that psychoanalysis could not help him personally. With a greatness characteristic of him, he concluded that something was wrong with him. The seeming failure of the system whose validity he trusted could only lie in a defect of his own—in this case, in a sin which he must have committed, but which he could no longer identify. "Why have I no sin, if I have one," he asks in one of his poems dealing with this obsession. Apparently he felt that if he could identify it, he would be liberated from it according to the rules of psychoanalysis. He could not find it, however, and as time went on, his situation deteriorated, and his hope dwindled:

> Hard ropes tie me to torture,
> I am woven in from every side,
> and cannot find the knot
> that I should release with a single jerk.
> And I suffer, but there will be no mercy:
> if she who is one with me releases me,
> all the pain will fall upon her.

The feeling that nobody could help him did not mean his situation was completely hopeless. It left open the possibility of his eventually finding that knot and releasing himself. It is frightening that the idea that he must have sinned because he could not be cured endowed him with a deeper insight. It was at this time that he began to write strange poems about God.

> I stood on all fours and my standing God
> looked down upon me and did not lift me up.
> This freedom made me understand
> there will be power in me to raise myself.
>
> He helped me by not being able to help.
> He could be the flame, but never its ashes.
> As many kinds of truth, as many kinds of love.
> He stayed with me by leaving me alone.
>
> My body is weak, fear should protect it.
> But my companion I await here smiling,
> for faithfulness is present with me
> in this world reeling in an empty void.

The relationship between this God and his sin, the cause of his suffering, is quite intrinsic. The sin that exists though it does not exist is paralleled with an absolution—solution, release, God—that exists though it does not exist. The link between the non-existence and the existence of God, the solution, is the effort that can raise a man.

> I don't believe in God, and if there is a God
> he shouldn't care for me.
> I'll manage my own absolution,
> and he who lives will assist me.

he said when he still felt more powerful and energetic, suggesting that he was speaking of his personal problem in terms of the human condition. The God who had left him alone and the God who should not care for him are similar notions. In both cases he believes that a solution exists and he must come to it by himself. What he calls "faithfulness" is his commitment to the effort of achieving it.

His task to raise himself was a mental task. It meant the shaping of his own mental activity, holding out for consciousness and control against unconscious and irrational forces. He was still carried by the hope that man can shape his own fate. If his commitment to this hope was not complete because of his fears, at least his commitment to the effort of controlling himself was complete. Out of this effort to maintain his conscious grip on the world and to master the unconscious by the conscious, to tame and absolve it, come great poems of exceptional intensity. In his last two years, he wrote more poems than in any other since 1928; he had not written more in his youth, when he frequently poured them out in haste. Now, however, the intellectual quality of his work and his craftmanship were at a level that his own poetry, and Hungarian poetry generally, has rarely reached. The power, penetration and shrewd simplicity of his last poems are unique. The only poet with a comparable output who comes to my mind is Yeats. It is hard to believe that these poems were written by the same sick man described in his sister's book and in the accounts of his friends.

During his last years, he developed schizophrenia and lived in a disturbed state. Finally, in the last summer of his life, he was taken to a sanitarium, but when he was released, he was no better. Sometimes he sobbed for days, often hysterical. It is not inconceivable that on that particular November evening, he did not make a conscious decision.

But the astonishing thing about his mental disorder was that it did not affect his work. We do not have a single line by him that shows the loss of his consciousness as an artist, and while time and again certain obsessions appear in his poems, he controls them by treating them symbolically. Some of his best work was written in his last year, and even in the last days of his life. Desperately clinging to his ideal of order, he has never preserved it more faithfully than at the time of impending catastrophe.

József's final collapse, however, was due to yet another blow. He said in his "Ars Poetica" that man had two parents, two guardians: Spirit and Love. Now after spirit had betrayed him, love betrays him too. The blow that destroyed his innermost being took the form of two hopeless love affairs, one in 1936, the other in 1937.

In his love for a woman, he encountered nature, the world. Nature means attachment, living contact. The world gives meaning, and a being is human and loving in his capacity to attain that attachment and that meaning. Love and humanity are synonymous for József, as are spirit and humanity. His beloved gave him "the door-knob of the locked world," and he could step out into the open, into nature and the world. This, then, is the "warm world" in contrast to the cold one wrought in iron and discipline. In the human gift of love, the poet's eyes perceived the microcosm hidden in the beloved, and by perceiving this microcosm, he could see himself in a world of living order, of warmth.

This miracle involved two loves. Hers was giving, and that was important; but his was receiving, and that was equally important, for it makes the act of giving possible. Applying here József's metaphor, the wooden door that locked him in suddenly changed by the touch of his vision into a glass door, and he could perceive the world of living order, though he still could not be within it; he was still locked out. Her uniqueness was not enough; it only proved that there *was* a warm world.

To understand what such love meant for József, it is necessary to recall his desperate love for his mother, who died when he was still a boy. She represented nature:

> Only now do I see how immense she is:
> her grey hair flutters in the wind,
> she dilutes blue in the waters of the sky.

She was the warm world that abandoned him when she died. And she was a woman:

> You lay down at the side of death,
> like a slender easy girl when given a sign.

> You are a bigger cheat than any woman
> that deceives a man and feeds him with hopes.

Psychoanalysis further deepened this attachment of József to his mother, indeed it may have evoked its real force. But if it evoked it or deepened it, it was only because his original vision, the special quality of his imagination was working in that direction. His ideal of order, his attitude toward the woman he loved, his love for his mother can only be understood as three aspects of the same basic attitude. Sometimes they appear intricately interwoven, as in this desperate love poem:

> My mother locked me out - I lay on the threshold -
> and wanted to crawl into myself, but in vain -
> stones below me and emptiness above.
> I want to sleep. I knock at your door.

The horror of being alone, abandoned, and locked out is powerfully suggested by his wish to crawl even into himself, so as to be in a safe place, in a warm world. In this stanza, the world cannot open up for him and accept him unless there is a woman who, in the role of his mother, accepts the man in the role of a boy.

The significance of love, not intrinsically, but rather its momentum, increased for József as his immediate hope in the social as well as the psychic spheres degenerated. It was his final tragedy that the two women whom he loved in his last two years did not love him. As far as he was concerned, they failed in their humanity when they were unable to come to his rescue; and through them, humanity was proved defective. He did not lose faith in love, just as he did not lose faith in Marx and in Freud, but he felt ultimately abandoned, and died, because there was really nothing left for him. The last stanza of his last poem written in his very last days sums it up soberly:

> Spring is good, and summer is also good,
> but autumn is better, and winter is the best
> for a man who can wish only for others
> a fireplace and a family.

He died before winter came, because he could not face it. Or to put it more correctly, he confronted winter with winter, death with death.

His sacrifice for serving order was truly symbolic. He was born of a working class father from the city who abandoned his family one day, as God abandoned his son, and of a mother from the village who died when he was still a boy, leaving him alone in a world which systematically destroyed him. He was equally at home in the city with its factories and offices, and in the village with its fields and forests, for he worked in both. He shared his passions with the people, and he trained his mind in mental disciplines, sharing his concern with millions who were active in changing the world, whether following Marx or Freud.

It was due, perhaps, to his gift of identification with social aims that his despair never took on cosmic proportions. His personal protest runs parallel to his "collective" social protest, and even if the latter seems to abate (especially during the last three years of his life), it never ceases. His despair remained personal, if not subjective. It was immense, but not apocalyptically exaggerated, because his ideals, his yearnings for order, were never discredited objectively. His personal fate appeared to him utterly hopeless because it seemed inevitable. But this inevitability was not based on any historical or objective necessity. If he could have believed that there was no hope for mankind, this might have alleviated the plight of his own case by offering him the satisfaction of a cosmic, Satanic despair. His despair, however, remains human, and the more shattering for it.

That József collapsed while trying to raise himself is tragic, but he only symbolized the age which one year after his death saw the end of the Spanish Civil War, the Munich conference, the culmination of the purges in Moscow. Looking back upon it, it was the year of collective European suicide. One can conclude that the conscious powers of mankind failed society as they did József.

József was aware of the symbolic implications of his life, and he expressed them in his poetry. But it is better to say that he grew aware of them in and through his poetry. In his case, life and poetry were dialectical—he lived his poems' insights. To be a socialist for him was to be a man freed from the tyranny of his unconscious. In his "Causal poem About the Standing of Socialism" he says,

> Passion is wasted into passing fits
> Unless reason in advance pervades it.

The Hungarian word for "pervading" also suggests absolution. What he called Order was a state in which reason pervaded and absolved passion, and his poetry reflects such a synthesis. He died when he saw he could no longer maintain it.

He died after sphere after sphere of his life was destroyed. The yearnings themselves remained intact. He still wished for others the children with whom he could no longer play, and a fireplace at which he could no longer warm himself. There it was, and there it is, a wheel wrought in iron and ice, glittering with the relentless perfection of the silver light in a black winter night, and a man broken upon it.

ATTILA JÓZSEF (1905-1937) is thought by many to be the greatest Hungarian poet of the first part of our century. Born in a poor family, his adolescent years were one long stretch of starvation and destitution. His higher studies were interrupted by his dismissal from Szeged University for a poem "smacking of anarchism." He lived for some time in Vienna and Paris, then returned to Budapest to join the ranks of the 'intellectual unemployed'. In the last few years of his life he co-edited *Szép Szó* a short-lived review of liberal Socialist intellectuals. His mental illness steadily worsening, he threw himself under the wheels of a goods-train in 1937. His poetic stature was fully recognized only after 1945. ANDRÁS SÁNDOR (b. 1934) has done research in both Hungarian and German literature. He holds degrees from the universities of Szeged (Hungary), Oxford, and Los Angeles; he has taught at Princeton and at the University of Southern California, Los Angeles. At present, he is Lecturer in Hungarian at the University of California, Berkeley.

translated by Vernon Watkins
ATTILA JÓZSEF

Behold I have found my land...

Behold, I have found my land, the country
Where my name's cut without a fault
By him who is to bury me,
If he was bred to dig my vault.

Earth gapes: I drop into the tin,
Since the iron halfpenny,
Which at a time of war came in,
Has outlived its utility.

Nor is the iron ring legal tender.
New world, land, rights: I read each letter.
Our law is war's, the thriftless spender,
And gold coins keep their value better.

Long I had lived with my own heart;
Then others came with many a fuss.
They said: "You kept yourself apart.
We wish you could have been with us."

So did I live in vanity.
I now draw my conclusion thus.
They did but make a fool of me,
And even my death is fatuous.

I have tried all my life to keep
My footing in a whirlwind fast.
The thought is ludicrously cheap
That others' harm matched mine at last.

The spring is good and summer, too,
But autumn better and winter best
For him who finds his last hopes through
Family hearths he knew as guest.

translated by George Gömöri and Matthew Zion

I want to breathe!

Who forbids that I tell what troubled me
on my way home?
A cooling darkness settled on the grass,
a velvet spray,
and under my feet turning sleeplessly
like children beaten and subdued
the dry leaves groaned.

The bushes squatted in a circle watchful
along the outskirts.
The autumn wind stumbled amongst them softly.
The cool black earth
looked suspectingly toward the streetlights,
and where I passed a startled wild duck
began to quack.
I thought: whoever wants to can attack me
in this deserted place
when suddenly a man appeared, but he
just walked away—

I watched him go: he could have taken
my money, for I wouldn't defend myself
I am so beaten.

They wire-tap what I say on the phone,
when, why and to whom.
They place my dreams in secret files, and even
who can decipher them.
And I can't know—when will they have a reason
to dig out those files
which violate my rights?

And those fragile villages in the country
—my mother was born there—
they are torn from the tree of living justice
like these leaves here,
and when Adult Misfortune stomps heavily
they rustle to announce their misery
and crumbling fall to dust.

Ah! I imagined something different.
My soul is not
at home where he who is most sly
gets on the best
and where the people are scared to vote
speak with downcast eyes to hide their thought
and revel at a burial feast.

Yes, I imagined a different Order.
Although when small
I rarely understood why I got spanked—
I would have done
anything for a good word. I knew that somewhere
I had some relatives, I had a mother.
These here were not mine.

I have grown up. Strange matter fills my
teeth as does death
my heart, but still I have some rights
and am not yet
spirit or matter, nor is my skin so precious
that as a man I can endure silently
my lack of freedom.

My leader commands me from within!
For we are men with minds,
not savages. Our heart, where desires ripen,
cannot be itemized.
Freedom, *you* bear me Order, come
teach with good words, and let your thoughtful son
play in his times.

The pain is sharp

From death which waits
for you within yourself and without
when you become excited you escape

to woman as,
into its hole, a mouse
that she protect you in her arms, knees and lap.

Tempted not just
by the warm thighs to thoughts of the undressed
body, need also pushes you to her each night.

It's for this reason
that all live things which find a woman
hold her until their lips turn white.

It is a double
burden, a double treasure that one love:
he who loves and finds no companion

is as weak
and homeless as a beast
when it relieves itself against a stone.

It's your one refuge
although still sucking at her breast
you might have murdered your own mother, brave son!

I had found her
who heard and understood these words
yet shoved me back when I was most alone.

Now I have
no place to go among those who live;
embellishing the pain my head pounds.

It is the way
when a child is left alone to play
through the bright afternoon the rattle sounds.

But what can I
do for or against my desire?
I dare to guess and feel not the slightest shame

because the world
rejects even so those dazzled
by the sun and shocked by the dream.

I shed culture as
another man sheds his clothes
during the course of a happy love affair.

Where is she now
to watch death toss me around,
to see how utterly alone I suffer?

Mother and infant
both suffer at birth—a two-fold torment
can be lessened by humility.

My song of pain
brings me a reasonable gain
and so but one companion: infamy.

You little boys,
when she walks by let your bright eyes
shatter like mirrors and turn dark.

Innocent one,
scream under the jack-boots when
they nail you down—the pain is sharp.

You faithful curs,
go get your paws ripped off by cars
and yelp at her—the pain is sharp.

Woman with child,
while you abort let out your wild
and anguished cries at her—the pain is sharp.

You sane and sound
people, get smashed and broken down
and mutter in her ear—the pain is sharp.

You men who wound
each other fighting for a woman,
don't keep silent—the pain is sharp.

You horse, you bull,
you who've been castrated so you'd pull
a yoke, bemoan with me—the pain is sharp.

You dumb fish, bite
under the ice the bait
and gape on it—the pain is sharp.

All you who for
so long ached and trembled, set fire
to your field, your home, your yard—

around her bed,
when she dozes off, you who are half-dead,
croak out with me——the pain is sharp.

While she's alive
let her hear this, for she denied
her worth: out of sheer comfort she refused

to grant a man
who needed to escape within
and without——his last appeal for refuge.

translated by Vernon Watkins

Grief

In my eyes grief dissolves;
I ran like a deer;
Tree-gnawing wolves
In my heart followed near.

I left my antlers
A long time ago;
Broken from my temples,
They swing on a bough.

Such I was myself:
A deer I used to be.
I shall be a wolf:
That is what troubles me.

A fine wolf I'm becoming.
Struck by magic, while
All my pack-wolves are foaming,
I stop, and try to smile.

I prick up my ears
As a roe gives her call;
Try to sleep; on my shoulders
Dark mulberry leaves fall.

MATTHEW ZION is a young American poet and translator living at Berkeley. His translations were published amongst other reviews in *Ramparts* and *Poetry Northwest*. VERNON WATKINS, the distinguished British poet, lived in Swansea most of his life. He died suddenly last year in Seattle where he was Visiting Professor in English Literature. These translations of Mr. Watkins are reprints from the collection of Attila József, *Poems*, London, 1966.

Stanislaw Ignacy Witkiewicz

a Polish writer for today

CZESLAW MILOSZ

Stanislaw Ignacy Witkiewicz fascinated my literary generation in the somber thirties and today, many years after his death, he is no less facinating to the young in Poland. He might be proposed now as an honorary member of the "situationists" or the "provos". To write about him is to explore the continuity of certain themes which go back to a more cosmopolitan era of Europe on the eve of World War I.

A few biographical data. He was born in Warsaw in 1885 as the only son of an eminent art critic. His childhood and adolescence were spent in the mountain village of Zakopane in Southern Poland, then a newly discovered "primitive area" with its rich folklore and fine specimens of peasant wooden architecture. Already fashionable as a center of mountaineering, Zakopane was a meeting place for intellectuals and young Witkiewicz grew up in a refined milieu. Perhaps a contrast between his physical vigor and the mood obligatory in those circles—that of "decadence", of "fin-de-siècle"—is one of the keys to his development as a thinker and as an artist. A student of fine arts in Kraków in 1904-1905, he travelled to Italy, France, Germany, and in 1914 went to Australia, through Ceylon and the Malayan archipelago, as a secretary to the anthropologist Bronislaw Malinowski. The outbreak of World War I caught him in Australia. As the holder of a Russian passport, he had to go back, arrived in St. Petersburg and, without waiting to be drafted, which was unavoidable anyway, volunteered. He fought as an infantry officer in an élite Tsarist regiment, was decorated for bravery with the highest Russian distinction, the order of St. Anne, and probably was loved by his soldiers, for at the outbreak of the Revolution they elected him a commissar. We know little, however, of this or of any other wartime incidents, as he did not like to talk about them, except for a casual remark in a conversation with a friend, for example, that counting the minutes before an attack is one of the most dire experiences in the life of man. In 1918 he returned to independent Poland where he lived mostly in Zakopane and Kraków.

The experience which he acquired was of an exceptional scope—in art, in life, in historical situations. His formative years were marked by the ascendancy of the "Young Poland" movement whose great master of ceremonies or witch-doctor was Stanislaw Przybyszewski, formerly a student of psychiatry in Berlin and a highly regarded member of the bohemian groups known as "Young Germany" and "Young Scandinavia". Przybyszewski proclaimed a manifesto in 1899 of the absolute supremacy of art over any other human activity and its complete independence from moral, social, or political considerations. Today, his formulae sound curiously pre-Freudian: "in the beginning there was lust"; art is an outflow of "the naked soul" uniting man with the unconscious life of the universe. Hence Przybyszewski's preoccupation with satanic forces revealing the illusory character of "poor, poor consciousness", with medieval witches, Sabbaths, hysteria and insanity. But Witkiewicz's plays and essays on drama would be incomprehensible without reference to another leading figure of "Young Poland", Stanislaw Wyspiański, from whom the entire modern Polish theater stems; the staging of his *Wedding* in Kraków in 1901 was a revolutionary event. Wyspiański broke with "imitation of life" on the stage; he conceived of a theatrical spectacle as a unity of color, movement and sound, and in his dramas fantastic, symbolic creatures appeared on an equal footing with life-like characters. Using today's language we would say he invited the spectators on a "trip", for after each of his plays in verse people used to leave the theater reeling. Parenthetically, let us add that contrary to Przybyszewski he advocated a committed art: drama, not unlike Greek tragedy, should be, in his view, an instrument for exploring all the problems of a national community and a call to energy—but through a peculiar medium of its own, having nothing to do with photographic naturalism.

Shaped by the Polish vanguard currents in literature, in painting, and in the theater, Witkiewicz landed in Russia at the very moment of her creative eruption, a period that remains unsurpassed in the excellence of its achievements. The most incredible "isms" were proliferating, the first purely abstract paintings were simultaneously being done in Germany by a Russian, Vassily Kandinsky (1910), in Russia by a Pole, Kazimierz Malewicz (1913), in Holland by Piet Mondrian (though his canvas of 1911 is still entitled "A Blooming Apple Tree").
Cubism was debated in Moscow and in St. Petersburg (a school of poets called themselves "cubofuturists") and in Moscow Witkiewicz saw the paintings of Picasso.

Witkiewicz was one of those who by their very behavior give fuel to a personal legend. Perhaps his oddity and humorous eccentricity increased with age but already as a young man he was puzzling: a huge, taciturn beast of prey in an invisible cage or a jester disguising some unavowed potential. He attracted women magnetically. One of them, who remembered him from Zakopane before World War I, related: "He was beautiful like an Archangel with those gray-green eyes of his. When he entered a café, my knees shook. And I guess all the women felt the same." In Russia, he shared the peculiar way of life led by élite officers (mostly from aristocratic families), divided into encounters with death and crazy pleasures. It was a time not only of alcohol and of sexual orgies but of a fashion for new drugs. Witkiewicz got acquainted with cocaine and tasted peyote. Later on, he experimented with the influence of drugs upon his painting and wrote a book on the subject (many years before Aldous Huxley and Michaux), *Nicotine, Alcohol, Cocaine, Peyote, Morphine, Ether + Appendix* (1932).

The Russian Revolution, as we may guess from his writings, left traumatic traces. Witkiewicz was brought up, let us not forget, on the basic premise of "decadentism", namely, that Western bourgeois civilization was living out its last decades, if not days. The upheaval of the masses in Russia seemed to confirm that view and for Witkiewicz gave it a more tangible shape. He became convinced that universal communist revolution was unavoidable. As for himself, he belonged to a world in decline. Revolution would have meant a victory of justice, but he was not primarily interested in "happiness for all", an aim he relegated to the realm of "ethics"; revolution, in his opinion, was but a stage in the general trend towards social conformity and destruction of the individual. This explains his subsequent friendly polemics with Polish Marxists, in which he showed a good knowledge of dialectical materialism.

Upon his return to Poland, Witkiewicz joined a vanguard group of painters and poets in Kraków who called themselves "Formists". His book *New Forms in Painting and Resulting Misunderstandings* (1919) as well as his essays on the theater published in magazines from 1920 on, and gathered in a book *The Theater* (1923) demonstrated the application of his theory of "Pure Form" to all the arts. But it is time to ask who, after all, was he? A painter, a creative writer, or a theoretician? He painted—but announced to all and sundry that "his *atelier*" produced portraits at fixed prices and that he himself did not pretend to the title of artist. It is true, though, that not everybody acceded to the honor of posing as his model. His "psychological portraits", mostly of intellectuals, his friends, resemble, by their treatment of line and color, what we associate today with psychedelic art. He wrote plays, beginning with *Cockroaches* when he was eight years old, on cockroaches invading a city; and a two-volume edition of his collected plays, published in Warsaw in 1962, surpasses in daring "the theater of the absurd". He wrote a few novels, the first in 1910: *622 Downfalls of Bung or a Demoniac Woman;* two novels of his are major contributions to Polish literature of the years 1918 - 1939; yet he excluded the novel from the domain of "art". For him the novel was a bastard genre, a catch-all, a bag, a device to convey the author's quarrels with his contemporaries. He wrote essays on the theory of painting and of drama. He had, however, only one true passion: philosophy. Let me stress this, for his philosophical concepts underlie everything he attempted to do.

His first "metaphysical divagations", as he called them, date from 1904. For many years, between 1917 and 1932, he worked on a rather slim, concise treatise to which he attached much importance, *Notions and Assertions - Implied by the Notion of Existence.*

A dilettante, though highly esteemed by some university chair holders, such as Professor Tadeusz Kotarbiński, the dean of Polish philosophers, Witkiewicz was equipped better than many professionals. He read fluently in

Russian, German, French, and English, not to mention his native tongue. The state of European and American philosophy, as he observed it, strengthened his historical pessimism. Philosophers, behaving like the fox who pronounced the grapes sour because they were too high, were engaged in explaining away metaphysics as a semantic misunderstanding. Was not this a sign foreboding the end of a search for "unattainable absolute truth"? To quote from him: "Throughout the entire struggle with Mystery, veils dropped away one by one and the time has come when we see a naked, hard body, with nothing more to be taken off, invincible in its indifference of a dead statue." The fable of the fox applied not only to the neo-positivists. Witkiewicz raged against Bergson: "intuition" was indeed a meager substitute for striving towards clear cognition. Pragmatism and Marxism fared even worse. They exemplifed the approaching era when "ethics will devour metaphysics." Or, to use again his own words: "Every epoch has the philosophy it deserves. In our present phase we deserve nothing better than a drug of the most inferior kind, to lull to sleep our metaphysical anxiety which hinders our transformation into automatic machines."

Trying to salvage whatever survived from the ambitious ontological drives of the past, Witkiewicz elaborated his minimal "system," somewhat akin to Leibniz's monadology. Its analysis does not belong here and I limit myself to a few points. According to Witkiewicz nothing can be asserted about being except that it predicates "Particular Existences". Every monad embodies what he calls "The Principle of Factual Particular Identity." In man this gives rise to a "Metaphysical Feeling of the Strangeness of Existence", expressed by questions: "Why am I exactly this and not that being? At this point of unlimited space and in this moment of infinite time? In this group of beings, on exactly this planet? Why do I exist, if I could have been without any existence? Why does anything exist at all?"

Mankind looked for answers in religion, then in philosophy. Yet religion was dead and philosophy was dying. Art, which has always been a means of soothing the anxieties provoked by the "Metaphysical Feeling of the Strangeness of Existence", survived. Art in the past functioned, however, in a universe ordered by ontological concepts of religion or of philosophy. Its harmonious forms reflected that serenity which is granted when man has also other means of satisfying his basic craving. Art as the only channel, as a substitute for religion and philosophy, by necessity would change. Its "Unity in multiplicity" reflecting the increased sense of identity in its creator, could be achieved but only at a greater and greater price, namely, a savage intensification of components used, otherwise, the harmony would have an insipid taste. Here Witkiewicz's formulations are not quite clear. He seemed to believe that modern artists, as opposed to their healthy predecessors, became neurotics because of their inability to quench metaphysical thirst in any other way than through their art. They were condemned to endow it with their neurosis, by choosing as their material more and more ugly, jarring, garish images, sounds, lines and colors. They were the last representatives of a species marked by a metaphysical "insatiation" and threatened by mass ethics in which the craving that constitutes the very dignity of man was already being deviated. Art was moving towards insanity and the future was not far away when artists would be imprisoned in insane asylums. Mankind would be "happy," but it would know neither religion, nor a philosophy deserving the name, nor art.

However we judge Witkiewicz's pessimism, one thing is certain: his creative work combines a rare vital energy with a conviction that art should select procedures adapted to its final phase. It should achieve "Pure Form." A painting, for instance, should be no more than a set of "oriented tensions" of line and color (he deviated from his principle when making his "psychological portraits" and that is why he dismissed them as merely an income-bringing hobby). In his stress upon "purity" he was, of course, no exception in the Europe of his time. Even the French Academy of Literature listened, as early as 1925, to Henri Brémond's lecture on "pure poetry." Yet of great consequence was Witkiewicz's application of the concept to the theater. If modern painting tended towards a refusal to represent anything, could not drama be conceived as "pure action" without any care for reproduction of reality? While posing the problem, he did not want to go so far: "If we can imagine a painting composed entirely of abstract forms which, unless we indulge in an obvious auto-suggestion, would not provoke any associations with objects in the external world, no such a theatrical play can even be thought of, because a pure becoming in time is possible only in the sphere of sounds, and the theater without actions of characters, even most strange and improbable characters, is impossible, since the theater is a composite art and not art based upon homogenous elements as are the pure arts: music and painting."

But "deformation" (as in cubist art) is not beyond the playwright's reach: "In painting, a new form, pure and abstract, without a direct religious background, was achieved through a deformation of our vision of the external world, and in a similar manner Pure Form in the theater can be achieved at the price of a deformation of psychology and of action." Since he presents rather clearly his intentions, let me continue quoting him: "What matters is the possibility of freely deforming life or an imaginary world in order to create a totality, the sense of which would be determined by a purely internal, purely scenic construction and not by any exigencies of consequent psychology or action, corresponding to the rules of ordinary life." The date when those sentences were written - around 1920 - should be kept in mind. It was in Europe a period of radical experimentation. Witkiewicz explains what a play written according to his recipe would be like: "Thus, three persons, dressed in red, enter and bow, we do not know to whom. One of them recites a poem (which should make the impression of something necessary exactly at that moment). A gentle old man enters with a cat he leads on a string. Until now everything has been going on against the background of a black curtain. The curtain is drawn apart and an Italian landscape appears. Music of the organ is heard. The old man talks to the three persons. He says something which corresponds to the created mood. A glass falls from the table. All of them, suddenly on their knees, are weeping. The old man changes into a furious brute and murders a little girl who just crawled out from the left side. At this, a handsome young man runs in and thanks the old man for that murder, while the persons in red sing and dance. The young man then weeps over the corpse of the little girl saying extremely funny things, and the old man changes again into a tender-hearted character chuckling on the sidelines. The sentences he pronounces are sublime and lofty. The costumes may be of any kind, stylized or fantastic—and music may intervene in various parts. So, you would say, this is a lunatic asylum. Or rather the brain of a madman on the stage. Perhaps you are right, be we affirm that by applying this method one can write serious plays and if they are staged in a proper way, it would be possible to create things of extraordinary beauty, they may be dramas, tragedies, farces or grotesques, but always in a style not resembling anything that exists. When leaving the theater, one should have the impression of waking up from a strange dream in which the most trite things have an elusive, deep charm, characteristic of dreams, not comparable to anything."

Yet, for Witkiewicz, programmatic deformation, for its own sake, not justified by the real need for formal unity, was to be categorically condemned. He underlined this: "Our aim is not programmatic nonsense, we are trying rather to enlarge the possibilities of composition by abandoning in art any life-like logic, by introducing a fantastic psychology and fantastic action, in order to win a complete freedom of formal elements."

In spite of those reservations, it is doubtful whether the recipe is conducive to anything but the monotony of a few devices repeated *ad infinitum:* once all improbabilities are accepted, no increase of their amount could ever stir the spectator. Fortunately, Witkiewicz as a theoretician and as a practitioner are two not quite identical persons. In his next to thirty plays written between 1918 and 1934, he gives free vent to his ferocity, a virtue rarely praised by "pure artists". He is in them a high-school prankster and makes us think of Alfred Jarry more than of any other writer. His characters, through their roars and their mad thrashing around resemble the abominable Father Ubu with his exclamations "merrrrdrre" and his machine for blowing up brains. Witkiewicz delighted in coining names for his characters, appropriate to their behavior. Many are untranslatable puns; some, often a cross-breed of several languages, can give an idea of his buffoonery. Thus we are confronted with Doña Scabrosa Macabrescu and her teenage daughter Świntusia (Piggy) Macabrescu, with a psychiatrist Mieczysław Valpurg and an attorney general Robert Scurvy (meaning in Polish both scurvy and s. o. b.); with Gottfried Reichsgraf von und zu Berchtoldingen, the Great Master of the Teutonic Order, and two hassidim, Haberboaz and Rederhagaz; with princess Alice of Nevermore, Minna Countess de Barnhelm, Maxim Grigorevich prince Bublikov-Tmutarakanskii, a counteradmiral, with Richard III in person, with vice-count Wojciech (Adalbert) de Malensac de Troufieres, a naturalist painter Oblivion Grampus etc., etc.

The titles of the plays are often no less promising: *Metaphysics of a Two-headed Calf; Gyubal Wahazar or On the Passes of Nonsense, a Non-Euclidean Drama in Four Acts; Mister Price or Tropical Nuttiness; The Ominous*

Bastard of Vermiston; The Independence of Triangles. On his characters two remarks can be made. All of them, men and women, are oversexed; practically all of them are on the verge of bursting asunder, victims of inexpressible yearning. Sex, since it is intimately connected with "The Metaphysical Feeling of Strangeness of Existence", was for Witkiewicz akin to art. Yet no discharges are able to calm down his weird puppets. They are under the pressure of a cosmic reality which is felt by them as "too much". And since they are not supposed to be "probable" as to the language they speak, they deliver tirades mixing slang and terms of modern philosophy, whether they are artists, princes or peasants.

The composition of his plays may be defined as a parody of psychological drama. Instead of middle-class husbands, wives and mistresses, bizarre mathematicians of genius, artist-misfits, unashamedly lurid women, with the author's obvious predilection for the international set, for aristocrats and proletarians as well as for meetings between figures taken from different epochs; instead of dialogues in a living room, ravings moved into a dimension of *opera-buffa;* instead of murders out of jealousy and suicides, sham murders and sham suicides, plenty of corpses, yes, but they soon resurrect and rejoin the conversation.

Witkiewicz's imagination, nourished by the apocalyptic events of war and revolution in Russia, was ill adapted to what prevailed in the literature of Poland after 1918. The country was independent but provincial, confronted with immediate tasks, and the radical vanguard schools of 1918 - 1920 soon declined or entrenched themselves in little magazines for the élite. Fortunately for him, Poland was a theatrical country, with good repertory theaters directed by people who continued the line of Stanislaw Wyspiański. A few plays of Witkiewicz were staged and some reached 15, 30, even 40 performances. He obtained the support of intelligent theater critics, and won notoriety as an *enfant terrible* of Polish letters. Yet it is significant that performances of his plays date from the twenties. After this he was more and more isolated, and the majority of his dramas were neither published nor staged in his lifetime. Because of his language with its humorous-macabre exuberance, puns, parody of styles— he is difficult to render into other languages, but even had he been translated what a chance would he have abroad, if "the theater of the absurd" conquered Paris and London only some thirty years later? At least in Poland the theater was not as commercialized as in Western Europe and directors, if not the public, understood what he was after.

Today, while considerable "freedom of formal elements" has been attained everywhere, Witkiewicz still fails to fit into any accepted category. He started from other premises than *Angst* and alienation; not being-in-an-unbearable-situation but Being as such was his primary concern. If we assume that Beckett's *Ah, les beaux jours* is the highest achievement of the theater of the absurd (François Mauriac compared it to Aeschylus) the insect-like, weak buzz of its heroine sinking into the sand (symbolizing time) does not recall anything in the plays of Witkiewicz. Curiously enough, a melancholy perception of transience is absent from his writings. On the contrary, his characters have to cope with a superabundance of Being as an eternal *now*.

More perhaps than the insane action, the intellectual contents of his dramas estranged the public. After all, in spite of his theoretical claims, he conveyed his philosophy in them by the very choice of his heroes. A lunatic fringe, the last of a perishing tribe, artists, aristocrats, descendants of rich factory-owners, represented an intensification of individuality through delirium and decadence, a kind of "last stand" before universal grayness, historically preordained, swallows them in. The scene hints rather at Russia on the eve of the Revolution than at Poland or any other country, unless one shares (which was not easy at the time) the author's belief in a doomsday awaiting the precarious "normalcy" that was patched together in 1918.

Witkiewicz abandoned writing plays after the twenties, except for one, in 1934, the closest to a parable, full of transposed realistic details, a response to the oncoming doomsday which was already announced by the rise of totalitarian dictatorships: *The Cobblers*. It is not accidental, in my view, that departing from "Pure Form" and injecting the work with "contents", he succeeded so well. As to "contents", to put it shortly, there are the cobblers (social rebels hungry for good living and sex galore) who are destined to be, after the revolution, playthings of the Super-Worker, a potential bureaucratic operator; a primordial, male-devouring female, princess Irina personifying the rotten system which is defended by attorney general Robert Scurvy. The attorney makes an alliance with "the Brave Boys" (a native fascist movement, the last phase of capitalism) and ends his career on all fours, chained as a dog (smoking a cigarette). Altogether, though it is no less a lunatic asylum than Witkiewicz's other plays, *The Cobblers* follow an anticipated historical logic which is why it bears the subtitle: "a scientific play with songs".

The two novels by Witkiewicz: *Farewell to Autumn* (written 1925, published 1927) and *Insatiation* (published in 1931) are populated with the same kind of personalities as his dramas—often appearing under the same names—and deal with similar problems, though the author is less bound by his search for "Pure Form". As I have said already, he excluded the novel from artistic genres. All of his creative activity, and I hope I am making this clear, was the result of a tension between his agressiveness and his concept of art as unity in multiplicity, indifferent to the "gut-level" (by which he designated "everyday life" feelings and emotions). He was more inclined to attack than to whine and "contents" did explode in *The Cobblers* (which reminds one the most of his novels). Once he had decided the novel was a "bag" with freely invented rules of the game, beyond any exigencies of "art", he could pack it with philosophical treatises, digressions and polemics. His novels are powerful, however, for the very reason that in scorning form he hit upon a specific novelistic form of his own. In this he was probably helped by his readings as an adolescent, by the science fiction of Jules Verne, H. G. Wells and other authors. Science fiction, before World War I and immediately after, was undergoing a mutation (not without some contribution brought by the genre of ironic allegories—Anatole France's for instance), into a novel of apprehensive anticipation, a novel of anti-utopia. Usually the future was visualized as dominated by machines winning their independence and crushing human beings. To give a few examples: in the twenties appeared Karel Čapek's *Krakatit*; in Poland, futurist Bruno Jasieński's *Legs of Isolda Morgan* (1923) and the dialectical stories of Aleksander Wat on the twists and turns of history to come, *Lucifer Unemployed* (1927). Witkiewicz's anti-utopias concentrate upon social mechanization, not upon the negative aspects of technology. His vision is close to that of the Russian writer Eugene Zamyatin whose *We* was published in England in 1924. Whether he read Zamyatin has never been ascertained. His Polish sources are obvious and acknowledged by him: first of all, the wild theosophical imagination of Tadeusz Miciński (killed in 1918 in Russia by a mob who mistook him for a czarist general) who, shuffling together epochs and countries in his dramas and novels, was, in his turn, a descendant of Polish romantic historiosophy.

In both novels, the action is placed in the future, yet the present—namely the Poland of his day—as material reshaped, magnified, seasoned with the grotesque, is easily reconizable, and it has been justly said that all the "realistic" fiction of those years could not match Witkiewicz's insights into social and political imbroglios. The names of the characters are construed in his usual prankish way. For instance there is a Polish verb *"zipać"*—to breathe with difficulty; he makes a French verb out of it: *"ziper"*, concocts a phrase: *"je ne zipe qu'à peine"*, changes spelling and obtains the name of one of his heroes: Genezyp Kapen. His style is not unlike that of Polish fiction before 1914, with its tendency to the profound and the sublime, especially in love scenes. He pushes the pedal just a bit more, so that the boundary between seriousness and joking is blurred. This serves him particularly well in his erotic passages. As might be expected, for his heroes the sexual act acquires an ontological magnitude comparable only to the act of artistic creation. His women, enamored with their genitalia, spider-females, do not wear ordinary bras and pants: "she took off her metaphysical hyper-panties". Yet because of this overemphasis and ironic grandeur, the brutality of his sexual duels (there is a fundamental hostility between his males and females) is not naturalistic and would not provide excitement for any shy pornographer. Sex for him equals an experience of the overwhelming, orgiastic monstrosity of existence.

Not a brave new world but the last phase of decay preceeding the advent of a brave new world is the subject of his novels. This renders questionable their classification with the genre which in our century begins with Zamyatin's *We* and embraces Aldous Huxleys' already proverbial *Brave new world* (1932), as well as George Orwell's *1984* (1948). A particular society drawn from observation and anticipation lurks behind the artistic and pseudoartistic milieu on which he focuses. Death of religion (sarcastically treated attempts at "neo-catholicism"), death of philosophy (whole pages of discussion with logical positivists) art going mad (music being the most tenacious, hence his frequent identification with composers)—such are portents of the approaching change of the social system. In *Farewell to Autumn* it is brought about by two successive revolutions: first, bourgeois-democratic (echos of Kerensky in Russia and of the Leninist theory), second, of the "Levellers". The last chapters depict a new order in quite Orwellian terms, but emphasize universal grayness and shabbiness, not terror. The central figure in the novel, Atanazy Bazakbal, more gifted in sex than in art, though he wanted to be an artist, returns home from India at the news of the revolution, is given a small job in one of the state offices and meditates upon the impotence of the individual to reverse the course of events. While in Zakopane, he decides to escape across the mountains; Witkiewicz was excellent in his descriptions of mountain scenery and the dawn over the summits as seen by Bazakbal, who is high on cocaine, is treated in a grandiose manner without a bit of mockery. The final pages summarize the author's dilemma throughout his whole career. If what awaits us is an ant-hill in which it will be forbidden to confess one's metaphysical craving, should not those few who are aware of it launch a warning? Bazakbal, under the influence of cocaine, has a revelation: a warning *must* be launched and it *must* be effective. He retraces his steps but is caught by a border patrol and shot as a spy.

In *Insatiation*, America and most of Europe have participated in counter-revolutionary "crusades", with the result that "the West" is half-Communist. Russia has gone in an opposite direction and has been ruled for a while by white terror. Poland did not join the anti-Bolshevik crusades (echo of 1919 - 1920 when Pilsudski refused to cooperate with White Russian generals, Denikin and Wrangel) and has a native brand of semi-Fascism. Europe, however, is threatened by Communist China who has conquered Russia and whose armies are already near the borders of Poland. All hopes turn to the charismatic commander of the army, Kocmoluchowicz (from *kocmoluch*—sooty face). The imminent danger does not disturb Witkiewicz's milieu too much, except as an oppressive atmosphere of futility and paralysis, exacerbating their sexual and metaphysical "insatiation". The reader follows the story of a young man, Genezyp Kapen, opening on the night when he is erotically initiated by a homosexual composer, Putrycydes Tenger and princess Irina Vsievolodovna de Ticonderoga. A new element is added to Witkiewicz's normal paraphernalia: a magic pill. If the society in this novel, thanks to the author's extrapolation, brings to one's mind more Western Europe and America of the sixties than of the twenties, the role ascribed to chemically induced states of "oneness" with the universe sounds short of prophetic. No more and no less, he writes a report on LSD. The pill is of Eastern provenience; it has been devised by a Malayan-Chinese ideologist Murti Bing (and Chinese Communism is in fact "Murtibingism") as a means of pacifying the minds. Those who take the pill, provided by mysterious peddlars, become indifferent to such trifles as wars or changes of political systems. Witkiewicz, as it was already mentioned, experimented with drugs and was not a philistine, yet the pill is for him a signal of the end, both the chemical compound and the philosophical "drugs" of pragmatism, marxism, "intuition", and its growing popularity shows that man is ready to renounce what torments him and makes his true stature—a confrontation with unmitigated nakedness (one is tempted to say: "otherness") of Being.

The plot of *Insatiation* leads Genezyp Kapen to the immediate surroundings of General Kocmoluchowicz, a magnificent beast relying only upon instinct and his intution of a leader, and of his lash-wielding mistress Percy Zvierżontkovskaya (*zwierzątko* in Polish means a little animal; transcribe it into Russian phonemes and add a Russian ending—the outcome is hilarious to anybody familiar with Slavic languages). The general—no brains, only animal vitality—on the eve of a decisive battle with the Chinese has one of his intuitive strokes of understanding: it is of no use to oppose "historical necessity". He surrenders and, with all ceremonies due to his rank, is beheaded. In the new order under Chinese rule no harm is done to lunatics such as Genezyp Kapen and his friends. Well paid, they participate in a cultural revolution under the auspices of the Ministry of the Mechanization of Culture and develop a perfect schizophrenia, in the clinical sense too.

Since both his novels only in their last chapters carry the action into a new "happy" society (modeled upon what he knew of post-revolutionary Russia), they do not suffer from a certain leanness of psychological design, so typical of science fiction and of its social satire mutation. Their density and allusiveness relate them to the psychological novel with a contemporary socio-political setting, though its pattern is pushed to a caricature. Some critics maintain that through his handling of plots and characters as mere pretexts for a philosophical debate, with the author's direct commentaries and even footnotes, Witkiewicz merely rejuvenated the eighteenth century techniques. Probably this is true, provided, however, that we see the genealogy of all "fantasy" fiction as specific, different from that of a "realistic" portrayal of a psyche in its conflicts with the externally imposed laws and mores.

Many years separate us from Witkiewicz's death. In September 1939 he left Warsaw, then being surrounded by the Nazi armies, for the Eastern provinces and committed suicide on September 17, at the news of the Soviet army's advance in fulfillment of the Molotov-Ribbentrop pact. This suicide (he took sleeping pills in a wood, woke up and slashed his wrists with a razor) remains, rightly or wrongly, blended in the mind of his readers with the tragic ends of both his novels, where the splendor of Polish landscapes in autumn is used as a background.

In post-war Poland, Witkiewicz for a long time was a disquieting case and a taboo. He did not oppose Marxism on political grounds. On the contrary, few Marxist writers or sympathizers could compete with him in his disdainful appraisals of the "free world" and he grasped perhaps even better than they the workings of fascism. Yet Western technology, mass dementias of the "Brave Boys" and Marxist revolutions were for him phenomena of an immense twilight, in which he preserved loyalty to a belief in "decadence" shared by European bohemians around 1900. If he was disquieting, it was above all because of his sophistication; a literature able to produce such a writer probably called for more subtle methods of investigation (and direction) than a few vulgarized precepts of "realism". The less one spoke of him, the better. His writings were unhealthy as they prophesied what everybody lived through, especially after 1949: boredom and fear.

The revival of Witkiewicz in Poland after 1956 seems to deny his utter pessimism as to the irreversibility of the historical trend. His plays have never been performed with such a zeal and have never attracted so numerous audiences. They are already a permanent position in the repertoire of the Polish theater. His theatrical essays are a must for every theater director. One of his novels, *Insatiation,* has appeared in a new edition (not *Farewell to Autumn,* as it is a too exact an image of Poland after the revolution of the "Levellers"). His philosophy is avoided but his admirers managed to give it attention, profiting from a temporary relaxation of censorship, in a symposium *Stanislaw Witkiewicz, Man and Creator,* Warsaw, 1957. He is an acting force in Polish letters, thus his "hope against hope" is at least in part revindicated.

His significance transcends, however, the limits traced by one historical moment and one language. It depends upon the judgment we make about the theme of decadence, so persistent in the history of European civilization since the second half of the nineteenth century.

Desperate Jules Laforgue, Spengler, T. S. Eliot in search of "live water" in the wasteland, as well as those playwrights and film makers of today who popularized what they stole from poets—all are relatives of characters in Witkiewicz's plays and novels. As the transformation of social organisms into abstract Molochs gathers momentum, we observe, in both East and West, a parallel rebellion against society as a machine nobody can control, with a resulting proliferation of bohemian attitudes of withdrawal.

It is possible Witkiewicz was not dialectical enough and underestimated the resourcefulness of our species, its sly, water-like flowing around obstacles which are but a solidified, frozen vestige of our creative powers. In all probability we are going through another crisis of the Renaissance man when "the world was out of joint." Yet Witkiewicz was hardly wrong, it seems to me, in his realization that something strange had happened to religion, philosophy and art, even though their radical mutation does not signify their disappearance.

STANISLAW IGNACY WITKIEWICZ (1885-1939) is one of the most provocative and challenging writers of our century. Playwright, novelist, aesthetician, painter, he was equally seminal in many genres. He wrote two novels, *Farewell to Autumn* and *Insatiability,* the latter and his aesthetic writings were republished after 1956. The last few years saw a renaissance of Witkiewicz's theatre in Poland; he is now widely acknowledged, besides Artaud, as the precursor of the 'theatre of the absurd'. Witkiewicz committed suicide in September 1939.

CZESLAW MILOSZ (b. 1911) began his poetic career before the war and soon became known as a leading poet of the so-called "Second Avantgarde". He lived in Vilna and Warsaw, and during the German occupation edited an anthology of underground Polish poetry. Since 1951 he has been living in the West, recently as Professor of Slavic Literatures at the University of California at Berkeley. Milosz is the author of many novels and essays; a long essay of his on the Polish critic Brzozowski was published in the *California Slavic Studies.* He translated and edited the anthology *Postwar Polish Poetry,* Doubleday, 1965.

translated by Walter L. Solberg

The Kafkorium

BOHUMIL HRABAL

EVERY MORNING the landlord tiptoes into my room. I can hear his steps. And my room's so long you could ride a bicycle from the door right up to my bed. He bends over me, turns and signals to someone in the doorway and says: "Mr. Kafka is here." And he pokes his finger into the air three times, and then steps away again and slowly goes back towards the door where my landlady hands him a tin tray with a roll and a mug of coffee and because his hands are shaking the mug clatters around on the tray. Sometimes after being awakened like that I get to thinking: what if that landlord of mine would announce while he's waking me up that I'm not there? I'd be terribly alarmed, because they've been going through this with me for several years in commemoration of the first week when they brought me breakfast every day and I wasn't to be found in bed.

It was raining then like it did during the Tertiary. A river, with one and the same rhythm, continually drained off the water and I stood there in the incessant rain, not knowing whether to tap with my fingers or go away. Olive drab leaves chattered in the crowns of the trees; several lamps squeezed out through the wickers, and in the doorway into the room a form could be seen undressing for sleep or for love-making. The night-light chased the shadow to its shattering on the enamel doors. And I wondered, was he the author of that shadow himself or was someone else there too? That night I just shivered, because at night rain is cold, and footprints get obliterated in the muddy downpour. But, living in anxiety and in fear of hearing your teeth chatter is good; it's good to drag your life to ruin, and then, in the morning, to start all over again. So too is it good to say goodbye forever and to praise misfortune like Job, the sly old fox, did. This time, though, I stood there in the incessant rain and didn't know whether to knock or go away, because I didn't have the guts to poke out that jealous eye of mine in my mind. I said a prayer: "O rainy night, don't leave me standing here; o rainy night, don't abandon me to the mercies of banal beauty, but let me kneel here in the mud contemplating this locked-up house." In the morning I asked; "You still like me, Poldinka?" "Do you still like me?" she answered. Next time, when I wake up, I'll ask: "Hey pope, you asleep?" Once maybe I'll hold a mirror up to her lips,—once maybe it won't cloud up at all.

Now I'm strolling through Ungelt and I look at St. Jakub's where the Emperor Charles was married. At the corner of Malá Stupartská my landlord got slapped in the face, not because he's a detective on the vice squad, but because he pulled a couple of drunks away from each other. There in Ungelt is the little building where I once lived in the attic where the blind accordion player used to cross through my tiny little room on the way to his own. I'd really like to know how the Emperor Charles wanted that princess who could straighten out horse shoes and twist a metal tray into a cone with her hands. That's what I'd like to know—and I look at the arbor where the Marquessa de la Stade used to stroll, the Marquessa who they say had such fine skin, that when she drank red wine it was as though she were pouring it down a glass tube.

And so I enter the house where I live. Once, in the old days the tolling bell broke loose from the belfrey of Tyn Church, flew through the air, across the tiled roof and then broke through the roof and plopped into the room where I live. The landlady is leaned up against the gloomy window, the curtains blow out and the invisible world comes to life. I lean out of the fourth-floor window, the stone wall of Tyn Church is almost within arm's reach, and the landlady lets loose on me her mistletoe-like blonde tresses and exhales the fragrance of elderberry wine. I look over at the Mother-of-God, cemented to the wall, as stern-looking as a teutonic knight. Pedestrians are walking around the town hall and saluting the unknown soldier.

"You know what?" I hear the landlady behind me whispering, "come here, how's about just a friendly little kiss. Well then, Mr. Kafka!"

I reply: "Please Ma'am, no offense. But I'm true to my darlin' ".

"Oh sure," she hissed, "but when it comes to hellin' around, you're really a top hand." She said this and ran out, leaving behind her in suspension the fragrance of elderberry wine. The curtains puff up, then fall back freely and thousands of hummingbirds grab the organdy in their tiny beaks as though it were a queen's train and the curtains puff up again in the breeze. Somewhere in our building someone's playing the "First Book of Classics" on the piano. Under the window an unkempt man stands and his face is as crinkled-up as his vulcanized fiber suitcase. Mercury oozes out along the cathedral walls. The puffed-up owls and baboons have fallen asleep on their cornices.

"Can I show you my toothbrushes?"

"Really, that can't be so."

"Got them from France. You bet. Nylon. 258 crowns per dozen."

"No, no! that's not possible!"

"Too much? Well, maybe, but look, your clients will dance beautifully on a floor that's been polished with our product, Sir."

"So that's why she complained so much!"

"And in the way of something new I can inform you that we have children's hairbrushes in stock. Can I take your order?"

"Yes, but I can never leave her."

"Please, that's a hard currency item."

"I'll bury your place in curses and chrysanthymums."

"And I can give you a two per-cent discount for cash."

And I'd send the goods registered mail. They'd be here next week. And that? That's a preparation that the firm Hrivnác & Ass. puts out. Yes, that's right, the one who hung himself. And why? I don't know. You'd have to tell me first why the district judge lost his mind and why the coroner only smiled. Why, all you have to do is tighten up your tie a little and ask your shadow; 'Well, brother, how much life's left in you now?' "

I jump up from bed and lean into the street out the window like into a deep well. A woman's blonde head is trading kisses with a youth's—kisses like the lashes of a whip. And the breeze ushers all this right up to my bed.

"Don't be scared! Come on, don't you like me just a little?" pleads the blonde, and the bubbles of silence march off towards the moon who is working out up there on the high wire of the night. From three doors down I can hear the snoring of the cook with whom I used to live. Every day I had to buy fresh bread, or else, I wouldn't go to sleep. That cook could snore so, that I had to put tampons of the soft bread in my ears, being sure to barricade myself up for the night. Now the blonde tenderly flops down on the sand pile and pulls the lad down on top of her. Lime splattered hubs wheel across the lovers; the mason's junk starts clattering away, but they don't hear. A whitened wheel rolls through the alley like a full moon. The Mother-of-God's hands are cemented into peace; she can't even veil her baby boy's eyes.

Then they're closing up the Bar Figaro, the Spider, the Chapeau Rouge, the Rumania, and the Magnet. Someone's getting sick around the corner. On the corner of Old Town Square a citizen shouts:

"Sir! I'm a Czechoslovak!"

And somebody else gives him a slap in the face and says:

"Well, so what?"

A woman peeps out from under the arbor—blood is pouring from her nose as though a minute ago she too had affirmed to the roughneck:

"Sir! I'm a Czechoslovak!"

And in the middle of the square a man in black drags a good-looking woman in a flowered dress, he drags her through a puddle and shouts sorrowfully to the skies: "Boy, what a fine slut I picked for myself!" and the girl holds on to his legs, but the man in black kicks her away and she slides down in the puddle, crunching all up there like a picture in a round frame and her hair floats about the scummy surface like seaweed. Only now is the man in the tuxedo satisfied. He kneels in the water, twists the wet tresses into a plait, turns her tear-stained face towards him and runs his fingers over those beloved features. Then he helps her up, they hang on to each other, kiss, and walk away with an unstrained step, just like the holy family. They walk away to the small plaza where, close by the Prince Regent, that tuxedoed man swings around as though he were pulling out his sabre and announces to the empty square: "Spirit has conquered Matter!"

Then a streetcar went by with several strung-up people hanging by their hands; a pedestrian fell down and tried to set the pavement on fire. Now over the city, straddling it, there stands an invisible bull, and of him only his rosy testicle is to be seen.

Sometimes even before noon I'm on the way to Kotce. At the corner I buy a horoscope for all the months. Colored ribbons flow from the noses of yardage brokers, as they measure them off with an elbow. The herbalists' crowns sprout sunshades. Old women often are seen staggering out of those lairs in Kotce, they have faces scarred with the signs of the Zodiac, and instead of eyes there are two patches of leopard's skin. They bring their ridiculous odds and ends out into the light of day. One of them is selling green roses made out of feathers, an admiral's sword and the keys off an accordion, another is offering military sweat pants, canvas pails and a stuffed monkey. At the Uhelný market the women peddlers have tulips of all colors in their kangaroo pouches. In the display cases on Rytířská St. the doves bill and coo and parakeets flit about in their cages like the similes in a poem. Some Canadian hampsters are working away at their freedom in the tall chimney of the pen. Once for three hundred crowns I became a saint for a day. I bought up all the finches and let them go free right out of my hand. Oh, what a feeling when a terrified little bird flies up from your palm! And then I go to the market hall where old women are selling fresh blutwurst on plates. Here it smells of new-born infants, wetted straw ticks, vinegar and butcher knives. From the freight cars they're always unloading lamb carcasses. Isn't it funny that the big feasts will make the poor little creatures pay? Christmas—fish, Easter—goats and lambs. I remember how we butchered a pig at home and we didn't stick him quite right and he jumped into the manure pile, and would have drowned in it rather than to have seen the sticker with the knife in his hand again.

Then I'm rushing along. But that's not necessary; the beer I bought has gone stale. At the office of Zinner Brothers' where there are some five-storeys of toys, the stock-keeper is shaking with rage and says: "Look here, Ponce, we sent you after beer, and not to the fountain of youth. Where have you been?" And the warehouseman pours some oil on the fire. "And when's your Uncle Adolf going to die again, the one who's always dying on you in next month's issue, Kafka?"

"Won't take long," I say, and take up the invoices and all day I check off and count over two carloads of children's toys.

Infantryman with a cannon, soldier with a boat, soldier with a helmet, officer in step, general in a trenchcoat, drummer, buglar, french horn, large drum, soldier lying with a gun, artilleryman with a ramrod, officer standing with a map. . . I check off these figurines and think, how they're always getting me mixed up with someone else; I've been away from home so many years, yet as soon as there's ever a vomit stain, or someone bawls at night, the neighbors will come running at me and give mother hell; "that punk of yours was bawling again last night, does he get a big kick out of it?"

Distance spotter, telephone man writing, motorcyclist, wounded man lying down, two corpsmen, doctor in a white coat, hospital dog, soldier lying down with a cigarette, dragoon on horseback. . . .

The Maryska's aunt was dying and in the morning Mrs. Maryska came to see mother and complained that I banged on their window during the night and auntie had the life scared out of her before she died, that it definitely was me that did it; that she had run after me and heard my grisly sniggering—even though I hadn't been home for so many years.

Cow feeding, cow mooing, calf standing, colt eating, piggies, cat standing with a bow, hens pecking, tiger cubs, speckled hyena, bear standing up, american buffalo, polar bear cub, monkey scratching, . . .

I watched how the vet leaned over a sick animal, how he told the bookkeeper that he's going to prescribe something, but then he roared at me to come over right now and get a brush and rub in between the hoofs like this. And he impressed upon me, that I should take an axe handle and open the ox's mug and paint his throat like this. And I just gaped and didn't know how to say, that I'm not the keeper of these beasts, that I'm just a bystander. Chamois, wild pig, little shepard, farmer, chimney sweep, cowboy standing, indian throwing a lasso, large rabbit sitting, scout with a hat, sheep dog. . .

So I go into the synagogue and a mud-splattered Jew leans toward me and whispers; "Sir, aren't you also from the east?" and I nodded yes. Then, when I dropped in for a beer, two fellows were sitting there. One of them says to me, "Ain'tchoo a baker?" And I nodded, and the kid rubbed his palms and says; "Knew it right away," and ordered cards and said, "We need a third" "One crown low and two for high. Low card deals."

Mary, Jesus, Joseph, standing king, black king, shepherd with a lamb, angel, bedouin, sheep feeding, sheep dog, ...

Two wagons of toys I check off at Zinner Brothers' on Majslova St., a department store with toys and fancy goods; that's why I like to take a walk after work. But all the time I keep stumbling on all the toys that I had in my hand today. I like walking through the Kampa quarter where the kids draw in the asphalt. They get down on all fours and continue their drawings up along the houses, as high as the hand can reach. Now I'm struck by the portrait of a man. His hat is painted from the front and from the back at the same time, and his hidden ear is drawn in above his head like a question mark, like an emblem.

"You draw that?" I ask a little girl who's finished that drawing and whose curls are blue, like shotgun shells.

"Yeah, but that's nothin'," she says, and erases that portrait that could have hung in a gallery, with her foot, "but, how's about combing my hair? Please?"

"If you want," I say.

And the girl sits astride of a bench, then draws one leg up under her. I sit behind her, she hands me a comb over her shoulder, and I comb her hair. And she squints her eyes, then watches a falling leaf and says; "That leaf's hands hurt so he let go." It gets dark in a hurry. Bicycle riders are coming down along the serpentine streets of Petrin hill wearing miners' lamps on their heads, small boats are rowing in the nephritine water, and with each stroke of the cars they churn up silverplate teaspoons by the dozen. Along the bench gropes a blind man and he leads a blind woman by the radar of his white cane.

"When you're drawing like this in the asphalt, what do you think about?", I ask.

"How that bird over there sings", she points to the branches and she presses her chin to her breast. I see that she's still completely a child, but in a few years there'll start to awaken in her the beautiful parasite containing that pungent stuff with the flavor of borax and it will slowly flood her life with happiness. I combed her hair, weighted it out in handfuls, then tied up a little bow. And the girl swung her hands in back of her head, placing her finger on the first knot so that I could make an extra special bow. Then she turned, untied the jump rope that girded her, stretched the two ends of the rope around herself, thrust out her tummy, and I placed my finger on the crossed rope, so that she could make a bow, and a little tie. All of a sudden she kissed my hand and took off.

From Kampa Charle's bridge looks like a long bath-tub where the pedestrians ride along on their bottoms in wheeled conveyances. Prague, with her broken ribs, groans in the river and the bridge's arches jump, one after the other, from shore to shore like coon hounds. I could go after my cousin at the brewery or drop in to see my landlady who invited me up for a bottle of elderberry wine, but I prefer walking about aimlessly. On Malá Karlova St. in front of an illuminated stall stands a shopkeeper and over his head there's a sign with the firms's name: Alfred Wieghold.

"My regards, Mr. Wieghold," I say.

And inwardly I apologize to him for gaping at his hands, hands cracked like those of the Virgin Mary of Czenstochowa. Synthetic hands.

"It must be going to rain," I remark, all the time staring at those artificial limbs.

"Young man," said Mr. Wieghold, "why are you walking around my shop on your hands? Put your hands in your pockets, get some use out of those pockets!" And he broke into an evil laugh, that Punch and Judy kind, and clanked the arms into the cabinet and both of his own creaked like flagpoles in Autumn.

Then I'm going down Michalská St. and I see a sign: The Iron Door. That gives a man strength just like ferrous wine. In the passage way I can see into the watchmaker's shop. The apprentice, who sweeps up, continually blinks and has eyes full of sugar crystals; he must have conjunctivitis pretty bad. Every morning I'll bet he has to pry open his eyes in order to make it to the wash basin. Today I keep coming across sequences of strollers, as though they were connected with an invisible chain. Ten people with bandaged heads, then again a dozen with meaningfully raised eyebrows, as if they wanted to tell me something, seven people with patches over their eyes. . .

But most of all my eyes are riveted to the women. This new fashion'll be the end of me. Each one looks around like she's just risen from the couch of love. What do they have there under that blouse? Some kind of scaffolding, or a skeletal corsage so that those breasts poke a man in the eye? And then there's that gait! A city fellow has to have a whole trunk-full of images stored up not to be driven to a crime of passion by those charms. Then a fellow caught up with me, and expounded all his wondrous doing to me—how he ran the first automat in the

Koruna, how he himself sat inside of the thing and first of all he looked to see if the coin that was dropped in was counterfeit, and only then put the sandwich on a plate and turned the mechanism with his hand; how he heard people marveling at the invention, just like the time when he had sat inside the five-meter clock at an exhibit with a pocket watch in his hand, and pushed the hand forward every minute. This he revealed to me and stopped short, astonished even now with these adventures of his.

I ask: "Who are you?"

"A practical philosopher," he said.

"Then please explain Kant's *Critique of Practical Reason* to me."

And we went up through Stepanska St. and Prague sank and sank, immersed by a hydraulic press, and the practical philosopher's hair struck against the incubator of the stars. He offered to treat me to a hot dog, and on the way to Rybnícek he gave me an interpretation. He crossed himself above his fly, and banged himself on the forehead so hard that the neon lights and the traffic signals sputtered.

I say; "that woman over there has good wieners now and then."

Then the acetylene lamp shined on that old woman, and Rembrandt rose up from the dead. The old woman's hands were resting on her stomach, as if feeling the back of her lost son. Her single tooth gleamed out of her mouth.

"So, it's midnight already, gentlemen?" she asked.

The practical philosopher raised his finger to the sky and at that moment he was really splendid; like Rabbi Low, like Vincent's severed ear. The night was full of slag, of silvered disks, of bolts and nuts. The air breathed amonium oxalate, lactic acid, feminine hygiene, essences, lipstick. And St. Stephan's clock struck the beginning of midnight. Then Prague's clocks struck from all sides; even those that were slow. The practical philosopher ate up his grilled wieners with real gusto, then, without saying goodbye, left.

In walked a whore. Pretty, dressed in white like an angel. She turned around and the pod of her mouth broke open and out popped white peas in two rows. I longed to inscribe some bright-colored words in her smile, supposing that she could read them in the morning in the mirror that she'll stand in front of with her toothbrush.

I say to the old woman: "Didn't you know Francis Kafka?"

"Oh, heavens yes". She said, "I am Frances Kafka. And my dad was a horse-butcher, and he was called Francis Kafka. And I knew a head-waiter at the station resturant in Bydzov who was also called Kafka," she said and leaned over and her one tooth gleamed in her mouth like a witches'. "But, if you wanted something special, Sir, all the same you're not going to die a natural death. Have yourself cremated and leave me those ashes of yours, and I'll polish my forks and knives with you, so that something extra special happened to you, something like a gift, like misfortune, like love, . . .hahahaha."

She said this and turned the hissing and sizzling hot dogs with a fork.

"I'm a fortune teller, too," she continued. If you hadn't been enshrouded in a cloud, Sir, you'd have done great things. . . here, get out of here, you! Here it is back again!" she said and swept off her skirt and kicked something away with her feet.

"What is it?", I ask.

"Nothing," she said, "It's just Hedvicka, the Polish countess'es daughter who got drowned, her ghost. . .you know: She's hanging around me all the time, and here she's pulling at my apron, you see?"

"I see", I say and I retreated from the radius of the acetylene lamp.

Then I was on my way home. In the entry of the Turandot someone's showing the bouncer that he does have money. At Smelhauz' music rises out of the cellar and two old laughing men too. Kozná St. is full of unchaste signs and motions. In the gutter there lies a fresh rose, as if it fell from a bouquet. Then I sit down by the pool at the Old Town Square, and my shadow is green with a violet border. Someone is carrying a huge cactus, each of whose arms is bound by a little red bow. A woman, who looks like she might have looked in from a Ibsen play, marches down Parízská St. Over her pajamas she has on a dress coat; she probably can't sleep and is walking over to lean on the railing over the river. Now a man has leaned up against the streetlight, as though he were listening to classical music. But then he throws up. The liquid flows out of his mouth as though his pocket watch were falling out on its chain. I can see the lighted windows of my apartment; the curtains are puffing out and my landlord walks back and forth and makes the sign of the cross. He's probably got a pot on the table again and an opened bible leaned up against it. From Dlouhá Ave. out stepped a policeman looking like both his hands had been plunged in plaster up to the elbow.

Poldinka, I think of you. Of how you told me; "It's you I hate least of all. In your mouth I can feel a bottomless pit that's been dredged out by love, on your teeth I can feel a wall along which sorrow oozes out. Honey, you've been having bologna for dinner, 'cause I've got a little piece on my lips, but that's all right. Kiss me once and kiss me twice and kiss me once again! Chew on the flesh around the pits of my eyes, around the crater of my mouth, And. tell me again that neither was Solomon in all his pomp and splendor, that neither are the flocks of the heavens or the flowers of the fields as pretty as I am. Tell me again, and ignite the burnt offering between my legs again, and kindle in me that pelvic fire. And when you go home in the morning and see women's clothing hanging from the window, don't pay any attention. That means I'm embracing a house shrouded in memories. They say you can feel the sun's lost pinpricks in an iron picket fence."

This is what Poldinka told me that time; she stepped towards the river where the town walks on its hands. This time I was amazed at why the upside-down cars travel in the river with their wheels up, as though they were sledding along the roofs, why the pedestrians greeted each other though dipping water in their hats.

Poldinka said to me: "Man o'mine, where did you ever get what it takes to sell all those crazy toys, those combs and brushes, all the time dreaming so intensely?"

And I said: "Poldinka, it's you alone who understood the words that I flooded your mouth, your hair, the breath deep in your lungs with, with words right out of the evening paper. It's you alone who always divines when the light in my eyes grows dim, and you alone also understand what will remain after I leave you with a metallic and mute looking face, because I too, just like you, never wanted to be happy according to a recipe, I never wanted, like you, to not have the right to pain and sorrow . . . Poldinka, you perverse and degenerate woman, you, why do you have to bring panic into my life? Like a stalactite, a bat?"

I jumped up from the bench in Old Town Square. Before me there was standing a straddled-out policeman with sleeves that had been soaked in lime. No one else was walking by so I confided in him: "So, from now on I won't be able to be rid of the longing to stroll with the Arameic professor of laughter, you know? From now on I won't be able to get rid of that fissure in the cranium because to be free, that's joy. So I'm sinking down in happiness itself, in weddings and joys; at Zinners' I check off Easter bunnies, and cottontails, miniature memorial chapels, angel hair, Christmas glass, toys. You understand? We're all brothers, *l' art pour l'art* brothers, as beautiful as *entartete Kunst,* as truthful as the nightingale, as degenerate as a rose. Do you really understand? Without a cranial fissure, you just can't live. You can't delouse a person out of his freedom, brothers! Do you understand?"

And the policeman sternly said: "Don't shout like that! Why are you shouting like that? Mr. Kafka! There's gonna' be hell to pay again!"

BOHUMIL HRABAL (b. 1914) studied law at the Charles University in Prague, later tried all sorts of jobs, including that of an extra in a Prague theatre. His first book was published in 1956, but his talents won full recognition only in the sixties, after the publication of *Perlicka na dne* and *Pábitelé* (*Pearl at the Bottom* and *Palaverers*). WALTER L. SOLBERG currently lives and teaches in Berkeley.

King Popiel

Popiel, a legendary king of Polish
prehistory, is said to have been
eaten by mice on his island in the
middle of a big lake.

Those were not, it is certain, crimes just like ours.
It was all about dugouts carved out of lime
And some beavers' pelts. He ruled over marshes
Where the moose echoes in a moon of acid frosts
And lynxes walk in springtime onto the drying holms.

His palisade, his timber fort and the tower
Built by the fins of the gods of night
Could be seen beyond the water by the hidden hunter
Who dared not push aside the branches with his bow.
Until one of them returned with the news. The wind chased over the deep
Into the rushes, the largest boat, which was empty.

Mice have eaten Popiel. The diamond-studded crown
He got later. And to him, who vanished forever,
Who held in his treasury three Gothic coins
And bars of bronze, to him who went away
Where, no one knows, with his children and women,
To him lands and seas were left by Galileo,
Newton and Einstein. So that for long centuries
He might smooth, on his throne   his javelin with a knife.

translated by Joy N. Humes

The early writings of Georg Lukacs

LUCIEN GOLDMANN

Georg Lukacs already appears as one of the most influential figures in the intellectual life of the 20th Century.[1]

His thought and his work, however, embrace such a vast number of objects, and present such a great variety of intellectual positions and levels of analysis, that it would be difficult to judge the work in its entirety without at once adding a number of clarifications and reservations.

We will therefore try first of all to trace schematically the concept of *significant dynamic structure* which Lukacs formulated for the first time in 1923 in *History and Class Consciousness* and which constitutes, in our opinion, his most important contribution to the development of the human sciences as positive scientific disciplines; and secondly, to trace an equally schematic portrait of his intellectual evolution, which will permit the reader better to understand the significance and importance of his work. The concept of *significant dynamic structure* is not, in fact, a discovery of Georg Lukacs. As a general, abstract and philosophic idea it was already at the center of Hegelian dialectic.[2] Marx, who afterward reexamined this idea, eliminating from it all that, in Hegel, was speculative, made of it an instrument of concrete empirical research.

Unfortunately he did not leave us what might properly be called methodological study; that is why, as important for the methodology of the human sciences as are the numerous reflections scattered throughout Marx's writings and most notably in the famous *Preface to the Critique of Political Economy,* it is to Lukacs that belongs the merit of clarifying and thereby rendering accessible to others the fundamental methodological principles of Marx's work, among them being those three most important concepts of dialectical methods in human sciences: 1) *significant dynamic structure* 2) *possible consciousness* (*Zugerechnetes Bewusstsein*) and 3) *objective possibility.*

Dialectical materialism, which is a generalized genetic structuralism founded

[1]Extract from *Temps modernes,* No. 195, August, 1962.

[2]Which explains the very great number of penetrating concrete comprehensive analyses which are to be found in Hegel's work. *Translator's Acknowledgment.* The translator wishes to thank Edward S. Casey, Department of Philosophy, Northwestern University, who read this manuscript and offered many helpful and pertinent suggestions.

on these concepts, implies that every human fact presents itself both as a comprehensible significant structure through the analysis of the constitutive relations between the elements which compose it (elements which are, in turn and on their own level, significant structures of the same type) and as an constitutive element of a certain number of other, larger structures which embrace and integrate it.

In this perspective every human fact has a dynamic character and cannot be understood except through the study of its past evolution and the internal tendencies oriented toward the future. Therefore this study always presents itself as an evolutionary process having two complementary aspects: *destructuration* of an old structure and *structuration* of a new structure undergoing self-formation. To the foregoing must be added that, in the positive study of significant structures which constitute history, it is impossible to separate factual judgments from value judgments, the mental categories of the researcher himself being a constitutive element of the existence of a social group which acts within global structures.

This position implies, first, that all positive research in the human sciences ought to be at once *comprehensive* and *explicative,* the *comprehension* consisting in the description of the essential links of which the Becoming (*le devenir*) constitutes the structure, the *explanation* in the comprehension of larger structures which include the Becoming of partial structures[3]; second, that for research of this type, the study of real or theoretical states of coherent *structuration* constitutes a particularly privileged conceptual instrument.

Finally, let us be very clear, in concluding this introductory part, that Lukacs never employs the term "significant coherent structure" and only speaks in his first two works of "Forms" and, in *History and Class Consciousness,* of "Totality".

In 1910, 13 years before having clarified in *History and Class Consciousness* the concept of significant dynamic structure, Lukacs, after having published in Hungarian a work which to our knowledge has never been translated in any western-European language, became known to the German public through a book, *The Soul and Forms,* which seems to us for several reasons to mark an essential date in the history of contemporary thought. First of all because, after long years of academic philosophy, Lukacs rediscovered in this work the great tradition of classic philosophy by placing at the center of his preoccupations the problem of the relationships which exist between human life and absolute values. This was an important intellectual event, for this tradition seemed entirely forgotten.

Neo-Kantian, neo-Hegelian and neo-Marxist social democrats had in effect obscured the work of the great classic philosophers, Kant, Hegel, and Marx, with

---

[3]To understand a structure is to grasp the nature and significance of the different elements and processes which constitute it as dependent upon their relations with all the other elements and constitutive processes of the whole. The Lukacsian description of the "Forms" of the Essay, of Romanticism and of Tragedy in *The Soul and Forms,* of the Novel, in the *Theory of the Novel,* of classic German Philosophy or of the proletarian Revolution, in *History and Class Consciousness,* are such comprehensive descriptions.

To *explain* a social fact is to insert it into the *comprehensive* description of a process of dynamic structuration which encompasses it. To take an example in our own research: the Lukacsian concept of tragic vision has been a capital instrument in the *understanding* of the writings of Pascal and Racine, the *understanding* of the Jansenist movement as a dynamic structure has, on the other hand, an *explicative* value in relation to these writings; in the same way the comprehensive description of the history of the Nobility of the Cloth has an explicative value for the understanding of the genesis of Jansenism, the *comprehensive description* of the evolution of the structure of class interrelations in the French global society of the sixteenth and seventeenth centuries has an explicative value for the dynamic processes which constitute the development of the Nobility of the Cloth, etc.)

a veil of dusty erudition which made the latter appear to be rather penetrating theoreticians, whose work although sufficiently complex to demand innumerable commentaries, seemed to have lost all real and immediate contact with daily life and the problems which it raises.

Philosophic reflection, moreover, seemed progressively to reduce its scope to epistemology, to the philosophy of sciences, and to the history of philosophy. It is true that this last in particular was attaining in the works of the great scholars a degree of erudition rarely before achieved.

Lukacs in no wise lacks this erudition, and even a casual reading of his book shows that he had no cause to envy the eminent doctors on that score. But if, as Pascal maintained, the mark of an honest man is to be well acquainted with a large number of different fields without ever appearing to be a specialist, Lukacs realizes this goal in the highest degree, for it is precisely. his exceptional erudition which allows him never to make a show of it. Thus his book which, as we will see later, rediscovered behind the academic deformations of neo-Kantianism the authentic sense of Kantian thought, never refers explicitly to Kant; in the same way one finds only rare references to Hegel in that eminently Hegelian work which is *The Theory of The Novel*.

Explicitly, *The Soul and Forms* is uniquely concerned with the relation between the human soul and the absolute, and those "forms" which express the different and privileged modalities of this relation.

Under what conditions can human life be authentic? What are the circumstances and the attitudes which make it lose its authenticity? Are there, between the authentic an inauthentic, the true and the false, any intermediary values? Can error engender any valid "forms", if only on the aesthetic or philosophic level? These are the only problems which Lukacs' book raises and even then, not on the level of general theoretical reflection but as an essayist, who, "at the right moment" treats a certain number of great literary and philosophical realizations: Montaigne, Plato, Kierkegaard, Stefan George, Kant, Pascal and Racine.

GEORG LUKACS, although still relatively unknown in the United States, is a major figure in European literary and social criticism. His Marxist humanism has mitigated the crudity of much Socialist Realism criticism, and he is already something of a legend among the young intellectuals of Eastern Europe, though still regarded with some suspicion by the Party. Gyula Borbándi has called him the "finest Marxist critic since Marx." Born in 1885 in Budapest of a wealthy Jewish-Hungarian family, Lukács studied in Berlin, was influenced by neo-Kantianism and in 1911, published his first book, a collection of essays, *The Soul and Forms (Die Seele und die Formen)*. During World War I Lukacs joined the Communist Party and as Commissar of Education, took part in the short-lived Bela Kun government in Hungary in 1919. Following its fall he fled to Austria, was arrested in Vienna, released, but forced to remain in exile. In 1923 his next book, *History and Class Consciousness (Geschichte und Klassenbewusstsein)* was attacked by Zinoviev at the Fifth Congress of the Communist International. Although Lukacs himself criticized the book in 1925, he was excluded from the central committee of the Hungarian Communist party. Suspected of deviation, Lukacs nevertheless survived Stalinist purges by avoiding open criticism of the regime. In 1956 Lukacs served in the cabinet of Imre Nagy, and when Russian troops entered the capital he fled with the latter to the Yugoslav embassy. He was taken by the Russians to Rumania, kept under house arrest, but spared public trial. The best documented study of Lukacs' life and writings may be found in *Soviet Survey* (London) nos. 23-27, 1958-59. His *Studies in European Realism* is available in this country from Universal Library, with an introduction by Alfred Kazin. Lukacs now lives in retirement in Budapest and is devoting himself to a three-volume work on aesthetics. JOY N. HUMES is presently an instructor in Romance Languages at Northwestern from which she holds her M.A.

In this sense it is probably with *The Soul and Forms* that the philosophic renaissance in Europe which followed the first World War, and which would be later designated as existentialism, began. No doubt Lukacs remained in the line of classic philosophy, and never adopted positions analogous to those later to be taken by a succession of thinkers, among them, Jaspers and Heidegger. But he was the first in the twentieth century to raise the problems which would dominate philosophic thought and which, since the death of Hegel, had more or less disappeared from European consciousness (one must not forget that Kierkegaard, who had only been translated at the beginning of the century, was still almost unknown).

Let us emphasize, however, that Lukacs' book is not a sudden creation without antecedents: the author had the merit—or the good fortune—to find himself present at the meeting of the three great currents in German academic thought of his time: the neo-Kantianism of Heidelberg, Dilthey's examination of the concepts of significance and understanding, and Husserlian phenomenology; and it is perhaps in part this situation which allowed him to rediscover the tradition of classic idealism, by defining *significance* as the *relation between the soul and the absolute,* while, having renounced this relation, the three currents mentioned above had in fact broken with the great philosophic tradition.

The encounter between phenomenology and the neo-Kantian school at Heidelberg was already effective before its theoretical expression appeared in *The Soul and Forms*. Husserl published in *Logos,* the neo-Kantian organ in Heidelberg[4], his famous article on "Philosophy as a Rigorous Science"; the Heidelberg group was resolutely oriented towards the human sciences and beginning to be interested, although in a way which might be contested, in Hegel, in dialectics; finally, Max Weber and Lask (after Windelband and Rickert, the third representative philosopher of the school) exercised a decisive influence on a few young thinkers who were beginning to publish their first works and whose names were: Lukacs, Jaspers, and Heidegger.[5]

As for Lukacs' book, it appears first to be a synthesis of two essential ideas of phenomenology and of the Diltheyan current, that of *atemporal essence* and that of *significance,* a synthesis which permits the author to elaborate the concept which he will later modify and make more precise, but which will remain the central element of his thought, i.e., *essence as significant structure.*

Moreover, the encounter between the phenomenological concept of atemporal essence and neo-Kantianism would result in the elaboration of the concept of *tragic vision* and in the rediscovery of the authentic meaning of Kantian philosophy, a meaning which the neo-Kantians had totally deformed.

We have already said that the idea of essence as a significant structure was not a new discovery to the extent that this concept was already, without being explicity formulated, the center of Marxist and Hegelian dialectic. But academic thought of the second half of the 19th century had lost contact with dialectic traditions to

---

[4]It was in the same review that Lukacs published the principal chapter of *The Soul and Forms* before the appearance of the volume.

[5]The first two books of this last explicitly showing the influence of Lask, the second being dedicated to him.

such a point that the simple use of the concept of significance by Dilthey—superficial and approximate as it was—seemed like a discovery.

By joining, to the vague and fluid ideas of Dilthey in regard to significance and understanding, the methodological demand for precision which characterized phenomenology, Lukacs made at once a step forward and a step back. A step forward, to the extent that he replaced the vague Diltheyan concept of significance by the idea of rigorous and precise description, such as phenomenology had demanded and the possibility of which it had demonstrated, a description which alone allowed the concept of significant structure to become an operable scientific instrument. A step backward, however, to the extent that, under the influence of this same phenomenology, he resolutely abandoned the historic conception of Dilthey in favor of the Husserlian idea of *atemporal essence.*

Lukacs thus arrived at the idea of *significant atemporal structures,* of "forms" as expressions of different and privileged modalities in the relationship between the human soul and the absolute.

Finally, it is this atemporal conception of significant structures which explains the fact that, contrary to Dilthey and to his masters of the neo-Kantian Heidelberg school who were oriented towards Hegelianism and history, Lukacs resolutely returned to the Kantian position, the authentic significance of which he rediscovered.

At the center of this book is the description of a particular atemporal significant structure, the *tragic vision,* which Lukacs considers at this time as the *only* true one and which he opposes to the other inauthentic forms of escape and pseudo-rejection of daily life.

We will see later that this position in *The Soul and Forms* is not rigorously coherent; let us stress, however, that in rediscovering the tragic significance of Kantianism and in presenting it, not as a historical fact but *as a universal human truth,* Lukacs touches on a problem which will dominate the philosophical renaissance of the twentieth century.

In fact, he is the first to pose in all its acuteness and force the problem of the relation between the *individual, authenticity* and *death.*

As paradoxical as it may seem, the development of individualistic thought since the sixteenth and seventeenth centuries had, in progressively eliminating from the consciousness all ideas of transcendence and of supra-individual values, relegated this problem to the background of philosophical thought.[6] For Christian thought in the Middle Ages, which integrated the existence of the individual to a vision of the whole, death was a particularly important event charged with significance for the individual. By suppressing, more or less radically, any idea of totality and of the whole, individualism in its different forms had made of life and of individual thought a priori values which could not and had no need to be exceeded, and, since these individual values were not called into question, it became progressively blinded to the problem of the limits of the individual and most importantly the problem of death.

---

[6]See on this subject for the sixteenth century *Lucien Febver: Au coeur religieux du XVIᵉ siecle,* Sevpen Paris 1956, pp. 55-58 and for eighteenth century B. Groethuysen: *Origines de l'esprit bourgeois en France,* Gallimard, Paris, 1956, pp. 61-69.

In 1910 bourgeois society lived in full confidence and optimism in the present; the period of the revolutionary disturbances of 1789 to 1848 was long in the past, the ruling classes, who in no wise felt themselves menaced, had even integrated the socialist positions and had ended by transforming them into a constitutive element of the existent equilibrium; the few local wars and even the Commune had only been limited episodes too unimportant to shake their good ideological consciousness and their confidence in a future which would eternally resemble the present. As for the great philosophic period of this bourgeoisie, which had corresponded to the enthusiasm of a group conscious of creating a new society and a new world, it too, was long past. The second half of the nineteenth century had been the period of acceptance of the *status quo,* of the birth of great industry, of great speculative financial successes, the prosaic affluent period of economic history, the social and intellectual triumph of the western bourgeoisie, the period of "get rich quick." This was the period, also, in which philosophers had been replaced by professors of philosophy, while those few great writers or thinkers who, like Nietzsche or Flaubert, had expressed their aversion towards this vulgar and prosaic society, had been relegated to the margin of social life where they were, for all practical purposes, neutralized and posed no threat.

In fact, in 1910, although few men realized it, this period was almost at its end, and invisible faults were cracking an edifice, the facade of which still seemed intact. No doubt a few Marxist thinkers had developed the theory of imperialism, but their ideas were not penetrating into the official and academic circles. Four years later World War I would erupt.

On this point, Lukacs' rediscovery of the tragic vision represented a total break with the scholars of the academic world. Neither Husserl nor Dilthey nor the neo-Kantians of Heidelberg had even been touched by the eventuality of the oncoming catastrophe. The conflict would erupt in an unforeseen and brutal way for moralists and official philosphers. Some years after its end, a new period would begin in western philosophy, and no one would again take the nineteenth century professors seriously. The values of individualism having been profoundly shaken, thinkers and writers would declare with horror that their predecessors had been totally blind to a fundamental and disquieting problem, *death.*

In effect, whatever were the individual values on which one claimed to found human existence, they now appear insufficient and outdated by the very fact that they were individual and that their foundation had to disappear with the limit of the individual and his inevitable disappearance. Pascal in the seventeenth century, Kant in the eighteenth, had made of this limit the very center of their philosophic thought. The nineteenth century, especially in its second half, had completely eliminated it from the consciousness.

Lukacs, in *The Soul and Forms,* once more takes up the problematic of Pascal and Kant in its most radical form. He affirms the absolute nonvalue of the social world for the individual, his inauthenticity and that of all life which participates in it in the least way or has the slightest illusion as to the possibility of a valid intra-mundane existence. Man is mortal and by that alone the only authenticity which could be accessible to him resides in the unequivocable consciousness of his limits, of the nonvalue of the world which these perforce entail, and of the necessity of his radical refusal. The distinction between *the* life which is conscious of limits, solitude and refusal, and the *life* which is on the contrary illusion, weakness and acceptance of quotidian reality, corresponds rigorously to the distinction Heidegger would later make between authentic and inauthentic existence. Heidegger's position, however, seems contradictory to us (because, while placing authenticity in the consciousness of limits, in *Sein zum Tod*, he nonetheless imagines that this existence could become authentic by its insertion in history) whereas Lukacs will always be more coherent and more radical on this point. In 1910, situating authenticity in the consciousness of limits and of death, he drew the inescapable consequence that no intra-mundane life could obviate these limits or confer on existence any validity whatsoever.

In 1923, when he was to admit the possibility of authentic historical existence and consequently, of the future of the community, he would conclude from this that the character of the individual limits, important no doubt, was in the last instance secondary. These two positions are coherent; that of Heidegger, on the other hand, seems to us a poor and not very philosophic compromise. However this might be, in so posing in all its acuteness the problem of limits and of death, Lukacs' book introduced into European thought a set of problems which would be the main concern of the philosophical renaissance following the first world war.

And yet Lukacs thought, in this book, is not rigorously coherent, for if on the one hand he defends a tragic Kantian position, opposing the authentic and radical refusal of the world to all inauthentic forms of pseudo-refusal and evasion that he studies, he also defends from another aspect the existence of intermediary values between the true and the false, the authentic and the inauthentic, values which are situated on the level of philosophic and aesthetic creation, and which he calls "forms." Along with the *Essay on Tragedy*, the *Essay on the Essay* constitutes one of the pillars of his work.

Lukacs defines the essay (and in this sense he himself has always been a great essayist) as an autonomous "form" situated between literature and philosophy. The first expresses coherent attitudes of the soul on the level of the imaginary creation of individual beings and particular situations; the second expresses the same attitudes on the level of conceptual creation. One and the same vision may be expressed in the work of Pascal and that of Racine; however in the former there is only *death*, while in the latter there is never death, but only *Phaedra dying*. As to the essay, it is an intermediary autonomous form. A conceptual work like philosophy, it can only raise conceptual problems (for it deals only with problems and never categorical answers) at the "instance" of a concrete and individual reality; and as conceptual problems cannot be posed separately from the complex and inexplicable confusion of daily life, the essayist must do this at the instance of those privileged aspects of this life which are "forms". The great essayists, Plato, Montaigne, disengaged the forms beginning from a real empirical life (that of Socrates or that of Montaigne himself), essayists of more limited scope posed problems having their origin in those forms, already purified and coherent, which are the great figures of universal literature. The essay is thus necessarily an ironic work having two dimensions. It seems to treat such and such a book, and such and such a person or concrete reality; in fact the book, the person or reality is only an "instance" which permits the author to pose the fundamental problems of human existence on the conceptual level. But, because of this, all these "forms" represent for the essayist privileged, and in part, positive realities.

Now, there is a contradiction between the tragic attitude categorized by *all or nothing* which only admits to the existence of true or false, or authentic and inauthentic without intermediary, and that of the essayist for whom all the coherent attitudes which he is analyzing (even when he does so only to expose their insufficiency) are privileged realities and thus constitute on the esthetic or philosophic level complementary values in relation to those of truth and error.

Thus, since 1910, Lukacs has merited an important place in European thought by disengaging for the first time the principal operative concept in the human sciences, that of *significant structure* (or "forms" as he called it then); by calling attention to the fissures which, behind an apparently intact facade, had profoundly shaken western bourgeois society.

The second work of Lukacs, the *Theory of the Novel*, appeared in 1920, but was written much earlier since, as we know, Lukacs had by 1917 gone beyond the positions defended in this book to support Marxism. Thus this work probably dates from some time during the war.

From a methodological point of view the positions of Lukacs here are very close to those developed in *The Soul and Forms*. It is a question of describing a certain number of atemporal essences, of "forms" which correspond to the literary expression of certain coherent human attitudes.

The change involves most importantly the manner in which Lukacs thinks of the relation between man and society, and, as a consequence of this change, the significant structures which he proposes to describe. For Lukacs, as we have said, is not only a philosopher and a scholar, but also a great essayist; which means that he does not limit himself to a positive and scientific study of any significant structures whatsoever, but that he chooses those for which the study may constitute "the occasion" for posing on the conceptual level the problems which appear to him most urgent.

All his essays are at once scientific studies and essays, and it is the problems raised in the essay which determine the choice of objects for positive analysis.

In 1910 Lukacs had only studied the forms of refusal or evasion; that is why he could entitle his book *The Soul and Forms*. This time, in the *Theory of the Novel*, he studies the great epic forms which, contrary to those he had chosen before, are *realistic*, i.e., are based, if not on an acceptance of reality, at least on a positive attitude toward a *possible* reality, the possibility of which is founded upon *the existing world*. That is why, in spite of the analogous conception of essence as an atemporal significant structure, this book could not have had the same title. For, if the exterior milieu was not essential for the "forms" studied in the preceding book—romanticism, essay, tragedy, etc.—in *epic* literature the "forms" are the expression of complex and multiple relationships between the soul and the world, which thus become, alongside of the soul and on the same level with it, their essential and indispensable foundation.

Thus, at a time in which the crisis of Western society had become manifest for all those who, a few years before, had not the least suspicion of it, Georg Lukacs, who had been one of the first to uncover it, affirms the category of realistic hope, and outlines the central category of his later thought, that of *objective possibility*.

Based on the category of "all or nothing", *The Soul and Forms* was an unequivocable work which affirmed the greatness of the authentic and solitary conscience, the greatness of refusal; categorized by "yes and no", by contradiction, the *Theory of the Novel* is a dialectic Hegelian book which affirms that the most valid human type in the present world is the complex and problematic individual.

Nothing in this book would lead one to suspect a knowledge of the Marxist theory of reification, the importance and richness of which Lukacs would be the first, in 1923, to show; and yet, in studying this book, if one analyzes the essence of the human condition in modern western society (it is, of course, ourselves who are thus limiting the historical and social background of the work), Georg Lukacs is already disengaging the psychic manifestations of this phenomenon.

The novel is for Lukacs the principal literary form of a world in which man is neither completely at home nor altogether a stranger. For an epic literature to exist (and the novel is an epic form) there must be a fundamental community; if there is to be a novel there must be a radical opposition between man and the world, between the individual and society.

Between the čpopče which expresses the sufficiency of the soul and of the world, of the interior and of the exterior, the universe in which the answers are presented before the questions are formulated, where there are dangers, but no threats, shade but no shadows, where the significance is implicit in each aspect of life and asks only to be formulated, not discovered,—and tragedy, which is the literary form of pure essence, of solitude and negation of all life, the novel is the dialectic form of the epic, the form of solitude within the community, of hope without future, of presence and absence. To use one of Lukacs' images, between that literature of consciousness and death which is tragedy, the novel is the literary form of virile maturity.

However, it is not a question of examining analyses which the reader can himself read in the text, but of trying to facilitate their comprehension by relating them to Lukacs' later positions and also to our own works.

In the realm of scientific esthetics, and of a positive study of forms, the first non-Marxist works of Lukacs have the merit of having succeeded in describing, by a series of brilliant intuitive insights, a certain number of significant structures corresponding to different literary genres, structures that it has been possible to insert later into a genetic and global analysis of the societies in which they had developed.

Nothing, in effect, seems at first glance further from Marxism or from all sociology than the conception of essences as significant atemporal structures. And yet, it is on the basis of these works that a certain number of analyses have been elaborated which have permitted the construction of the first elements of a positive sociology of literature and of philosophy. Let us mention here, besides the later works of Lukacs himself, our own studies of the philosophy of Kant, Pascal's *Pensées*, and Racine's theatre, growing out of *The Soul and Forms*, and the remarkable work of Erich Kohler on Chrétien de Troyes, growing out of a few pages of the *Theory of the Novel*.[7] But the most important step towards a Marxist study of literature seems to us to have been the description in this book of the significant romanesque structure, a description which we were later able, in research now in progress, to relate to the Marxist analysis of merchandise fetishism, showing that in both cases it is a question of *homologous* significant structures.

It has been clear for a long time that the novel was the principal literary form corresponding to bourgeois society and that its evolution was closely linked to the history of that society. No one, however, to our knowledge, has better succeeded in exposing the intelligible link which engenders this correspondence.

We think that the comparison between the Lukacsian analysis of the novel and the analyses of value and of merchandise fetishism in the first chapters of *Das Kapital* permit us to advance a little in the elucidation of this problem and also permit a clarification of one of the most important chapters in dialectic epistemology.

Let us begin by tracing schematically the Lukacsian analysis of the novel as a significant structure, an analysis which Lukacs himself limits to a portion of romanesque literature, eliminating what he calls decadent forms, *escape literature* (*littérature de divertissement*), but in which he tries, wrongly it seems to us, to include one of the most important romanesque forms, i.e., the work of Balzac.[8]

The romanesque form analyzed by Lukacs is at once characterized, as we have already said, by the community and by the radical antagonism between the hero and the world: the *community* has its basis in the common decadence of both in regard to the authentic values which govern the work, to the absolute, to the divinity; the *antagonism* is based on the different and opposed nature of this decadence.[9]

In regard to authentic values, the world is conventional and radically decadent, devoid of all which might be a homeland, a hearth for the soul; the hero, on the contrary, remains bound to these values even though in an indirect and decadent manner, a manner which Lukacs will call "demoniac" as opposed to an immediate bond, to the positive, the divine.

We will perhaps clarify the analysis of this structure by saying that the values which govern the work are nowhere explicitly manifested: neither in the world, nor in the consciousness of the hero. That is why the romanesque structure analyzed by Lukacs is a literary form of *absence*. And yet these values act effectively within the universe of the work which they govern *implicitly*.

Their only manifest presence is in the consciousness of the author, where moreover, they are only presented in the peculiar and insufficient manner of *conceptual*,

---

[7]Erich Kohler, *Ideal und Wirklichkeit in der Höfischen Epik.*

[8]The pages which Lukacs consecrates to Balzac are incontestably penetrating and full of useful information. It is nonetheless true that in accepting them in their entirety, they are a description of certain traits in the romanesque form to which is lacking the problematic individual who, very justly, constitutes according to Lukacs the central element of all the other works that he analyzes.

[9]It is not a question, of course, of preconceived values on the part of the critic or the reader, but of values which govern the structure of the work and which could differ from one work to another.

ethical, "*should-be*" necessity, and not as realities entirely and effectively lived; without which, the author would probably have written an epic poem and not a novel.

No writer could, in effect, create a valid work by posing problems which he himself had already resolved. That is why, if the novel were only the testimony of past experience, if the values were presented in a non-problematic way in his own consciousness, the author could and should have presented them in the work itself. It is thus the insufficiency, the problematical character of the values, not only in the consciousness of the hero, but also in that of the author, that explains the birth of the romanesque form.

A history of a problematic and demoniac search which cannot end because the end would exceed the rupture between the hero and the world and by that, exceed the romanesque universe, the novel is a biographical form *par excellence* and at the same time a social chronicle to the extent that this search takes place within a given society.

There is, no doubt, a necessary and organic end in any authentic novel. But this end, of which the death of the hero is only the symbolic expression, results from the latter's awareness of the vain and demoniac character of his earlier hopes, and not from any effectively discovered harmony.

This is a common element of the three fundamental types of novels which Lukacs distinguishes in his work. The novel of abstract idealism, of the demoniac character with too narrow a consciousness for the complexity of the world, (*Don Quixote* or *Le Rouge et le Noir*); the psychological novel with the passive hero whose soul is too broad to adapt itself to the world (*Education Sentimentale*); and the educative novel of conscious renunciation which is neither resignation nor despair (*Wilhelm Meister* or *Der Grüne Heinrich*). The romanesque form thus implies what Lukacs calls the irony of the author in regard to his work, an irony which results from the fact that this author is at once aware of the vain and demoniac nature of the search of the hero, the conventional character of the world in which this search takes place, the insufficiency of the final conversion, and the conceptual aspect of the values as they exist in his own consciousness.

Thus the hidden character of the values which govern the romanesque structure characterizes not only that structure but also the larger structure—essential for its comprehension—which at once encompasses the author and his work.

The hero of the novel is a *problematic* being, a fool or a criminal, because he is always looking for absolute values without knowing them and without living them integrally and without being able, as a consequence, to approach them. A search which is always progressing without ever advancing, a movement which Lukacs has defined by the formula: "The road has been covered, the journey begins."

In the analysis of the second type of novel, that of the passive hero with too vast a consciousness in relation to the narrow world in which he lives, Lukacs introduces a problematic which will have a primordial importance for philosophic thought in the twentieth century: *temporality*. There also it is not a question of an original discovery, and Lukacs does not present it as such, but refers explicitly to Hegel and to Bergson.

And yet, there is a notable difference between the thought of these two philosophers and Lukacsian analysis, a difference which is all more worthy of note as it is the most important point which separates this eminently Hegelian book from the effective thought of Hegel. While time has a positive and progressive significance for Hegel and Bergson in that it is a means of accomplishment and realization, Lukacs envisions it in the *Theory of the Novel* only as a process of continuing decadence, as a screen which is interposed between man and the absolute.

However, like all the constitutive elements of that dialectical structure which is the romanesque structure, temporality also has a nature at once negative and positive. A progressive degradation of the hero, it is at the same time a passage from a first inferior form to a more authentic and clearer form of the consciousness of the problematic and mediated relations of the soul with values and with the absolute, from authentic and illusory *hope*, which guided the search to the *memory*, conscious at once of the vanity and the authenticity of this hope, an authenticity which is itself problematic and contradictory, because it resides in the nature of the search and not in the possibility of accomplishment.

The novel thus presents itself as a dialectic structure characterized by the fact that nothing in it is unequivocal: neither the problematic hero who is searching, in an inauthentic, decadent way, for absolute values; nor the world which, while being conventional and fixed, retains a character sufficiently positive for the hero's search to be possible in it; nor time which, while being a proess of decomposition and decadence, retains a complex and mediated relation with the authentic values in the double form of illusory hope and conscious memory despoiled of illusion; nor the consciousness of the writer which is— and this is one of the particular characteristics of the romanesque form—a constitutive element of the work, a consciousness itself problematic, normative, a "should-be" in a structure of which the epic character denies the "should-be" and makes of it a non-value.

The *Theory of the Novel* is limited to the analysis of the romanesque structure as a significant essence which it scarcely relates to the historical conditions in which this structure appeared and developed. Only a few passages allude, not to real history, but to a transcendental Becoming to which would correspond an essential succession of "forms": epopee, tragedy, philosophy, novel. In this sense, Lukacs' book is no doubt idealistic, and the dogmatic "Marxists", who recognize books as valuable only to the extent that they are 100 percent "orthodox" and faithful to all the commas of the Master, and see books as without value to the extent that they are heretical or strangers to Marxism, are no doubt right in putting the first works of Lukacs in the second category.

They are merely forgetting that Marx himself, far from denying *in toto* the results of contemporary or earlier theoretical works, had utilized a number of them which he has partially integrated in his own work. To say that the *Theory of the Novel* is an idealistic work is no doubt true, but is of only limited interest. The importance is to know what is its value as a limited and partial study and to what measure, (admitting as we do, that valid analysis ought to be global, historic and dialectic), the significant structure disengaged by Lukacs constitutes, not a final stage, but an important step in its elaboration.

Now it happens that it is only by beginning with the work of Lukacs and going beyond it, obviously, that a dialectic and Marxist analysis of the romanesque form is revealed as possible, and that this analysis allows us not just to understand the genesis of this form, but to integrate it into the Marxist study of capitalistic society and even to clarify certain elements in the latter.

Lukacsian description of the romanesque structure, a description written with no implicit or explicit reference to Marxism, is in effect *rigorously homologous* with the description of the free market as it has been elaborated in *Das Kapital* (notably in the passages on merchandise fetishism) in such a way that the relationship, long recognized, between the history of the novel and the history of the bourgeoisie becomes, if not entirely, at least partially comprehensible.

The romanesque universe is described by Lukacs as a world which could not have a positive hero for the simple reason that all the values which govern it are *implicit* and that, in regard to these values, all the people in the novel have a character at once negative and positive. To which must be added the existence of a radical opposition between the world, conventional and without significance, whose relation with the values is mediated in the extreme and just sufficient to permit the epic structure, and the problematic hero, whose life consists uniquely of the search, decadent and demoniac, for these authentic values.

The possibility of inserting the *Theory of the Novel* in a global Marxist analysis is justified by the later evolution of Lukacs himself who, after having joined the Hungarian Communist party in 1918 and having been the peoples' commissar in the Bela Kun government, published in 1923 one of the most important and most discussed of Marxist works: *History and Class Consciousness*.

The historical events surrounding the publication of this book are fairly well known in the European intellectual circles. Hardly had it appeared when it caused an extraordinary reaction, and gave birth to a sort of theoretical "school" whose principal representatives were: Karl Korsch, Herbert Marcuse and Karl Mannheim, but it also elicited very energetic reactions in the traditional Marxist milieux linked to the great international currents of social-democracy and communism. The communist party of which Lukacs was a member officially condemned the work, and Lukacs, who did not wish to repudiate it, accepted a sort of "gentlemen's agreement"; he stopped writing and the party forebore asking him his theoretic opinions. It was only much later, in the face of the growing Fascism in Germany and especially after its victory, that Lukacs, sincerely modifying his positions, would himself criticize his first theoretical works and to begin to write anew.

It is from this time that the second period — quantitatively by far the most important—of his work dates, a period entirely different from the first.

Unfortunately, Lukacs' situation within Marxist thought since he had begun to write again has elicited some misunderstandings. For, on the one hand, official communists have always regarded him with a certain suspicion and distrust because of his past which they are unwilling to believe he has entirely repudiated, and on the other hand, the "oppositionals" and nonorthodox Marxists as well have often imagined that his "submission" was purely on the surface and that he was writing works contrary to his most intimate convictions.

These suppositions were of course erroneous. Nevertheless they had for the history of ideas and for Lukacs' own attitudes unhappy consequences, restraining his liberty of expression in the extreme. Suspected of defending, even in a veiled and partial manner, his former positions dating from *History and Class Consciousness*, Lukacs has had to establish beyond any doubt the fact that he had totally abandoned them, and no longer cares to refer to the valid, even ingenious scientific and methodological ideas developed in this work. In the same way, suspect in the eyes of the directors of a party to which he belongs, he has limited himself in his publications to philosophic and literary critiques, enjoying even there a much more restricted freedom of expression than any other member of this party who does not have to bear the onus of such a past.

Leaving aside however, the numerous and no doubt important but secondary details resulting from the situation, it suffices to state that while *History and Class Consciousness* defends political positions which have been later exposed as erroneous, this book has a capital importance far beyond these errors for all it has contributed to philosophic thought and especially to the methodology of the human sciences.

It is noteworthy that many people attribute to those who praise this book on the scientific level, the political ideas which are defended in it and which may be totally foreign to them and, inversely, distrust its scientific methodology because they refuse its political themes.

On the methodological level, the importance of *History and Class Consciousness* resides in the decisive progress which Lukacs made by replacing the *phenomenological* idea of significant *atemporal* structure which had dominated the preceding historical works, by the Marxist and dialectical concept of significant temporal structure and a dynamic founded on the idea of totality, and by developing from this the two other fundamental Marxist concepts of *possible consciousness* (*Zugerechnetes Bewusstsein*) and *objective possibility*, with which the human sciences acquired at last the status of operative and positive disciplines[9].

Totality, significant dynamic structures, the necessity of genetic study of these structures, the use of the future as an explicative factor of the present, the maximum of possible consciousness, objective possibility: no doubt none of these concepts in particular, nor their global synthesis represent new discoveries; these are constitutive concepts in the work of Marx, and Lukacs presents them, moreover, as such.

But as he himself remarks, the majority of these, and most notably totality, were absent from the *Anti-Dühring* and also, we might add, from Lenin's *Materialism and Empirical Criticism*. Now, in the last instance, it is the *Anti-Dühring* and not the writings of Marx which had formed Marxist thought in the European socialist parties. In this sense, Lukacs' work broke with an already old and solidly established tradition, to return to the sources. Nothing could better illustrate the

---

[9]See on this subject Lucien Goldmann: *The Human and Philosophical Sciences*, P.U.F. 1962. Le Dieu caché, Gallimard 1956. Recherches dialectiques, Gallimard 1958. English translation *The Hidden God*, P. Thody, New York Humanities Press.

importance of the work than this fact which today seems to us almost inconceivable: coming into a discussion between the principal Marxist thinkers on the philosophy which best corresponded to historical materialism, a discussion in which Kautsky preconized the thought of Darwin, Bernstein, Max Adler, and a number of others less well known Marxists, the philosophy of Kant, Plekhanov, that of Spinoza and Feuerbach, the team of Russian thinkers against whom Lenin would write *Materialism and Empirical Criticism*, the thinking of Mach and Avenarius, Lenin himself, a mechanical materialism quite close to Feuerbach[10], Lukacs was, with perhaps the one exception of Antonio Labriola, the first to point out that the philosophy closest to Marxism was the Hegelian dialectic.

In fact, it is certain that even on the methodological level, Lukacs' work goes too far in the Hegelian sense by affirming the *total identity between subject and object* on the level of social life and knowledge of society. No doubt this idealistic and Hegelian formula, much too radical and difficult to defend on the level of positive science, is related to the faulty political judgments of the work, judgments of which we will speak later.

On this point we have been led to propose a more moderate formula, that of the *partial identity between subject and object*, an identity the nature of which is variable in each particular case and which it is necessary to clarify at the moment that one undertakes the study of it.

One must not however forget that the most important methodological error of the positivist sociology which still today dominates most western universities as well as mechanistic Marxism, be it of Stalinist or social democratic hue, has been precisely the *opposite* affirmation of the *radical difference* between the subject and the object, and the possibility of an objective sociology for which the discordant intervention of value judgments would only be very frequent, but avoidable, accidents.

Within this perspective and given this evolution, Lukacs' idealism in *History and Class Consciousness* no doubt seems erroneous to us, but the error is much less serious than the scientistic and mechanistic position which has sterilized Marxist thought for the past thirty-five years.

On the level of concrete research, the work, like all Lukacs' books, contains a great number of remarkable analyses, the most important of which seems to us to be that of *reification*.

There too, Lukacs is only re-examining a Marxian theory, elaborated in *Das Kapital* (to which he explicitly alludes), a theory whose operative value in the realms of epistemology and the study of the artistic, literary and intellectual life, he demonstrates.

On the political level, Lukacs, who has in this work identified the revolution as a global "form", as a significant dynamic structure, places himself, with certain corrections imposed by the experience of Bolshevism and the Russian revolution, within the perspective of a current most notably represented by Rosa Luxemburg, for whom Europe, and beyond Europe, the world, is faced with the imminent

---

[10]*Cahiers sur la Dialectique* was not yet known in the West.

prospect of a worldwide revolution exclusively proletarian in character. Now, the stabilization of western capitalism after 1923, the fact that territorial extension of the socialist societies took place only much later, after World War II, and that it took place almost exclusively in countries which were industrially underdeveloped and predominantly peasant, clearly proved the erroneous nature of this judgment. That is why it seems to us that there is reason to be astonished at what point partisans and adversaries are still—even while they admit that Lukacs is a very great thinker—suspicious about his criticism of a position, the erroneous nature of which must be evident on the slightest serious reflection.

Finally, on the philosophic level, Lukacs, with *History and Class Consciousness,* arrives at Marxist positions which he will definitively retain thereafter.

In the last analysis, Lukacs has always been a great essayist. However important have been the positive analyses of those significant structures—Tragedy, Essay, Novel and Revolution—they constituted for him only a first level: the exposure "at the instance" of realities from which he could formulate, on the conceptual level, questions and reflections which seemed to him important concerning human life and its meaning.

If the consciousness of the limits of solitude and death seem to him the fundamental categories which permit the meaning of the human condition to be grasped at the time that he wrote *The Soul and Forms*, if absence, contradiction and problematic existence were the categories of *The Theory of the Novel*, study of revolution in *History and Class Consciousness* allowed him to formulate a philosophy based on the community, the future, and an objectively-founded hope of authentic values, values which could be realized through revolutionary action on the part of the proletariat and humanity.

Kant, Hegel, Marx; through his three books, Lukacs has re-traveled on his own the road of classic German philosophy.

For long years, during which he had disappeared from intellectual and philosophic life, the problems which he raised would be at the center of a powerful philosophic renaissance which would plunge its roots into the profound crisis of western bourgeois society and into the anguish that this would excite among the bourgeois thinkers.

It is certainly not accidental that the two most important thinkers of this renaissance, Heidegger and Jaspers, belong to the same generation as Lukacs and come from the same restricted academic milieu, the philosophic school of Southwest Germany.

We do not think that one can understand this philosophic renaissance, anguished and decadent as it was, if one does not take into account the fact that it was permanently formulated during the temporary absence of the one thinker who, forgotten and in the silence of retirement, nevertheless had foreshadowed it, tracing the framework and outlining the scope of discussion, and the problems which it would concern, but who had always affirmed the dignity of man, the value of a clear conscience, of courage and hope.

Much later, toward 1933-36, Georg Lukacs would again undertake a considerable project, which is, however, within an entirely different context, and which, of all the former discussions, would allude only to that of another thinker, Ernest Bloch, who has also moved closer to Marxism though never integrally adhering to it.

We do not here have the time or space to analyze either this discussion, centered about the historic value of the clear conscience and utopic illusions (Lukacs defends the first, Bloch the second), or the properly communist works of Lukacs after 1932.

That does not mean, of course, that these relate to questions of secondary importance and we hope to be able to study them in the near future. Our primary concern here has been to situate *The Theory of the Novel* and to stress its importance for the understanding of the intellectual history of the 20th century in general and philosophic thought in particular[11].

[11]To obviate any possible misunderstanding, let us emphasize that, in regard to *History and Class Consciousness*, Lukacs has modified his positions not only in regard to political analyses and the affirmation of the identity of subject and object, but also concerning the critique of Engels, and that he today defends the dialectical character of the natural sciences. We cannot follow him on this last point.

LUCIEN GOLDMANN is one of the leading Marxist literary critics in Europe today. Born in Bucharest, he received his secondary education in Rumania, later emigrated to France. He received his law degree in Paris, his PhD. from the University of Zurich, and his Docteur des Lettres in Paris. He is now a French citizen. He has lectured widely in Europe, as well as in Canada, the United States and Mexico. In addition, as Visiting Professor, he has taught at the Universities of Montreal, Brussels, West Berlin and Johns Hopkins, in Baltimore. He is currently Director of Research at the Institute de Sociologie, University of Brussels. Mr. Goldmann's works have been widely translated, and include studies of Racine, the philosophy of Kant, and most recently, the important *Pour une sociologie du roman* (Gallimard, 1965). The article here reproduced was written to accompany the French translation of Georg Lukacs' *Theory of the Novel* (Editions Gonthier, Switzerland, 1963).

translated by Teresa Fand

Amor 43

MAREK HLASKO

The boy was nine, he was in love and he knew that it was forever. Anyway, he told his father about it, first asking him to keep it a secret but later, giving in to father, agreed to disclose it to his mother, even though he seriously doubted that mother would understand. The girl whom he loved was called Eva; she was one month and twelve days younger than he. She lived with her parents in the next house and she used to come to see him in the evenings.

'Can't you come earlier?'—he asked one day.

'No'—she said.

'Why?'

'My father doesn't let me. I am allowed to go out only when it's dark.'

'I'll have a talk with your father'—said the boy.

'He won't agree'.

'We'll see'.

They were sitting in the shed where once the boy had kept rabbits until some-one broke in at night and took them away. After that he no longer wanted to raise rabbits, he only asked his father to be allowed to keep the shed and to arrange it for himself and to promise that no one should ever enter there, and his father agreed and only asked if in autumn the boy would permit the wood which they were to saw together to be dumped there. So it was agreed. Now they were sitting together on a pile of sawdust—loose, bright, and fragrant; it was evening, silent, and he felt his heart beat and also the beating of her heart. When one is nine, one does not yet know what desire is, for at that time curiosity about another's body and amazement take the place of desire and it is then that one's throat goes dry, one's heart beats faster; and the hair on one's head stands upright as on a dog's back. But the boy did not know that this curiosity is stronger than desire. He sat next to the girl on a pile of sawdust, passed his hands over her body, and knew only that he was in love for the remainder of his days.

'Come earlier tomorrow'—he said.

'I'll try'.

'Are you sure you wouldn't like me to have a talk with your father?'.

'Father is ill'—she said. 'Perhaps another time'.

'Tomorrow I will find it out'—he said.

'From whom?'

'From a fellow who used to go to school with me'—he said. 'I am going to see him tomorrow. I said I would give him the cages for it.' The boy sighed. 'He didn't want to tell me anything until he saw the cages first.'

'Do you think he knows?'

'He knows for sure'—he said. 'You know who it is? It's Nadera.

'Nadera'—repeated the girl.

'Yes'—he whispered. 'It's the other Nadera's brother, you know. His father works on the railway. When he goes out, he locks the other one in the cellar or chains him down by his leg. He is already seventeen, the bigger Nadera. And this one is his brother. He will tell me'.

'Do you think that we'll be able to do it?'

'If only he tells us how. And he is sure to tell us. Do you see these cages? My father and I made them; you only have to pull the string and they open'. He suddenly turned and looked at her but could only see the glitter of the saw which stood in the corner.

'Are you going to be afraid?'—he asked.

'I don't know'—she said.

'When you have a child, they'll have to let you out during the day'—he said. 'Your folks. They won't have a thing to say. You'll be grown up and you'll be able to do as you please'.

'I have to go now'—she said.

'Yes'—he said. 'I'll walk home with you'.

The next day he waited; he was impatient, angry but there was no sign of his friend. It was evening again and dark; he was with Eva, sitting on the pile of sawdust which was warm from their bodies, and then he heard the whistle. He got up and went out into the courtyard.

'Why so late?'—he asked.

'I couldn't make it earlier'—said the other. 'Father got drunk and was raising hell at home. Now he's asleep. Where are the cages?'

'Come on'—said the boy.

They entered the shed.

'This is Nadera's brother'—the boy told Eva. 'The one whose father chains him down. He has come for the cages!'

'But I have to go'—said the girl.

'Don't you want to wait?'

She shook her head.

'Excuse me'—said the boy to his friend. 'We have a secret. Just a minute'.

'I'll have a look at these cages'—said the other.

'O.K.'

He took the girl into a corner.

'Why don't you want to wait?'—he asked. 'After all, he has come especially in order to tell us.'

'If I don't go home now, tomorrow they won't let me out at all'—she whispered.

'You don't know my father.'

He squeezed her hand.

'Yes'—he said. 'Go back. Meanwhile I'll take care of everything here. But come earlier tomorrow'.

'Will it take us long?'—she asked.

'I don't know'—he said. 'You know that I have never done it before. But a child is a child. I don't suppose that it's as quick as all that.'

The girl left. Nadera followed her with his eyes until she went inside the house and closed the door.

'Who's this bird?'—he asked.

'A girl, that's all'—said the boy.

'From Warsaw?'

'Yes'.

'She is black'—said the friend pensively. 'Her hair is black and her eyes are black'.

The boy placed his left foot forward and pressed his chin to his chest.

'You don't think she is pretty?'—he asked. 'Just say that you don't think so'.

The other gave him a sudden blow in his stomach, but knowing him, the boy was not unprepared. His father had taught him a bit how to fight; he now jumped towards the other one, twice hit him hard and jumped back remembering about the footwork and that the foot should follow the movement of the hand.

'I'm going to tell my brother'—sobbed the other.

'I'm not afraid of your brother'—shouted the boy, at this moment he believed what he was saying; he was holding the other one by the lapels of his coat and was shaking him. 'I'm not afraid of anyone, not anyone'. Then he pushed him away and the other ran across the yard.

He entered the house holding up his blood-stained hands to the light.

'Did you fall down?'—asked the father.

'No'—he said. 'I had a fight with Nadera's brother.'

'What about?'

'What?'

'You know very well. I am asking, what was it all about?'

'I can't tell you'—said the boy quietly.

'You can't tell me?'

He pleadingly pointed towards his mother.

'I can't'—he said.

'That's different'—said the father. 'Go to bed'.

And later when the boy was already in bed, he sat down and leaned over him. 'Did you tell him where Eva lives?'—he asked.

'He knows'—said the boy.

'And do you know?'

'What, daddy?'

'Do you know who Eva is?'

'Eva?'—repeated the boy. 'What do you mean, daddy?'

'Nothing'—said the father, 'that's good. But this Nadera. I think he works for the Germans. Anyway, that is what people say'. Suddenly he rose and went towards the wardrobe; he pulled out a rucksack, sheepskin and ski-cap. 'They won't harm you'—he said. 'But I prefer to disappear for a few days. And he said to mother: 'Go there and tell them that it would be better if they, too, are not seen during the next few days. I am afraid of these Naderas. I may be wrong, but I prefer to wait this out.'

Mother went out.'

'Did you know daddy'—said the boy, 'that this Nadera is tied down with a chain when his father goes out? And once he even locked him in a cellar and Nadera sat there for three days.' Then he forgot Nadera; he only thought with regret that he failed to find out what he wanted to know and that Eva will have to wait a while longer and leave her house only at dusk. He did not hear his mother return.

'Well?'—asked the father.

'They don't want to go away'—she said. 'They say that they have nowhere to go. And that it's bound to happen sooner or later. She looked at his thickened, dark hands which were struggling with the string of the rucksack. 'And you want to go now?'—she said.

'In any case I would be unable to defend you'—he said. 'You won't be harmed. I am certain. But they are going to clobber those over there'.

'Isn't there anything that can be done?'

'It's too early now to talk about that'—he said. 'We will think about it when the war is over. Perhaps God will preserve the Germans and He is certain to do so. I think that God needs them more than any other nation and for this reason he will preserve them. So that everyone will know and feel what evil looks like. If only for one reason, so that it will be possible to choose goodness.'

'You ought not to speak like that'—she said. 'If ever you are to teach again, I hope that it won't be this sort of thing.'

'I was a bad teacher'—he said. 'But I did learn something, after all. When the war is over I shall talk about it. And now I am going out to kill them and pray to God to preserve them. I'll keep in touch.' He slung the rucksack on his shoulder, went up to the boy and kissed him. Then he went over to the stove, cautiously removed one of the tiles and took out a pistol wrapped in a greasy cloth. 'Tomorrow take some plaster and replace this tile'—he said.

'May the Lord be with you'.

'Yes, the Lord'—he said. 'And tell him to watch carefully when they kill them. Let him look and learn. And let him remember them all his life.'

The father went out quietly closing the door behind him. But the boy slept soundly and did not hear his father leave. He did not even hear them when they drove up to the house at four in the morning; he did not even hear their voices and banging on the door and the barking of the dog; he continued to sleep, unaware of their presence and the noise which at four in the morning they brought with them, acting according to the principle that any hour is suitable for the victors. He awakened only when his mother shook him and he sat up in bed, alert and rested like a young animal.

'Get dressed'—said the mother.

'But it's Sunday'—said the boy.

'Yes'—said the mother. 'You can go back to sleep later, but get up right now.'

He put on his clothes and went out of the house. He wanted to run towards the car but his mother caught him by the hand. She stood on the veranda of the old wooden house and breathed loudly; he could feel the warmth of her palm.

'What's going to happen?'—he asked. 'Is anything wrong, mommy?' She did not answer, so he repeated: 'Is anything wrong?'

He looked at the car glistening with dew, at the dog lying with its tongue hanging out and at the gun barrels; then he softly whistled and the dog raised his sensitive pointed ears. The policeman who had been standing on the side, now stepped forward and said,

'Follow us'.

'Where are you taking us?'—asked the boy's mother.

'It's not far'—said the policeman. 'You will look on for a bit and then you may go home.'

'I will go alone'—said the mother. 'It's not necessary for a child to see such things. You understand that.'

The policeman hesitated for a moment.

'We have our orders'—he said unwillingly. 'They said everyone was to watch. It's to be an example'.

They walked behind the policeman and the Germans. His mother kept on holding his hand and the boy was embarrassed; he attempted to free himself a second time, but his mother held him tightly. He was sorry that his father was not there; father would never do a thing like that. At most, he would simply put his hand on his shoulder and then it would look like two friends walking home together from work.

Then they stood and watched how Eva's father and the farmer in whose house he lived dug a hole, working rapidly and in silence. He saw Eva, whose mother was holding her by the hand in the same way as his mother, and he threw himself in her direction, but mother was stronger. So he stood and he looked. He saw one of the Germans go up to Eva who was crying and stroke her head.

'Bring her a doll'—he said to the policeman.

'A doll?'—the policeman was surprised.

'Yes'—said the German. 'Something to play with'.

The policeman entered the house and after a moment came out holding a plush bear.

'How old is she?'—the German asked Eva's mother.

'Eight.'

The German handed her the bear and now Eva stood there holding the bear.

'Now there'—he said. 'Don't be afraid. Do you know the story about the wolf and the seven kids? No? One day Mother-goat said to her children: "Don't open the door for anyone while I am gone," and she left. Then the wolf came up to the house and knocked on the door with his paw. "Who is there?" asked the kids. And he answered "It is me, your grandmother". "But why is your voice so low grandmother?"—asked the kids. . .'

The policeman went up to him and said:

'It's ready. Do they have to undress?'

'No'—said the German.

The policeman reached out his hand in Eva's direction.

'Give me that bear, little girl'—he said.

'Why are you taking it away from her?'—asked the German.

'I wanted it for my child'—said the policeman.

'Don't you see that this also is a child'—said the German. 'You certainly are a strange man. You ought to be ashamed of yourself.'

Afterwards they were walking back to the house, and crying the boy now was glad that his mother was with him and not his father. Because he would have been ashamed to cry in front of his father, and he had to cry and could do nothing to stop himself. During the next few days the partisans killed Nadera and his oldest son; on the platform of the railway station some young man shot a German to death in broad daylight, and some Jewish family committed suicide by lying down on the rails at night. The boy knew all this, heard about it all, and gradually began to forget. Although from time to time he cried, especially at those times when he reminded himself that never, never would he be able to have a wife and children, for he had sworn fidelity and that he is in love for life.

MAREK HLASKO (b. 1934) became widely known in Poland with the publication of his fine collection of short-stories *First Step in the Clouds* (1957). In 1958, during a trip to Germany the Polish authorities refused to extend his passport. Since then Hlasko has been living abroad, currently in West Berlin. His books translated into English include: *The Eighth Day of the Week, The Graveyards,* and *Next Stop Paradise*. TERESA FAND is an American of Polish origin, a specialist on Russian literature. Many of her translations from Russian and Polish were published in American journals. Now she is teaching Russian literature at Sheffield University, England.

On artistic freedom

LACO NOVOMESKY

YES, WE HAVE to learn everything, to master all the techniques, go elsewhere, look around, but then we must speak about ourselves. We sometimes
show a certain inclination to autarchy which is, of itself, nonsensical, but still
based on our situation. The one and only way of overcoming this is progress at
home. But we must never confuse national pride with national arrogance; the
story of the "people's party"[1] no doubt taught everyone that this can only
result in harm. Yet here again: such trends can, and must be corrected by the
Slovak environment. . . .

It is just this everlasting conflict, this quarrel—if you wish—which is characteristic of our national cultural life. I would say straight away that in this also
lies a justification for the side-by-side existence of two national cultures: in
their dialogue and in how they quarrel with each other, how everything in them
always appears in two aspects, seen by two pairs of eyes. This is no America,
even Stur[2] knew that and, of course, Salda[3] who used to say about himself that
he did not understand "Slovak affairs", although he understood them in their
substance as only few others did. It was he who, in a dispute with someone else,
pertinently pointed out the inevitability of Czech and Slovak creative work—
whether literary or otherwise—being in constant quarreling touch, in dispute
through which they both grow.

A certain Slovak national modesty is, of course, very appropriate in order to
stop every querulous grumbler from claiming a right to chastise, though he himself is not capable of sweeping his own door-step and tidying up his own house.
And this tidiness means, among other things, if not first of all, the ability to distinguish between friendly and suitable advice and quarrelsome grumbling.

But the same thing applies vice versa too. In Czech quarters there is again the
same old tendency towards condescension for their backward younger little

---

(1) "People's Party (the Hlinka-Party)—autonomist and later separatist Slokak clerical party, became the
ruling party in the Slovak Republic in 1939-1945 when it collaborated with Hitler's Reich.

(2) *Ludovit Stur* (1815-1856), Slovak writer and political and cultural leader mainly in the Revolution of
1848-49; together with *J. M. Hurban* and *M. M. Hodza* they established the use of Central Slovak as
literary language.

(3) *F. X. Salda*, Czech literary critic.

brother, and that is no better. I lived in a Czech environment, with Czech people —e.g. in Devetsil[4]—where all this was absolutely clear to us and none of us thought of me being a Slovak and you being a Czech. I was always far more interested for instance in Czech poetry, in an effort to find its specific characteristics, than in disputes or quarrels about national differentiation.

A sort of ethnic arithmetic has found its way among us today: two Czechs here, one Slovak there, and I believe this to be a basically unsound thing which is merely a substitute for what ought to be, but is not self-evident: to till the common field, to breathe the same air. All this should be replaced by a different formula as soon as possible, by a formula based on quality. After all, Fulla[5] is just as important for the Czechs as Síma[6] is for us. . .

Ethnic motives are, of course, absurd in these relations. But the strange absurdity of all this arithmetic begins at the moment at which there are in Czechoslovakia such artists as Fulla, Bazovsky[7] or for that matter Filcík—and we, instead of trying to make them into at least a national institution, if not an European one, allow them to fry in our own fat at home. In the end, someone remembers them merely because of that proportionate arithmetic and not because of the high quality of their work which has been beyond doubt for a long time.

We once stood in opposition, in unambiguous opposition and that was, of course, a very firm cement, more so than any family kinship. Sometimes it happened to be just two people frequenting the same cafe as the others, and through them oozed in both directions. And those two again incessantly dragged with them once Nezval,[8] another time Teig to, let us say, Ružomberok[9] or who knows where, and our national community was thereby refreshed.

But during the war and after something happened. Both communities developed in a different way, on the Czech side there were hard feelings because of 1939,[10] and the Rising[11] was accepted as an essentially good thing and, at the same time, as a means of vindication. But that wasn't it at all. The Slovaks were vindicating first and foremost themselves through the Rising and, after all, also undoing the consequences of the mistakes of Czech bourgeois policy. . . . How to undo the consequences of those years? In my view there is no other way but to show that some sort of "transgression" should be sought not merely among the Slovaks, but also to show that many a Czech also has, in the past, his share of guilt; and the voices against Czech mistakes, and any echo of these which lingers even today, must come from the Czech ranks; because anything else would be

(4) *Devetsil*, Chech leftist literary circle of the 1920's.

(5) *Ludo Fulla*, Slovak painter.

(6) *Sima*, Czech painter.

(7) *Milos A. Bazovsky*, Slovak painter.

(8) *Vitezslav Nezval*, Czech surrealist poet.

(9) *Ružomberok*, a small town in Slovakia.

(10) 1939, the year in which the Slovaks seceded from the Czechs, then occupied by the Germans.

(11) The Slovak Rising of September-October 1944.

quite ineffective.

After all, nowhere in the world have the most progressive trends in culture become a state ideology. They didn't in our country either. Everything was simply pigeon-holed, added-up, the letter prevailed over the law. . . .

We shall understand the syndrome of these problems better if we approach it through the criteria of state interests. In the autumn of 1944 I went to London and, in the negotiations with Beneš, I demanded, together with the delegation of the Slovak National Council,[12] certain guarantees for Slovakia. Later we also discussed the matter with Comrade Gottwald, and I shall never forget telling him: We Slovaks must at last get ourselves out of a situation in which we stand between the goal-posts and are incessantly compelled to watch out so that the Slovak team will not be scored against. But the fear remains that Slovak interests and affairs will not duly be taken into consideration. Incidentally, this is also the result of Czech indifference to the whole problem.

I used to say to myself frequently in jail: why do they brand just me as a nationalist when I was always in favour of the aforesaid attitude? But my nationalism was perhaps something else; I knew that it was essential to stand between the goal-posts, no matter how much I desired this not to be necessary. And finally, Slovak nationalism is unthinkable without Czech chauvinism, paternalism, indifference. Without them it would be nothing, and would itself die. They are simply two linked vessels: if you pour something into one of them, the level rises in the other one. Of course, for many people communism simply covered up the defects and failings of both sides and all trends which, somehow, had got themselves under the same hat. Until we understand and disentangle all this, we shall still have to swallow all sort of things. Let us constantly bear in mind that if we, the communists who rule this country, are not able to achieve a solution of these problems, or if the people have such an impression, then it is only a tiny step to them thinking they will achieve more in a different way. And if we, both Czechs and Slovaks, got on better together, on a common path, we could each shout louder at home at those who are trying to trouble the waters and to foster their own interests.

Why do I speak so much about this? We stand on the eve of the congress of the Association of Czechoslovak Writers which is also a national organisation, and somewhat involved in these problems. At the Third Congress our minds were, of course, full of other questions. The issue then was to reject socialist realism as the one and only god, and to rehabilitate those who had to be rehabilitated. The necessity to defend all that is great in literature applied just as much to the Czechs as to the Slovaks. The Slovaks realised well enough that the rehabilitation of Seifert, Holan, Halas[13] etc. was a victory for Slovak literature as well. And it would be good if it remained like this always, both in our Association and elsewhere, that is the divide should be between what is progressive and reactionary, and not between what is Czech and what is Slovak. To divide things on an ethnic level is stupid, and it is even more stupid when somebody

(12) Slovak National Council, governing body under the Rising of 1944.

(13) *Seifert, Holan, Halas,* Czech poets.

attempts to assign some to progressive and to others regressive positions on an ethnic basis.

Very much has happened since the Third Congress, Seifert has become a National Artist, Holan was published and rapidly sold out, etc. At the same time a vast, wide field was opened for creative work, for a progressive trend in literature, and this field must be defended against all who would like to restrict it. All these great gains, however, exist in relation to what was, and not in relation to what ought to be. Here and there it is said: Interpret us as you like! But what sort of criterion is this? What ought to be, will arise only when everybody will be able to write—allow me to paraphrase Brecht—that in Minsk or Prague, Bratislava, or wherever you wish there is *boredom*. Someone told me recently he did not know of any banned books or manuscripts lying about anywhere. But the issue is not merely what has already been written. There are authors who should have written but would not write because they told themselves that it would not be published anyway; or because they are worn out by their anxiety for the freedom attained at last.

Thus the writers' next task, and by no means only theirs, will be to allow and to ensure completely free expression in its fullest form. At the same time I realise quite clearly that many people do not understand certain things (e.g. painting), and they ask why "for the workers' money" etc. This, however, means a great danger for cultural growth and development. On the contrary, I would put the problem thus: when and in what legal form can a writer or publicist say a frank and critical word about things "sacrosanct" or "tabu"?

This is what the problem looks like to us communists who were always the standard-bearers of freedom. And to put it in a concrete way, my purpose is to enable a Dostoyevsky of today to become Dostoyevsky, to allow him to have his say about people's gravest conflicts even in a socialist society. After all, no system is perfect, we have already got used to that. And what about a society which is choking in its self-complacency? This is the tragedy of Soviet literature. Surely we cannot solve things simply by quoting Lenin instead of Stalin. . . .

Does such artistic freedom conceal in itself the danger of restoring capitalism? No, this is not how the way to capitalism is opened. People accepted socialism among other things in the hope that it will open for them the way to the kind of freedom of thought and expression to which capitalism did not. I am not talking of Dostoyevsky because of his views but for the sake of a concept, not for his Russian orthodoxy but because of what he gave to mankind. I would, indeed, go even further. Namely, I claim the same right for those who—though no Dostoyevskys—have a share in creating an atmosphere which must become a general atmosphere. Socialism differs from capitalism in this—that it raises those barriers which capitalism was not able to raise any more. At the same time, I naturally admit that discipline is necessary in any society, but this discipline must operate inside the mechanism which will evolve from freedom of expression and not from its restriction. To restrict, to harness is no solution. I do not, of course, idealize capitalism, those who take advantage of the opportunities it still grants are by no means official writers of that society; neither Hochhut, nor

Böll or Weiss are. But the culture of a country was seldom built by official writers. And with us, the important thing will always be who has any real value, who is marching forward, removing obstacles, clearing the way.

Our cultural policy ought to have this single aim: to be in harmony with the endeavours of avant-garde writers and artists in general. Here, of course, arises a whole complex of questions around the autonomy of culture, as it is being discussed in the West, in Italy for instance. But beware of those discussions. Let us not forget that the Italian or French communists are in opposition, and that we have in mind an autonomy of culture inside this revolutionary opposition, apart from which there is a further wide cultural area arising from different ideas. Nor do we want in our country to see communist ideology dissolving itself in a multitude of views; it should be developed within itself and should keep its integrity. But our situation differs from that of the communists in capitalist countries in this, that we, as a ruling force, are and must be simultaneously the guardians of freedom for a different view, or even an opposite one. The moment we forget this, we have forgotten a very essential premise of socialism. Where, then, are the boundaries? I should say that these stand at private ownership of the means of production and the exploitation of one man by the other. This is where the dividing line lies, but beyond it there is, on our side as well, plenty of room for widely differing views.

And finally, "cadre" criteria must never be used in art, we must always judge by the work itself. Recently, working on our encyclopedia we were faced by a Slovak writer who lived in exile, I mean Hronský.[14] From a "cadre" point of view, one would say, a clear case. But if we examine his work, what he wrote, then we find that he goes beyond himself and that in many respects he is ours. In this we are in complete agreement with Lenin. Or again, take the Church. Popes John and Paul when they approach their reforms, understandably take church interests into account first and foremost, but in no case can this be indifferent to us. They have already found a way in which a Catholic can live in socialist countries without getting himself into conflict with his own conscience, and Catholics are very important for the building of socialism[15]—surely no one is going to deny that. And socialist philosophy is strengthened only in controversy, in conflict. It must always surpass the opposing view, and when it will not surpass it, it will succumb to it. Yet, then it will not be because it allowed controversy but because it did not have enough arguments. We do not adhere to the view-point of the Church: accept my faith and I shall enable you to exist. The views of others must always be respected. After all, Marx could never have become Marx if he had lacked the basic stimulant which was conflict, the argument that drove his thinking on.

The questions of Czech and Slovak literature are common questions, nothing is only Czech or only Slovak. When one half of the house is on fire, sooner or later the other one will burn too. And that applies to everything. I have already said

---

(14) *J. C. Hronsky* (Jan Ciger), Slovak novelist, administrator of the Slovak cultural institute *"Matica Slo-venska"* till 1945 (under Slovak independence), when he went into exile. He died 1964 in the Argentine.

(15) Over 80 per cent of the Slovaks are catholics.

that when progress or reaction are at stake there are no separate Czech or Slovak issues. Well, it would be a good thing if this applied to everything, so that all would represent the whole Czechoslovak culture, that equal rights and values would prevail and that apart from administrative trivia there would be no division into Czech and Slovak. Worst of all is indifference, in this case our mutual indifference to each other's problems.

Both literatures, both cultures must permeate each other. Take for instance Talich.[16] The Czechs say that at a certain time we saved him. It is pleasant to hear this but I am also interested in the other aspect of the affair: namely that we profited by it enormously. He contributed towards the creation and development of Slovak symphonic music. We must not be lone runners, and whenever it occurs to us that we should loosen the mutual link of both literatures—for instance, in the Association—let us always go back to Salda. The warnings against possible mistakes and faults sound strong enough there.

Regarding the heritage of the twenties and thirties: I am no theoretician and what I am going to say here is evidence of the speaker himself rather than of literature. So first of all: as always when something begins, there was a lot of maximalism in all the trends, but also there was an immense devotion to the program, and great enthusiasm. Today's young generation may possibly possess all this also; and perhaps it's just we who don't see this entirely. Obviously, I wouldn't like to sigh: oh, when we were beginning. . . I see it approximately this way: the twenties followed immediately after World War I, after the Russian revolution. The years 1945-1950 came also after a world war and we were literally engulfed by revolution. And yet there was a difference; everything is somehow less explicit than in those timés. I used to explain this to myself by the fact that the social changes, all that upheaval came to us as it were much too pre-fabricated; that there was no direct demand for an answer, everything was somehow already given. Decidedly, this was no analogy of the twenties in the sense in which I speak of them on behalf of one part of my generation. Dogmatism, the personality cult and God knows what, no doubt played its part in this. But the main thing is that then we were creating, we developed a conception, whilst afterwards we only became executors of a ready-made thing. And something that could be compared with the nineteen-twenties did not come till after 1956, after the XXth Congress, quite some time after it.

What did remain? It is not merely the specific field of literature that I have in mind. What happened was a great civilization and humanisation of literature, was torn down to earth from whatever towering heights. This, naturally, did not happen at a single blow. Srámek and Neuman gave an impulse a long time ago, as if they had a presentiment of what was to come. And this impulse became rather subconsciously the property of the young ones, it was carried on through further decades. The revolution of the past is an utterly self-evident thing today, and its harbingers have become National Artists.

So what did remain? In the first place, in each of us an immense desire for free-

---

(16) *Vaclav Talich*, Czech conductor and composer, fell from favour with the Czechs after World War II, but found "sanctuary" with the Slovaks in Bratislava.

dom, freedom to think and to act, which, in the complex situations of the nineteen-forties, brought us finally into conflict. The same thing happened also to many Czech poets, artists of our generation. Quite simply, they were not capable of bearing what society was demanding from literature at the given moment. And in this also lies the solution to the mystery why, at a moment when there is relaxation, when the conflicting situation is on the wane or is taking a different shape, all of them revert to places which in fact they had occupied previously. This is both our and their sanctification and curse. We cannot change and nothing can change. This is why our cultural situation is different too, and has its separate place in the context of world socialism, it has after all its own quite distinct past, its quite distinct tradition, its quite concrete youth.

And in literature? Each of the currents of that period brought something to literature, or rather a whole lot of things; about none of them can it be said that they didn't mean anything, that they did not leave any traces. I do not agree with any unequivocal expulsion or deification, nor do I therefore agree with those who maintain that surrealism alone, and nothing but surrealism, is the foundation of the whole literary revolution from the twenties until today. This is an unnecessary absolutisation of surrealism and surrealism does not need it at all. Personally, I am for poetry to remain poetry, and to that end all methods and means are good. The future will push aside certain things, it will highlight others, but I want to stress it in its entirety. I do not, and never did, belong to the surrealists. I do not identify myself with the surrealist view of the world and understanding of the world, but I have great respect for many things it brought with it. I would say something like this: the Bible—and in it, let's say, the Song of Songs, but not only that—is great poetry, and no matter in how many different ways it has been refuted, it does not cease to be a source of attraction and inspiration for poetry.

What has changed? I am very fond of reading the manifestos of all the literary schools, but personally I do not swear by any of them. There were times after the first war when the one and only expression of being modern was blank (unrhymed) verse, the shattering of old forms, and Teige cursed Nezval for no more than *"Edison"*,[17] he accused him of having betrayed himself. But did he really betray? In my view not only did he not cease to be a great poet but on the contrary, in *"Edison"* he even grew in stature. No one, of course, blamed him for this but he too attained a virtually classic form, and if we are going to compare with *"Na vlnách TSF"*[18] for instance, then he also had "betrayed himself". However, he achieved what only the great ones do achieve: he developed the achievements of modern times and their trends, and by doing so he arrived at a Neruda-like transparency.[19] Seifert's example will be discussed for a long time yet and there may never be enough of that. Literary schools . . . they are interlaced, they permeate and take over from each other, they influence each other, and that is the very substance of artistic development.

There is, of course, the difference between the generations. One cannot after

---

(17) *Edison*, Nezval's poem.

(18) *Na vlnach TSF* (On Wireless Waves), Seifert's poem.

(19) Novomesky has in mind the Czech classic Jan Neruda.

all wish different generations to have identical feelings, and experiences. The things which used to be sacrosanct and taboo for us are seen by the new generation in an entirely different manner; it has a different hierarchy of values, it feels its whole life in a different way from us. It is a great mistake—in literature just as much as in other fields—to believe that one generation just hands over its legacy to the next one which takes it over like some relay baton and carries on . . . On the contrary, each new generation brings with it a multitude of new problems and perceptions which are—from the point of view of the previous generation— as if from a different galaxy. They will deride us, they will condemn us, and, if only for our own sake, we ought to be wise enough not to condemn them. It is a commonplace truth that in the end they will find out all sorts of things, and it is just as true that they will always love their grandfathers more than their fathers. But we must first of all respect their completely different attitude towards life.

My generation and yours had in their lives one common, related experience, war—Wilhelm or Hitler—, the post-war period; and that is why we felt so many things in a similar way even though we were looking at them from a different angle. But what about the present generation? Does it think of war or doesn't it? It impresses me by not knowing fear. And as I am advocating things where fear has no place, I most certainly would not like to appear as if I was trying to intimidate. But I wouldn't like it at all if they took the present world lightly or if they thought that words about the danger of great world conflicts should be taken as only subtleties for elderly gentlemen.

But don't let me become didactic: it isn't all that simple with those generations either. Take for instance mine. People in their sixties or fifties, they are all divided by their personal experience, attitude to life, by what one or the other of them went through or had to endure. Some of my contemporaries guard their convictions, or rather the care of their convictions, like the very light of their eyes. Others did not get themselves into this "canned" state as yet, and, according to their powers and abilities, they are still, even today, trying to accomplish what they once wanted and still want. And finally, those of the third variety sit quietly and twiddle their thumbs and are very much bewildered by the fact that the later generations are not enthusiastic about what they achieved. We can find the categories of the satisfied and the seekers in every generation, as each generation is, in fact, thus divided. The first ones do not demand anything any more, the others are still persisting in their demands. I would like to belong to these others but my powers, my powers. . .

I am not able to rise and say: look how beautiful the present is, it tends towards the future! I am not able to sing praises or to glorify. Often I have the feeling that we have believed more than we achieved, that we have promised more than we could give. Nevertheless I am still convinced that this was and is a well-chosen path. And that it will lead somewhere, no matter how muddy it is at the present moment and no matter what well paved ways there might be all around. Not because, as a socialist country, we must be right. But for many other reasons that spring from both history and the present time; ours, the Czech and the Slovak ones, as well as the world around us. I do not know why many things don't function but I think we ought to hold on to the basic things, and to direct, to shape, to solve. It isn't here a question of sticking to something at any price only because we reached out for it at some stage. But after my experience with the world I do not know any better answer than the socialist solution of its problems. The only thing to do is to find the ways which will lead to a genuine attainment of genuine socialism. That, of course, is not easy. It never was and never will be.

Agamemnon Makris (Hungarian)

LACO (LADISLAV) NOVOMESKY, Slovak communist poet and politician, together with Clementis, Ponican, Okali, Horvath and others founded in the 1920's the communist literary and political review *Dav* which attracted a group of leftist intellectuals: hence "Davisiti" (the "Davists"). During World War II Novomesky was one of the leaders of the Slovak Rising in Sept., Oct. 1944; after 1945 he held high government office but fell into disgrace with the Czech communists, together with Clementis who was hanged and the Husak group of the then younger Slovak communist leaders. (All were accused by the Czechs of "Slovak bourgeois nationalism".) He spent several years in jail, then was rehabilitated as a poet but not re-instated to political power as none of the group were. He is now one of the leaders, a sort of "elder statesman", of the rebellion of Slovak intellectuals against the Czech Communist Government of Prague, demanding the liberalisation of communism. This piece was first published in the Bratislava literary weekly *Kulturny Život* (April 22, 1966) as an interview, "Two Days with Novomesky." The interviewer and some of the commentary have been deleted from the original in the interests of space and continuity.

translated by George Theiner
MIROSLAV HOLUB

'Heat with a Little Warmth'

They take
a bit of the world,
put it
in a pan,
heat it,
stew it
in its own juice,
listen
to the fervent sizzling.

All their life
they wait
for the fried meat-ball.

But under that lid
there are
equations,
frost
and flames.

The Fly

She sat on a willow-trunk
watching
part of the battle of Crécy,
the shouts,
the gasps,
the groans,
the tramping and the tumbling.

During the fourteenth charge
of the French cavalry
she mated
with a brown-eyed male fly
from Vadincourt.

She rubbed her legs together
as she sat on a disembowelled horse
meditating
on the immortality of flies.

With relief she alighted
on the blue tongue
of the Duke of Clervaux.

When silence settled
and only the whisper of decay
softly circled the bodies

and only
a few arms and legs
still twitched jerkily under the trees,

she began to lay her eggs
on the single eye
of Johann Uhr,
the Royal Armourer.

And thus it was
that she was eaten by a swift
fleeing
from the fires of Estrées.

translated by Ian Miller

Polonius

Behind every arras
he does his duty
unswervingly.
Walls are his ears,
keyholes his eyes.

He slinks up the stairs,
oozes from the ceiling,
floats through the door
ready to give evidence,
prove what is proven,
stab with a needle
or pin on an order.

His poems always rhyme,
his brush is dipped in honey,
his music flutes
from marzipan and cane.

You buy him
by weight, boneless,
a pound of wax flesh,
a pound of mousy philosophy,
a pound of jellied
flunkey.

And when he's sold out
and the left-overs wrapped
in a tasselled obituary,
a paranoid funeral notice,

and when the spore-creating mould
of memory
covers him over,
when he falls
arse-first to the stars,

the whole continent will be lighter,
earth's axis straighten up
and in night's thunderous arena
a bird will chirp in gratitude.

MIROSLAV HOLUB is an outstanding representative of modern Czech poetry. His first works were published in 1947 but as he became better known only after 1956. He is also internationally known as a research pathologist, at present working in a New York immunological research institute. Holub's poems have been translated into many languages, recently his *Selected Poems* were published by Penguins, with an interesting introduction by A. Alvarez. All poems of Holub published here are reprints from Miroslav Holub, *Selected Poems* (Penguin Modern European Poets Series), London, 1967.

Vasko Popa

TED HUGHES

Vasko popa is a Yugoslav and was born in 1923. He studied philosophy. at the University of Belgrade and now works in a publishing house. His two published books of verse are KORA (1952), and NEPOCIN POLJE (1956), and a third SPOREDNO NEBO, is yet unpublished.

He is one of a generation of East European poets—Holub of Czechoslovakia and Herbert of Poland are perhaps two others of similar calibre—who were caught in mid-adolescence by the war. Their reaction to the mainly surrealist principles that prevailed in Continental poetry in the inter-war years was a matter of personal temperament, but it has been reinforced by everything that has since happened, to their countries in particular and in some measure (more than ever before) to human beings everywhere. Circumstantial proof that man is a political animal, a state numeral, as if it needed to be proved, has been weighed out in dead bodies by the million. The attempt these poets are making to put on record that man is also, at the same time and in the same circumstances, an acutely conscious human creature of suffering and hope, has brought their poetry down to such precisions, discriminations and humilities that it is a new thing. It seems closer to the common reality, in which we have to live if we are to survive, than to those other realities in which we can holiday, or into which we decay when our bodily survival is comfortably taken care of, and which art, particularly contemporary art, is forever trying to impose on us as some sort of superior dimension. I think it was Milosz, the Polish poet, who when he lay in a doorway and watched the bullets lifting the cobbles out of the street beside him realised that most poetry is not equipped for life in a world where people actually do die. But some is. And the poets of whom Popa is one seem to have put their poetry to a similar test.

We can guess at the forces which shaped their outlook and style. They have had to live out, in actuality, a vision which for artists elsewhere is a prevailing shape of things but only brokenly glimpsed, through the clutter of our civilised liberal confusion. They must be reckoned among the purest and most wide awake of living poets.

In a way, their world reminds one of Beckett's world. Only theirs seems braver, more human, and so more real. It is as horrible as his but they do not despair of it to the point of surrendering consciousness and responsibility to their animal cells. Their poetic themes revolve around the living suffering spirit, capable of happiness, much deluded, too frail, with doubtful and provisional senses, so undefinable as to be almost silly, but palpably existing, and wanting to go on existing—and this is not, as in Beckett's world, absurd. It is the only precious thing, and designed in accord with the whole Universe. Designed, indeed, by the whole Universe. They are not the spoiled brats of civilisation disappointed of impossible and unreal expectations and deprived of the revelations of necessity. In this they are prophets speaking somewhat against their times, though in an undertone, and not looking for listeners. They have managed to grow up to a view of the unaccommodated Universe, but it has not made them cynical, they still like it and keep all their sympathies intact. They have got back to the simple animal courage of accepting the odds and have rediscovered the frontier.

In another way, their world reminds one of the world of modern physics. Only theirs is more useful to us, in that while it is the same gulf of unknowable laws and unknowable particles, the centre of gravity is not within some postulate deep in space, or leaking away down the drill-shaft of mathematics, but inside man's sense of himself, inside his body and his essential human subjectivity, his refusal to surrender his individuality to any impersonal abstraction, political or fashionable or whatever. They refuse to sell out their arms legs hair ears body and soul and all it has suffered with them, in order to escape with some fragmentary sense, some abstract badge of self-estrangement, into a popular membership safety. They accept in a sense what the prisoner must accept, who cannot pretend that any finger is at large. Like men come back from the dead they have an improved perception, an unerring sense of what really counts in being alive.

This helplessness in the circumstances has purged them of rhetoric. They cannot falsify their experience by any hopeful effort to change it. Their poetry is a strategy of making audible meanings without disturbing the silence, an art of homing in tentatively on vital scarcely perceptible signals, making no mistakes, but with no hope of finality, continuing to explore. Finally, with delicate maneuvering, they precipitate out of a world of malicious negatives a happy positive. And they have created a small ironic space, a work of lyrical art, in which their humanity can respect itself.

Vasko Popa uses his own distinctive means. Like the others, he gives the impression of being well-accquainted with all that civilisation has amassed in the way of hypotheses. Again, like the others, he seems to have played the film of history over to himself many times. Yet he has been thoroughly stripped of any spiritual or mental proprietorship. No poetry could carry less luggage than his, or be freer of predisposition and preconception. No poetry is more difficult to outflank, yet it is in no sense defensive. His poems are trying to find out what does exist, and what the conditions really are. The movement of his verse is part of his method of investigating something fearfully apprehended, fearfully discovered. But he will not be frightened into awe. He never loses his deeply ingrained humour and irony: that is his way of hanging on to his human wholeness. And he never loses his intense absorption in what he is talking about, either. His words test their way forward, sensitive to their own errors, dramatically and intimately alive, like the antennae of some rock-shore creature feeling out the presence of the sea and the huge powers in it. This analogy is not so random. There is a primitive pre-creation atmosphere about his work, as if he were present where all the dynamisms and formulae were ready and charged, but nothing created—or only a few fragments. Human beings, as visibly and wholly such, do not appear in Popa's landscapes. Only heads, tongues, spirits, hands, flames, magically vitalised wandering objects, such as apples and and moons, present themselves, animated with strange but strangely familiar destinies. His poetry is near the world of music, where a repository of selected signs and forms, admitted from the outer world, act out fundamental combinations that often have something eerily mathematical about their progressions and symmetries, but which seem to belong deeply to the world of spirit or of the heart. Again like music, his poems turn the most grisly confrontations into something deadpan playful: a spell, a riddle, a game, a story.

He arrived at this freedom and inevitability gradually. His earliest manner often owes a lot to a familiar kind of mildly surrealist modern poesy, though it is charming in Popa, and already purposeful, as in the poem titled FORGETFULNESS, which is from a series of landscapes:

> From the distant darkness
> The plain puts out its tongue
> The uncontainable plain
>
> Spilt happenings
> Scattered withered words
> Levelled faces
>
> Here and there
> An occasional hand of smoke
>
> Sighs without care
> Thoughts without wings
> Homeless glances
>
> Here and there
> An occasional flower of mist
>
> Unsaddled shadows
> Ever more silently bury
> The hot ash of laughter

That is from his first book, KORA, but the first poem in the same book already sketches out the essential method and Universe of his much later and more characteristic work:

Don't entice me sky-blue arches
I'm not playing
You are the arch of a thirsty palate
Over my head

Ribbon of space
Don't wrap around my feet
Don't carry me away
You are a wakeful tongue
A seven-forked tongue
Beneath my footsteps
I'm not going

My innocent breathing
My winded breathing
Don't intoxicate me
I foretell the breath of the beast
I'm not playing

I hear the well-known canine blow
The blow of tooth on tooth
I feel the darkness of the jaw

That opens my eyes
I see

I see I'm not dreaming

It is all there, the surprising fusion of unlikely elements. The sophisticated philosopher is also a primitive, gnomic spellmaker. The desolate view of the Universe opens through eyes of childlike simplicity and moody oddness. The wide perspective of general elemental and biological law is spelled out with folklore hieroglyphs and magical monsters. The whole style is a marvellously effective artistic invention. It enables Popa to be as abstract as man can be, yet remain as intelligible and entertaining and as fully human as if he were telling a comic story. It is in this favourite device of his, the little fable or visionary anecdote, that we see most clearly his shift from literary surrealism to the far older and deeper thing, the surrealism of folklore. The distinction between the two seems to lie in the fact that literary surrealism is always connected with an extreme remove from the business of living under practical difficulties and successfully managing them. The mind, having abandoned the struggle with circumstances and consequently lost the unifying focus that comes of that, has lost morale and surrendered to the arbitrary imagery of the dream flow. Folktale surrealism, on the other hand, is always urgently connected with the business of trying to manage practical difficulties so great that they have forced the sufferer temporarily out of the dimension of coherent reality into that depth of imagination where understanding has its roots and stores its X-rays. There is no sense of surrender to the dream flow for its own sake or of relaxation from the outer battle. In the world of metamorphoses and flights the problems are dismantled and solved, and the solution is always a practical one. This type of surrealism, if it can be called surrealism at all, goes naturally with a down-to-earth, alert tone of free enquiry, and in Popa's poetry the two appear everywhere together.

The air of trial and error exploration, of an improvised language, the attempt to get near something for which he is almost having to invent the words in a total disregard for poetry or the normal conventions of discourse, goes with his habit of working in cycles of poems. He will trust no phrase with his meaning for more than six or seven words at a time before he corrects his tack with another phrase from a different direction. In the same way, he will trust no poem with his meaning for more than fifteen or so lines, before he tries again from a totally different direction with another poem. Each cycle creates the terms of a Universe, which he then explores, more or less methodically, with the terms. And one of the attractions of all Popa's poems is that one cannot set any limit to how deeply into the substance of the Universe his intuitions may penetrate. The cycle called GAMES, for instance, is close to mankind as we know it. Nothing prevents these poems from being merely ingenious, or virtuoso pieces of phrasing and timing, except the shock of recognition they impart, and the Universe of grim evil which they evoke. It could as well be protozoa, or mathematical possibilities, playing these games, as anything in humanity. They are deeper than our reality as puppets are deeper than our reality: the more human they look and act the more elemental they seem.

In his latest collection, still to be published, the total vision is vast and one understands why he has been called an epic poet. His Cosmos is more mysteriously active and dreadful but his affection for our life is closer than ever. The infinite terrible circumstances that seem to destroy man's importance, appear as the very terms of his importance. Man is the face, arms legs etc. grown over the infinite, terrible All. Popa's poems work in the sanity and fundamental simplicity of this fact, as it might appear to a man sitting in a chair.

TED HUGHES the distinguished British poet, is the author of *Lupercal* and *The Hawk in the Rain,* and editor of *Modern Poetry in Translation.* A collection of VASKO POPA's poetry is forthcoming from Penguin books.

translated by Anne Pennington
VASKO POPA: FOUR POEMS

The Burning Hands

Two burning hands are sinking
In the depths of heaven

They do not grasp at the star
That floats around them
And twinkles and crosses itself

They are saying something with their fingers
Who can guess
The tongue of fingers in the flame

Solemnly they put their palms together
To signify a peak

Are they talking of an old house
That they left burnt down
Or perhaps of a new one
That they are just thinking of building

Heaven's Ring

Ring no one's ring
How did you get lost
How fall from heaven somewhere
Rather everywhere than somewhere

Why did you at once marry
Your old your ancient shine
To your young emptiness

They have forgotten both you
And their wedding night

Since then your shine has taken to drink
Your emptiness has run to fat
You are lost again

Here is my ring finger
Take a rest on it

The Death of the Sun Father

Three paces from the top of heaven
From the lime in everlasting flower
The old sun stopped

Turned red turned green
Turned round himself three times
And went back to his rising

(So as not to die in our sight)

They say there is a son and heir-apparent
Before the big-eyed one is born for us too
We shall have taught this darkness to shine

The Homeless Head

A severed head
A head with a flower in its teeth
Wandering circles the earth

The sun meets it
It bows to him
And goes on its way

The moon meets it
To him it smiles
And does not stop in its way

Why does it growl at the earth
Can't it return
Or go off for good

Ask its lips when the flower comes out

Věra Linhartová

Mirrors and masks

VERA BLACKWELL

Věra Linhartová was born in 1938. Her first stories, dated 1957 but published in 1964*, were thus written when she was only nineteen. This is quite remarkable, since all her writing—including the earliest stories—appear to be the work of an altogether mature mind; a mind, moreover, which has all the characteristics usually assigned to male intelligence. There is nothing feminine about Linhartová's writing, save her name.

Although Linhartová's prose does not seem to be unduly difficult to translate, her titles defy translation. The following are more-or-less literal renderings of them: SPACE FOR DIFFERENTIATION; INTERIM INVESTIGATION OF THE IMMEDIATE PAST; DISCUSSING THE ELEVATOR.

Linhartová is not a student of literature, as one might expect from her literary and linguistic preoccupations, but of the history of art. She was a member of the editorial board of the brilliant literary magazine TVÁŘ, suppressed by the authorities a year ago.

The public opinion polls—a favourite pastime of Czech journals, particularly around New Year's—show that her work is extremely popular with the readers. The critics, however, appear to be rather puzzled. Her work does not seem to fit into the Czech literary context at all: it is hard to file it under any of the obvious headings. Her stories are not real stories, her one "novel" DISCUSSING THE ELEVATOR is anything but a novel.

Because of her rejection of plot, character, and psychological motivation, and of all the formal trappings of the 19th-century novel, her work can be—and has been, though with great hesitation and uncertainty—related to the French *Nouveau roman*. There are differences, of course; some of them rather substantial. There is also no direct relationship (save for the relationship of the basic sources, independently acquired, namely: Husserl, Heidegger, Kierkegaard,

*In 1964 two of her books were published: *Prostor k rozlišení* and *Mezipruzkum nejblíž uplynulého*. They were followed in 1965 by *Rozprava o zdviži*.

Kafka, Sartre's Existentialism) for contemporary French writing was unobtainable in Czechoslovakia at the time most of Linhartová's stories were composed. She herself names Dostoyevsky and Stendhal as the writers who made the greatest impact on her.

Like Robbe-Grillet, but also like all the young Czech "post-Stalinist" authors, she rejects all *a priori* concepts, and finds her purpose, her "truth", not in any preconceived end, but in the very steps she takes, perilously, towards uncertainty. "So many laborious steps," she complains, "and none of them reaches the goal; the goal is in each step." There are no short-cuts to truth. Truth is no longer perceived as an ideal to be reached at the end of one's journey. "There are no direct routes any more", Linhartová says. "All the real routes are bent." If there is any truth at all, it is in the journey itself. Hence her stress on experimentation, her passionate concentration on the work, currently at hand, her anxiety that, outside her work, there is no certainty, nothing but the shifting sands of the world. And hence, too, the reason one is tempted to think of Robbe-Grillet when considering Linhartová's work. "What am I when I am not actually writing. Nothing. Less than nothing, in fact. A shapeless whisp of a cloud, prey to all the winds"; she says. And again: "If I believe in anything at all, it is in what I have yet to say."

To Robbe-Grillet and to Věra Linhartová the modern world has become inexplicable, vastly confusing, too vast to be grasped by a single intelligence, too confusing to be unravelled by an orderly intellect. But whereas Robbe-Grillet concludes that a writer therefore has no other choice but to describe, objectively, the opaque "things" which surround and help to determine his and everybody's life, Věra Linhartová refuses to recognize the reality of anything outside her personal experience. She goes even further, defining her personal experience as not that of the surrounding objects *per se*. What she experiences is not reality, but the artistic interpretation thereof. For her, as for Wilde, life imitates art. She seems to accept that part of Aristotle's definition of *mimesis* which says: "Objects which in themselves we view with pain, we delight to contemplate when reproduced..." For it is not life in its bare form that inspires her. Her most profound experiences are triggered off by human artifacts. Mirrors and masks are her favourite images. "I find I come closer not only to shapeless reality", she states, "but often to the work of a particular author as well, through what has been said about it, rather than the impact of the thing itself."

Therein lies the basic difference between Robbe-Grillet and Věra Linhartova. There is no such thing as an "objective" description of reality, of things. Every description is an interpretation. But Věra Linhartová, is too much of a logician to fall into this obvious trap. For her the answer to the opaque world is a descent into the infinite "confines" of her own being. And as for the outside objects, she appears to be tempted to agree with Berkeley: it looks to her as though things existed only by her seeing them. Or by somebody else having seen them first, and having expressed them in words.

To her it is only the verbal expression that counts.

"Don't put velvet under my fingers, say "velvety"; it is up to me to hold the word against the thing... it is up to me to fasten it tightly, because it is again uneasy, it flutters its wings and is about to fly off, leaving the thing here as it was before, naked and helpless." And elsewhere: "The words of others come always just in time: a moment after I've uttered them myself." Uttering words means creating reality. Reality which until then, unseen and unshaped, had not existed.

Like Robbe-Grillet, Věra Linhartová refuses to survey the whole of the plot, all the actions of all their characters at all times. This would mean making a dupe of the reader. Clearly, the author knows very well how the story is going to come out, and if he asks any questions it is only because he knows the answers already. For the sake of this laudable honesty they do not hesitate to risk boring their readers to tears. Both stubbornly refuse to face the facts; namely, that most readers expect to be cheated, that most of them look forward to this particular form of deception when they open a book.

There is the suggestion of contrivance in Robbe-Grillet's work which to some might appear repellent. Věra Linhartová's work, on the other hand, seems entirely genuine. She is obviously thrilled by every word she writes; the act of creating a literary artifact is her one, all-absorbing passion. Thus her personality emerges as more lovable than that of her cold, distant French colleague, and what she says—although she erects just as many formal obstacles to test the patience of her readers as Robbe-Grillet—is consequently much more readable. One can get entirely involved in her intricate, formal patterns, which take the place of the story in her narrative, because one feels they have been achieved through traditional love and suffering.

The patterns are often purely grammatical. Her primary concern is for the language. Robbe-Grillet's "objects" become "words" with Linhartová. She does not view a word, however, as an opaque "thing", as an *"être-en-soi"*, but rather as one of the building-blocks from which her world is to be constructed. Words—often as minutely described as Robbe-Grillet's objects—are the very material of her reality. On the contrary, when she catches a word in a charming posture, her impulse is to "break its back". Her "favourite occupation" is, according to her, "the correction of words". "I can seldom pass by a word and let it alone", she says through one of her characters. She is trying to purify the language from the muddying it has suffered in recent years. She is trying to re-charge specific words with specific meanings, words which have recently acquired the habit of expressing different things to different people, and often not expressing anything to all.

Yet she enjoys violating words and their conventional meanings. Hence her love of the paradox. She can "never resist the temptation to turn everything inside out". Because she believes that this way a word will show its true colours. Its real meaning may become clearer when it is exhibited outside its usual context. Her formal patterns are neither a genteel, abstract, artificial display of wit, nor any haphazard, sterile game a clever young lady might play in her spare time: they are eminently functional.

Her gestures are consciously heroic, though her manner, in spite of her witticisms, is often dry. She lives dangerously over the abyss of non-meaning, of chaotic vagueness, of non-being, in fact. For, as regards human existence, one may propose the following equation: Life = being, being = creation, creation = imposing order upon chaos. Thus Linhartová's writing—which is proudly, almost defiantly, intellectual—can be described as truly vital. Echoing Heidegger, she says, "The essence of poetry is poetizing about the essence of poetry" "Our only duty is to think... never to stop thinking about our own thoughts, without getting carried away by them."

One of the exciting things about Linhartová, a natural result of her constant experimentation on all levels—is that almost everything she writes defies definition. Including the very form of her narrative, which cannot even be safely called a narrative. It may be described, perhaps, as a mixture of meditation (cf. Marcus Aurelius), essay (in the manner of Montaigne) and diary, where the "I" is split into a narrator and a group of marionettes the narrator manipulates. The marionettes (characters of a conventional story or novel) are displayed as such, with all their wires showing; each wire, in fact, being blatantly exhibited and minutely described. Every time a marionette moves we are informed about its precise movement, as well as about the mechanics thereof. This peculiar way of presenting a "character" represents yet another aspect of her ethical position, which forbids her to offer as a live personage what in actual fact is a mere figment of her imagination. But this is not all. Even the "I" of Linhartová's narrative appears to be an (often male) marionette. "When I speak", she says, "I become something that is no longer myself... When I speak of myself I speak of somebody else." Hence the image of the mask, which is another name for the artificiality that bedevils thoughts as soon as they have been uttered, words as soon as they have been written down, faces as soon as they have been described. Once ascertained, this fact turns for her into an act of defiance. My face, she says, "needs its mask, it will progressively shape itself inside it, until one day the interpenetration will become complete and I shall be unable to take it off without tearing the skin off my face. We move towards greater naturalness with each artificiality, all the way to the last one, the only one that belongs to us entirely."

Step by step, as the "story" unfolds, she lets the reader see into her "kitchen". She exhibits not only the wires of her marionettes, but also all the rusty pipes and the rough planks of the scaffolding around the actual building, plus all the ungainly tools she is using in order to give it shape. She never lets anyone forget for a moment that what she is offering to the reader is no "slice of life", but an artifact. In the context of Czech letters, Věra Linhartová's work is quite unique. For although she shares with her generation of intellectuals many of her ethical preoccupations, she differs from them—and indeed from most Czech prose writers of this and preceding ages—by her cultivation of an intricate literary style. Whereas the main drift of Czech prose has always tended to be factual and simple, hers represents bold artifice and complexity. Her work to date has already made her into one of the most interesting young writers in the country. Providing she can sustain her exaltation and at the same time manage to remain in control of her style, Věra Linhartová may yet become one of the truly great writers in the Czech language.

Miklos Borsos, STUDY

VĚRA LINHARTOVÁ was born in 1938. She is an art historian by training and profession. Her special fields are surrealism and abstract painting. Until recently she worked at the *Ales* Gallery in South Bohemia. She now lives in Prague. She wrote her first stories in 1957 when she was nineteen. They were published in 1964. Her latest works (not discussed in the essay) are: *Prestorec* ("DESPITESPEACH"), 1966, and *Dům daleko* (DISTANT HOUSE), about to be published.

VERA BLACKWELL who lives in London, has translated works of Vaclav Havel and of other Czech writers into English. Havel's *The Memorandum* will be published in the U. S. by the Grove Press in her translation.

CITRA (110 X 100) V. Vasarely

translated by Jan Darowski
MIRON BIALOSZEWSKI

My jacobs of exhaustion

Higher:
Fanfares of form
inhabitations of touch
all weathers of the senses . . .

Lowest—I
it is from my breast
that stairs of reality grow

Yet I feel nothing.
Nothing of succulence.
Nothing of colour.
Not only am I not
one of your Old Testament heroes
but less than a sole
stuck to the sea-floor for dying
with balloon-clusters of breath
escaping up
less than a mother potato
sprouting her huge antlers of shoots
and herself—shrunken
almost to nothingness.

Smite me
construction of my universe!

Secret freedom

They bequeathed their walls
like living plasma.

They bred in families
great-grand-wardrobes
great-grand-door-handles.

When the spiral staircase unwound
and the floors caved in,
they still felt the wardrobe in their tiny livers,
they thought: the sideboard exists
by saying so.
The mouth creaks—
A door grins wide . . .

Through landscapes broken into syntheses
they went to the promised floor,
promised for each
by himself.

They did not sing Ecclesiastes.

Vanity is for the elect.

The elect are few.

Everybody—in the last resort
Elects only himself.

MIRON BIALOSZEWSKI was born in 1922 in Warsaw. His first volume of poems, *The Revolution of Objects,* was one of the literary sensations of 1956. Since then he has published three more books of poetry and for some time ran a small experimental theatre in Warsaw. His interest in linguistic patterns and the structure of the language makes Bialoszewski a leading poet of the present-day Polish avant-garde.

JAN DAROWSKI is a Polish poet and translator living in London, a member of the group of poets "Kontynenty."

translated by Czeslaw Milosz
ZBIGNIEW HERBERT

At the gates of the valley

After the stars had fallen
all were gathered under the guard of angels
on a meadow of ashes

from a hill that survived
the eye embraces
the whole lowing two-legged herd

in truth they are not many
counting even those who will come
from chronicles fables and the lives of the saints

but enough of remarks
let's raise our eyes
to the throat of the valley
from which comes a shout

after a loud whisper of explosion
after a loud whisper of silence
this voice resounds like a spring of live water
it is we are told
a cry of mothers from whom children are taken
since as it proves
we shall be saved each one alone

the guardian angels are unmoved
and let us concede they have a hard job

she begs
—hide me in your eye

in the palm of your hand in your arms
we have always been together
you can't abandon me
now when I am dead and need tenderness
a high ranking angel
with a smile explains the misunderstanding

an old woman carries
the corpse of a canary
(all the animals died a little earlier)
he was so nice—she says weeping
he understood everything
that I said to him—
her voice is lost in the general din

even a lumberjack
whom one would not suspect of such things
old bowed fellow
presses to his breast an axe
—all my life she was mine
she will be mine here too
she nourished me there
she will nourish me here
nobody has the right
—he says—
I won't give her up

those who as it seems
obeyed the orders without pain
go lowering their heads as a sign of consent
but in their clenched fists they hide
fragments of letters ribbons clippings of hair
and photographs
which they naïvely think
won't be taken away from them

this is how they appear
a moment before
the final division
into those who gnash their teeth
and those who sing psalms

ZBIGNIEW HERBERT was born in 1924 in Lwów. He took part in the Resistance movement against the Germans and wrote his first poems during the occupation, but for a variety
of reasons his first book of poetry was published only in 1956. Since then he has made
frequent visits to Western Europe and his poetry has been translated into many Western
languages. In 1965 he won the Lenau Prize for his contribution to European literature. A
book of his poems in English is now in preparation.

translated by Stephen Polgar, Stephen Berg, and S. J. Marks
MIKLOS RADNOTI

Postcards

From Bulgaria the huge wild pulse of artillery.
It beats on the mountain ridge, then hesitates and falls.
Men, animals, wagons and thoughts. They are swelling.
The road whinnies and rears up. The sky gallops.
You are permanent within me in this chaos.
Somewhere deep in my mind you shine forever, without
moving, silent, like the angel awed by death,
or like the insect burying itself
in the rotted heart of a tree.

In the mountains, August 30th, 1944

Nine miles from here
the haystacks and houses burn,
and on the edges of the meadow
there are quiet frightened peasants, smoking.
The little shepherd girl seems
to step into the lake, the water ripples.
The ruffled sheepfold
bends to the clouds and drinks.

Cservenka, October 6, 1944

Bloody drool hangs on the mouths of the oxen.
The men all piss red.
The company stands around in stinking wild knots.
Death blows overhead, disgusting.

Mohács, October 24, 1944

I fell next to him. His body rolled over.
It was tight as a string before it snaps.
Shot in the back of the head—"This is how
you'll end." "Just lie quietly," I said to myself.
Patience flowers into death now.
"Der springt noch auf," I heard above me.
Dark filthy blood was drying on my ear.

Szentkirályszabadja, October 31, 1944

Two years after he was shot in 1944, the body of the Hungarian poet MIKLÓS RADNÓTI
was found in a mass grave at Abda. In the pocket of his coat his wife discovered a group
of his poems (called "Postcards"—four of which are given above) which constitutes a
record of his last days during a long forced march. The place names and dates of the
poems indicate the line of march before its termination in Abda, where, no longer useful
as laborers to the retreating Nazi army, the prisoners were shot.

Miklós Radnóti published eight books of poetry; the last, *Cloudy Sky,* appeared posthu-
mously in 1946 in Hungary. All of *Cloudy Sky* and about seventy-five poems from his other
works are being jointly translated by the three poets named above. The work is proceeding
under a grant from the National Translation Center.

Polish poetry in a double speculum

TYMON TERLECKI

IN THE LAST few years Polish poetry—"la grande muette" of European literature—spoke up, at last. It became audible, accessible to our hearing and perception. We owe this to the appearance of several anthologies in various languages.*

The mere enumeration of these anthologies, all of the current decade, points out the differences between them. Some cover a long span of time, the whole, or what to the editor seemed to be the whole history of Polish poetry (Peterkiewicz and Singer, Pankowski, Jeleński); some are limited in their scope to the last 70 years (Gillon and Krzyzanowski), the first half of our century (Dedecius), the period after World War II (Milosz). Some are singlehanded, individual, or at best, fourhanded ventures (Peterkiewicz and Singer, Dedecius, Pankowski, Milosz), some are big collective enterprises, engaging a great number of translators, introducing several new especially commissioned translations. One of them (Gillon's and Krzyzanowski's Anthology) has a mixed character with a practical, didactic, educational purpose: its content is divided into fiction (300 pages) and poetry (some 120 pages); it renders good service to the steadily growing number of Slavic departments at American Universities. The other publications are dedicated to the common or rather uncommon reader displaying a taste for aesthetic adventure, a refined curiosity and a generous open-mindedness.

I shall concentrate here on poetry, and on books which open gates much more hermetically closed than the boundaries of fictional and essayistic prose. And among the poetic anthologies, I intend to focus my attention on the works of Jeleński and Milosz. They reflect Polish poetry in the mirror of two different and most universal languages. They supplement each other in their scope. And finally, they are linked by a personal bond: the author of the English anthology of postwar Polish poetry is the author of the preface to the French anthology, embracing

---

*Five Centuries of Polish Poetry 1450-1950. An Anthology with Introduction and Notes by Jerzy Peterkiewicz and Burns Singer (Secker and Warburg, London 1960); Anthologie de la poésie polonaise du XV-e au XX-e siècle, traductions et notices de Marian Pankowski, introduction de Claude Backvis (André Roche, éditeur, Bruxelles 1961; Introduction to Modern Polish Literature, An Anthology of Fiction and Poetry edited by Adam Gillon and Ludwik Krzyzanowski (Twayne Publishers, Inc. New York 1964); Polnische Poesie des 20 Jahrhunderts, herausgegeben und übertragen bei Carl Dedecius (Carl Hanser Verlag, München 1964); Anthologie de la poésie polonaise, établie par Constantin Jelenski, préface de Czeslaw Milosz (Editions du Seuil, Paris 1965); Postwar Polish Poetry, An Anthology, selected and translated by Czeslaw Milosz (Doubleday and Company, Inc. New York 1965). There exists also an Italian attempt of a kindred character (Carlo Verdiani: Poeti polacchi contemporanei, Milano 1961) which was unfortunately inaccessible to the author of this essay.

all, or allegedly all the ages of Polish poetry. However, whilst concentrating on these two somehow kindred, complementary achievements, I intend to refer to the other works mentioned. In a way they are all connected, interdependent both in their general tendencies and in their idiosyncrasies.

This is most true of the relationship between the earlier anthology of Pankowski and the later of Jeleński. In spite of what Milosz writes of the latter, it is not "la première anthologie française de la poésie polonaise". This honour goes to Pankowski; a bilingual Polish and French poet, who settled in Belgium after World War II and a nearly murderous stay in a German concentration camp; an original prose writer, a temperamental though sometimes biased critic of poetry, a budding historian of Polish literature, and lately "chargé de cours à l' Université Libre" in Brussels. Published by a small Belgian publishing house in a relatively small number of copies (one thousand), his anthology passed unnoticed and was not as appreciated as it deserved to be. The anthology of Jeleński followed Pankowski's example on a much bigger scale (it contains the works of some 100 poets, over 400 poems, as compared with the 34 poets and 60 poems of Pankowski's choice). This increase in numbers was possible through the application of a different method—collective instead of individual, of team work instead of the "domestic" or "cottage industry" system. The Parisian publisher was able to give it much more effective support, to assure it a much better presentation and much wider circulation.

The link between the two anthologies of Polish poetry in French is stressed by the fact that one third of Pankowski's smaller omnibus found its way into Jeleński's larger one. We are entitled to suspect that even those of Pankowski's translations which have not been incorporated into the later collection, rendered an important service as bases for new transpositions, done by native French translators. Such was the case with one of the masterpieces of Polish poetry, with Cyprian Norwid's "The Piano of Chopin". Its last French version is still a very far cry from the unique musicality of this free verse which, in this most original and amazing form, made its appearance in modern times on the European continent in 1863, before the "invention" of the thing and of the name.

But one feels the influence of the author of the earlier anthology not only "for the better" but also "for the worse". It is probably he who suggested the XVth century as "terminus a quo", the starting point of the later anthology. Even the wording of the first title is identical in both collections: "Auteur anonyme du XVième siècle" (Pankowski), "Anonymes du XVième siècle" (Jeleński). The same limitation characterized the choice of Peterkiewicz—but there it is somehow justified by the boundaries he imposed himself.

This can not be said of Jeleński's anthology. Even more stunning and less pardonable is that for the author of the preface to this anthology, Polish poetry also begins with the XVth century—five centuries after the inception of Poland's recorded history in the second half of the Xth century. It is true that for geopolitical, political and social reasons, the first centuries were by no means fertile in the literary and especially the poetic field. Or, let us say, that they are poorly documented in this respect because of conditions not befriending cultural continuance (invasions and ensuing ravages, internal divisions and struggles, foreign immigration). Nevertheless, there stands out in this wasteland, under those stormy skies, one solitary peak, there blossoms one flower of fascinating beauty—the song "Bogurodzica Dziewica" (Mother of God and Virgin).

It is one of the most mysterious, enigmatic poems in all European poetry. It was the object of research, of daring conjectures, of heated polemics for over a century. Careful scrutiny of Western hymnology did not trace any model to which it could be referred back and this fact suggested the possibility that "Bogurodzica" is an original, self-generated, autogenous work. But before World War II the vista was opened into the opposite direction—towards the Byzantine East. Some striking similarities were revealed between the ancient Polish song and two Byzantine species: the "kontakion", a versified homily, an elaborate metrical sermon sung to the accompaniment of music, and the "theotokion" (in Slavic "bogorodicen"), a hymn in honor of the Mother of God. The hypothesis concerning the Greek-Byzantine origin of the Polish archsong, was accepted by Maria Dluska, professor of the Jagiellonian University, the greatest living authority on Polish "versology", by the eminent American scholar Roman Jacobson of Harvard University and by the Danish Slavist Adolf Stender-Petersen. However, the poem is still pending in mid-air and probably will stay there forever. The links connecting the Eastern models and their alleged extreme-Western offshoot on Polish soil are missing.

What I have said so far could be dismissed as just a pedantic divagation, if "Bogurodzica" were not a truly astounding piece of poetic art, the proof of both an inborn creative gift and conscious, deliberate craftsmanship. Its lexical and syntactic parallelisms, its sophisticated antitheses, internal and external rhymes, its rhythmical pattern qualify it as one of the masterpieces of medieval poetry. It is true that "Bogurodzica" appears on the Polish firmament like lightning. It has no antecedents and for a long time had no "postcedents", no literary progeniture. But it exists. And to omit it, to pass it over in silence in the biggest, the most extensive anthology of Polish poetry ever published in any language, is a glaring truncation of this poetry. Without "Bogurodzica", without even a bare mention of it, the historical perspective is shortened. It is difficult to say by how much, since its established age is just as controversial as everything else concerning it—it oscillates between the end of the Xth and the beginning of the XVth century. The most cautious, the most justified and substantiated is the placement of "Bogurodzica"'s birth in the middle of the XIIIth century. And this becomes thus also the birthdate of Polish poetry, a hypothetical date, but rather under—than overestimated.

It is hard to understand why the editor of the French anthology and the author of its preface lightheartedly shifted this date to two centuries later. Since ignorance must be excluded, the only explanation of this mistake is, to all appearances, a capricious whim, a misapplied spirit of contradiction. One wonders why it did not play the other way round: it would have been tempting to introduce a note of discordance into the conventional image of Polish literature, a disquieting complication into its generally accepted but not generally appreciated allegiance to the Western heritage.

The other end, the *terminus ad quem* of Jeleński's anthology is less disputable. Its fourth part dedicated to the *jeunes poètes d'après-guerre* contains 18 names (the last representative of this group J. M. Rymkiewicz was born only in 1937), more than in Milosz's specialized anthology of *Postwar Polish Poetry*. The latter takes into account the works of 21 poets; but 9 of them belong to the prewar generation. In this respect, the editor of the French anthology is really generous, which does not mean that he is impartial and infallible in his choice and judgements.

The most striking point in hand is the case of Kazimierz Wierzyński. One can risk saying that, now in his seventies, he is the greatest living Polish poet, a potential Nobel prize figure, a "papabile". Wierzyński has only one real rival, one counterpart on the opposite, let us call it "constructivist" pole: Julian Przyboś. But whilst Przyboś is a poetic doctrinaire, a dogmatist, a poet's poet, although a communist—Wierzyński is a phenomenon of astounding vitality, of continuous renewal and transformation, of evolution through a variety of manners and forms, of thematic interests and lyrical commitments. His appeal to the reading public passed through many stages, had its ebbs and flows, but in sum, it was and is enormous, one of the biggest in the history of Polish poetry. With all that, he is a salient example of unity in diversity, a paradoxical mixture of spontaneity and classical measure. To an unbiased onlooker, the artistic stature of Wierzyński is beyond any doubt. And yet, in the anthologies of Peterkiewicz and Singer and that of Pankowski he is not represented at all, in the selection of Milosz, he is dismissed with one poem, in that of Dedecius with two—neither of them well chosen nor quite representative.

Unfortunately, here again Jeleński follows in the wake of his fellow-anthologists. Among the poets belonging to the "Skamander" group which triumphantly illuminated the arrival of the Second Independence in 1918, Wierzyński is represented with the smallest number of works. He is wronged in comparison with poets of other orientations, such as Przyboś, representing the "first" or "Kraków Vanguard" (7:12), as Milosz, representing the "second" or "Wilno Vanguard" (7:12), even in comparison with poets of the youngest generation, such as Bialoszewski (7:10). Jeleński's choice of Wierzyński is haphazard (i.e. the futile bagatelle "Un dessin de Léonor Fini"); the translations are done by second-rate translators, or at least less conscientious or happy ones. But the height of things is the introductory note. It reduces an adventure in poetry which has lasted now for more than half a century, to such negligible categories as "des poèmes historiosophiques", "des poèmes patriotiques". One of the most amazing upsurges and breakthroughs in Polish post-war poetry is dismissed with the label of descriptive "poetry of nature". Only the German translator understood even less and had even less to say in this matter. Fortunately, the "Introduction" of Gillon and Krzyzanowski gives Wierzyński his due. Generally speaking, the American lover of poetry, is—as far as this author is concerned—in a better position than the European one (English as well as French), thanks to the small but substantial volume of Wierzyński's *Selected Poems,* edited by Clark Mills and Ludwik Krzyzanowski

(Voyages Press, New York 1959), translated by 15 young American poets, prefaced by Donald Davie. It is, incidentally, a most interesting experiment in collective translation.

And now briefly about another "partis pris": Leopold Staff, a neo-classicist, a Polish Jean Moréas, but with an incomparably wider scale of inner experiences and displaying a much greater poetic generosity. I am not particularly fond of him, but I could not help feeling a violent indignation reading these two half-truths converted into full falsehoods: *Le prestige de Staff durant les cinquante et quelques années de son activité littéraire était largement dú a ses qualités personnelles. Il était toujours l'ami des poètes et l'évolution de son oeuvre démontre l'influence qú avaient sur lui ses jeunes contemporains.* Right but. . . Beside having really captivating manners, Staff was an inspired poet and an accomplished craftsman; beside his keen participation in the changing poetic reality, he was the teacher of two generations of Polish poets. Tuwim called him his "poetic father" and Wierzyński could easily do the same. Of the two arbitrary opinions on Staff, I prefer Peterkiewicz's: "a prolific but minor poet". It is more honest and more loyal.

Of the whole output of Jan Kasprowicz, the first great poet of peasant stock, one poem in poetic prose survived in Jeleński's anthology: "The Ballad of the Sunflowers", and one ballad using the type of diction called in French "vers en prose". The editor very sagaciously links the second work with that of Aloysius Bertrand; the first poem, however, is not his but Peterkiewicz's choice, who added to its translation the note: "This is beyond any doubt one of the best poems in the language". Yet Jeleński did not follow his predecessor in the tentative transposition of Kasprowicz's "Hymns", one of the greatest works of the period ("Young Poland", the counterpart of French symbolism, or strictly speaking, an original variant of European symbolism). He lost thus the opportunity of introducing the foreign reader to this gigantic attempt in the "vers libre", on a scale comparable to that of Claudel and Péguy, but independent of them. (The titillating question of Kasprowicz's dependence on Walt Whitman is open to conjecture).

One could multiply the examples of arbitrary choice and opinion, of uncontrolled idiosyncrazies and whims. It is not worthwhile quarreling with all of them. I personally do not mourn the omission of Adam Asnyk, a Polish Sully Prudhomme, though a better poet. He happily passed through the needle's eye of the two radical partisans of the poetic vanguard: Peterkiewicz and Pankowski and found a modest place in their anthologies, he did not pass through the larger needle's eye of Jeleński, and was not allowed a place in his much more spacious Heavenly Kingdom. As I said, I don't mind. But neither do I feel any elation about the alleged discovery of a certain Norbert Bredkrajcz, a fourth-rate romantic poet or poetaster, known to a handful of specialists, and rightly so. One of his poems was introduced into the collection, I guess only because of its violent anti-papist accents. If that was really the case, one could find much better, in this respect, in Polish poetry.

An even more striking example of whimsicality, of capricious predilection is the choice of Miron Bialoszewski. Born in 1922, he belongs to the so-called generation of 1956, to the group of poets who revealed themselves in the "Polish October", thanks to the "thaw" after the bleak and frosty period of Zhdanovism, imposed from above by Communist officials. He possesses undoubtedly a poetic profile of his own. Dedecius links him with the Russian cubo-futurist Velimir Khlebnikov and his theory of *somovitoe slovo*. There is indeed some affinity, but the question of dependence remains open. So much only is certain that Bialoszewski experiments with the language, that one could apply to his poetry Jacobson's term "poetry of grammar" and his definition of this term: "the poetic possibilities hidden in the morphologic, syntactic structure of the language". but Bialoszewski's "poetry of grammar" aims not at the discovery, the revelation of this structure, but at its decomposition, at its annihilation, at the reduction of the organised order to a dissolute disorder. After some striking and refreshing experiments (in a more restraint form, they can be observed in other post-war poets, such as Tadeusz Rózewicz and Tymoteusz Karpowicz), Bialoszewski landed in an impasse, in a blind alley. But the anthologist has a weak spot for him. He is represented with 10 poems, as many as Tuwim, one of the leading poets of the inter-war period, he beats by three points Boleslaw Leśmian, the greatest poet of symbolist inspiration and an existentialist *avant la lettre,* immensely appreciated in contemporary Poland, he beats by one point Maria Pawlikowska, whom somebody rightly called the greatest Polish poetess of all centuries. To his favorite, his pet-poet, Jeleński lends also his helping hand as a translator. In those poems in which Bialoszewski betrays his remote kinship with Francis Ponge, with the poetry of the humble, underprivileged object, the translations succeed in communicating something. Other poems, based on the play of meanings, have proved themselves uncommunicable, untranslatable into a foreign language. It is love's, or whim's, labors lost. One wonders whether they are worthy to be translated, at least to such an extent.

We have come so close to the editor of the anthology that it is time to say a word about himself. He is a dynamic, versatile, enterprising, prolific personality and an amazing polyglot. He speaks and writes in at least four languages (Polish, French, English, Italian). He is a temperamental political columnist, with a deep sympathy for and a deep belief in "revisionism"; a critic of fine arts, able to follow the minutest meanderings of fashions, propagating with an apostolic zeal every novelty, often for novelty's sake. His is at once a spirit of contradiction and a specific conformism of *être à la page.* Among Poles living in Paris, Jeleński is the most Parisian one, sometimes even more so that the Parisians themselves. He seems to have a limited understanding for the tragic approach, for the concept of life as a mortal game with fate, for pathos, even for the epic sense of history, he is more strongly attracted by the grotesque, the extravagant and strange, by irony and black humor. Very cosmopolitan, sincerely anti-nationalistic, he nevertheless appreciates national poetic distinctness in the same, or almost the same degree as he appreciates individual artistic distinctness.

Such was Jeleński's equipment as editor of the Polish anthology in the French language. Working on it, he made use of the experiences of his predecessors.

From Peterkiewicz he took the idea of interspersing lyric poems with excerpts from epic ones, with fragments of dramas, and to top a selection of learned poetry with a few samples of popular poetry. Both practices seem rather debatable.

Epic poetry is episodic by its very nature and lends itself to fragmentation. (Peterkiewicz made much better use of it to give a fuller presentation of the Polish Baroque epics, so enthusiastically approved by the Belgian scholar Professor Backvis). Dramatic poetry seems much more functional, "structural" and therefore resists division into smaller parts; none is sufficiently representative of the whole, except perhaps the soliloquies of Lear and Hamlet, of Faust and Byron's "Manfred", the epic or lyric inserts in Mickiewicz's "Forefathers' Eve" (the "Great Improvisation", for instance). The imitation of Peterkiewicz's practice permitted Jeleński to indulge in one more personal *parti pris* (the introduction of Witold Gombrowicz, a forcibly intellectual, principally "anti-poetic" writer into an anthology of poetry), but in an attempt on a larger scale, its lack of consequence and purposefulness becomes obvious. The choice from Slowacki, the most prolific romantic playwright, is neither typical nor representative. And if we are given Slowacki and Wyspiański (the greatest symbolist dramatist), one wonders why this aspect of Mickiewicz was omitted (for instance such an almost surrealistic, oneiric piece as "Eva's Dream" from "Forefathers' Eve"), why the translation of such a marvel of lyric poetry as the third chorus from Kochanowski's "The Dismissal of the Greek Envoys" was not attempted. ("The Dismissal" is a classical Renaissance tragedy, unique in Poland and of European standard). But the most regrettable omission in this context is that of Aleksander Fredro's poetic comedy, a comic poetry fascinatingly translucent, volatile, brisk in its verse form ("The Revenge" and "Maidens' Vows"). Instead, Fredro is dismissed with one fable which, to the French, must sound like rather second-rate La Fontaine.

As for the second enlargement of the range, it can be questioned on two points. Learned, artistic, written poetry is something intrinsically different from the spontaneous, popular, primarily oral poetry, although they often crossfertilized, and although at certain periods (Polish romanticism) the latter was considered the source and inspiration of the former. But even if one eliminates this objection, it must be said that the choice of popular poetry in Jeleński's anthology is so scanty, so casual, so fortuitous, that it does not pay justice to the phenomenon, does not present it convincingly to the foreign reader.

All these are, however, relatively minor questions compared with the main problem: the translations. Until our days it seemed insoluble, as far as poetry was concerned, or rarely soluble. It faces a single person with the requirement of a thorough knowledge of two languages; moreover, it calls for a poetic talent equalling, or at least, approaching the talent of the poet to be translated. Within the circle of attempts I am dealing with here, Peterkiewicz was the first to introduce a simple but affective improvement in the procedure. Himself a poet, linking peasant origins with poetic vanguard leanings, he studied during the war and graduated from one of the universities in Scotland. Later, he dropped writing poetry in Polish, and began to write successfully novels in English.

Currently, he is reader in Polish literature at the University of London, and already in this capacity, he embarked on his anthology. He had the idea of doubling the translator and formed a team with Bernard Singer, a young, intelligent English poet (of Scottish origin), prematurely deceased two years ago. The team worked in such a way, that Peterkiewicz prepared the literal versions, accompanied by notes on characteristics of the verse form; Singer proposed a draft poetic translation, and afterwards they both worked on it, confronting requirements of one language and the possibilities of the second one, striving to find the best possible equivalent of the Polish in English.

This method of having the translations done by a team of Siamese brothers, Jeleński applied, one could say, on an industrial scale. The progress was not only quantitative but also qualitative. Jeleński's anthology avoided the stylistic sameness, a certain levelling of stylistic distinctions between the various poets, which is discernible in Peterkiewicz's anthology. And no wonder. Jeleński managed to mobilize an echelon of some fifty French translators. There is no point in enumerating all of them. It will be enough to say that among them are representatives of all generations and orientations, names of first rank, poets of stature such as Pierre Emmanuel, Francis Ponge and Jacques Audiberti (only two great names are missing: Henri Michaux and René Char). Being masters, sometimes magicians and equilibrists in the language into which the translations had to be done, they did not know the language from which they had to be done. There were only a few exceptions to this rule: some bilingual Polish-French poets (as the already mentioned Pankowski and Jan Brzekowski), some French writers and scholars knowing Polish (like Professor Jean Bourilly, an authority on Slowacki, like Paul Cazin, an eminent prose translator from Polish into French of sometimes most difficult works; Cazin is the author of disputable and disputed prosaic rendering of Mickiewicz's "Pan Tadeusz", the greatest Polish epic poem of the XIXth century). Also some older translations were used by Jeleński. We find among the co-authors of the anthology such brilliant names as Paul Eluard and Oskar Milosz (or O. V. de L. Milosz), a poet of Polish origin, who belonged to the second generation of French symbolists, that of Claudel and Valéry (his transpositions from Mickiewicz, although masterly versified, change the ballad stanzas into prose novelettes, through a bizarre typographical arrangement). But the bulk of the anthology consists of freshly made translations, appearing in print for the first time. And this is the greatest achievement of Jeleński, a real exploit of organisation and inspiration. It shows him as the producer of a great polyphonic show, the commander-in-chief of a complicated battle. It gives the measure of how deeply he has penetrated into the French literary milieu, on what intimate terms he is with it, what a great personal credit he has acquired. Jeleński's anthology is the outcome of his adoptive Parisianism. It also testifies to his initiative, his driving force, his power of persuasion, his enthusiasm and perseverance. This counterbalances, compensates for all the weaknesses of his remarkable work. Perhaps it even explains and justifies some of them.

Other drawbacks are rather unnecessary and could easily have been avoided. This concerns the bio-bibliographical notes and the information about the systems of Polish versification. The notes are often shaky in their content. Biernat of Lublin, the first national writer, is called one of the first lay writers, but he was a priest (and doctor), his "Life of Aesop" is a versified paraphrase of a medieval comic romance, preceding a collection of fables. Fredro's family acquired the aristocratic title from the Austrian government after his service under Napoleon, not before. Wyspiański, a painter and visionary dramatist, never studied in Munich; he spent three decisive years in postimpressionist Paris and was in touch with Gauguin; he never published any collection of his poignant but occasional lyrics (not too well represented in the anthology). Maria Pawlikowska would turn in her unhospitable Manchester grave, could she hear that she served in the Air Force—she was a pacifist, mortally sick and, one can say, dead of the war, of her sorrow about the war. Such and many similar slips are not calamitous, but should have been prevented.

A more serious shortcoming is a hasty and blurred survey of Polish prosody in the closing editorial word. Jeleński mentions five metrical systems and characterises three. Five is too much, three too little. I must once more indulge in pedantry, but not for pedantry's sake. The clarification of this question will be useful for the appraisal of Milosz's anthology.

One could speak about five systems of versification only if taking into account the common Slavic and early Polish asyllabic poetry. Since its specimens are not of any remarkable artistic value and are not represented in Jeleński's anthology, only four systems are here to be considered. Three of them are numerical, based on the number of elements composing the verse line, the fourth is a non-numerical one. The numerical systems in order of their appearance are: syllabic, syllabotonic, and tonic. The syllabic is based on the number of syllables in the line, the syllabotonic combines the number of syllables with the number of measures (feet). The tonic disregards the number of syllables as well as feet in the line; its basis is the number of accentual groups. The last, the youngest system, called simply "System IV", abandons all these formatives: the equal number of syllables, the combination of an equal number of syllables with an equal number of feet, and the equal number of accentual groups, of accents. The basis of System IV is the phrase, the elements of syntactic construction or semantic relationship, the expressive intonation. With the help of intonation, it forms structures, unknown to pronouncements which are not aiming at expressiveness, at poetic emphasis.

All four systems of versification are of different age. The first covers the entire Middle Ages: it passed then through a long evolution of relative, approximate syllabism, to reach in the XVIth century, through Kochanowski, the "Polish Ronsard", the level of strict, absolute syllabism, an isosyllabism not tolerating any deviation from a fixed number of syllables within one poetic unit (stanza or poem). It is therefore wrong to say, as Jeleński does, that it was "of a rather loose structure" ("de structure assez libre"). Syllabotonism is the acquisition of Polish romanticism, an initiative to be ascribed mainly to Mickiewicz, and is not, as Jeleński assumes—of popular origin, but is due to the influence of antique Greco-Roman poetry. The tonic system appeared at the turn of the centuries and most probably was formed under the influence of English poetry; it was promoted by Kasprowicz, a remarkable translator of this poetry. The system without a name yet, let us call it the "intonational" system, made its first appearance in the period between the two world wars. But the most curious phenomenon is that, at that time, all four systems co-existed, sometimes within the work of one poet. To a high degree they still coexist today. A striking example of this symbiosis is Adam Wazyk. A representative of the radical poetic vanguard, a propagator of Apollinaire in Poland, author of the "Poem for Adults" (1955), marking the breakthrough towards the Polish "Thaw", he wrote during the same period as this latter work, two other poems: "Poslanie do przyjaciela" ("Message to a Friend") and "Qui tacent clamant", observing in both of them the riguours of the regular quatrain with full alternating rhymes (abab).

Milosz's anthology disregards, discards the fact of coexistence of different metrical systems in contemporary Polish poetry, the fact of "polysystematism". One can say that he is a "metrical monist", he gives preference to "System IV", and in so doing, impoverishes the poetic landscape at least in its formal aspect. Even when he ventures to translate poems written in "traditional metre" as he calls it, he is unwilling or unable to follow it consequently (that is the case of Antoni Slonimski, a representative of the "Skamander" group to which also Tuwim and Wierzyński belonged). I am opposed to this practice, and inclined to agree with Peterkiewicz that the rhythm and rhyme pattern forms an integral component of a poem. Together with Singer, he strove not to imitate the Polish diction in English, but to find approximate equivalents. They can boast some remarkable achievements in their search, in their valiant struggle with "the demons of two languages".

Translation of poems, making use of the "intonational" system, does not set the translator free from this struggle. If the working definition of this system, as given above, is right, the problem of "translatability" is as acute here as in poetry using the numerical systems. It is even more difficult, since it concerns factors more complex, more subtle, less palpable than the counting of syllables, or the hammering out of measures. Intonation, the musical phrasing, the expressive possibilities of the syntax, are different in Polish and English. I am not absolutely sure whether Milosz is always and fully aware of these implications. I had the impression that more than once he tended to obtain a clear meaning to the detriment of other constitutive factors of the poem. He is prone to treating poetry as a specific kind of intellectualized prose. "I must admit—he confesses himself —I am partial to poetry that sometimes attains the calligraphic quality of an ideogram".

This is visible in the prominent place given by Milosz to Zbigniew Herbert (18 poems, a record number, as against the 12 of Rózewicz, 7 of Grochowiak, 5 of Bialoszewski, 4 of Harasymowicz). Herbert (born in 1924) is undoubtedly the most outstanding and the most mature representative of the 1956 generation unit, to which all the other mentioned poets belong (except Rózewicz). Of them all, he alone obtained recognition abroad. He was printed and broadcast in England; a selection of his poems is to be published in the "Penguin" series. In

America, the anthology of Gillon and Krzyzanowski brings six of Herbert's poems (against 7 of Rózewicz and none of the other representatives of the group). On the cover of Milosz's anthology, Thomas Merton calls him "one of the most important poets of our time in any language".

The attitude of the anthologist towards the main star of his book is of a specific, rather complicated and delicate nature. Milosz is attracted to the younger poet by his affinity, by his imaginative and intellectualized lyricism. More or less consciously, he considers Herbert to be his follower, his continuator. He sees in him the fulfilment of the strive for this universally acceptable idiom which he himself did not fully realise.

The editor of "Postwar Polish Poetry" attained before World War II a considerable position in his country, and after this war, also abroad. In Poland he was the leading representative of the Wilno or Second Avant-garde, the most outspoken mouthpiece of "catastrophism", of apocalyptic forebodings. Abroad, he won fame through his protest against the reglamentation of literature in the Stalinist era, as the author of "The Captive Mind", which was translated into a dozen languages; his other works, although some of them remarkable, met with a weaker response. His essays, diaries, criticisms, prove that he is a keen, perspicacious observer of the international scene; he is equally at home in France, England and the United States. He has to his credit many translations into Polish from the French (among others the renderings of works of his uncle O. V. de L.Milosz, a comprehensive anthology of Simone Weil), the English (among others T.S. Eliot's "The Waste Land", also Jeffers, Whitman), from the Spanish and even occasionally from the Yiddish. He is now professor of Slavic Literatures at the University of California, Berkeley. In this capacity he wrote the preface to Jeleński's anthology. It does not go beyond elementary facts, but interprets them intelligently. It strikes the reader by such happy formulas as the one about Rózewicz: "la nudité de l'homme sur la terre impitoyable", by startling associations (he compares, for instance, Slowacki, the Polish romantic, the author of a mystical treatise with Teilhard de Chardin—perhaps a little too flatteringly).

In short, Milosz is a versatile, many-sided writer, but his poetry did not manage to force the language barrier. He was not (as yet) tempted by bilingual poetry, although it has in Poland a tradition of long standing, going back as far as Kochanowski, the greatest poet of the Renaissance, who wrote with the same mastery in Polish and Latin; there was also the curious case of the lately rediscovered minor poet Józef Dunin Borkowski (XIXth century), who wrote poems in Rumanian, or the pathetic instance of Leśmian, who gave up the possibility of writing in Russian, to write in Polish. The fate of Milosz's poetry must be attributed to its specific character. In spite of what he thinks of himself, and what some critics think of him, he is closer to such Italian hermeticists as Montale and Ungaretti, than to anybody else.

This brings us back to Herbert and the attraction he has on Milosz, to the preponderant place given him in Milosz's anthology. The younger poet intellectualizes emotional states, he "verbalizes feelings", like his elder patron, but he reaches an unusual level of transparency, of translucency in his poetry, without loosing any of its mysteriousness, ambiguity, evasiveness. Herbert's poetry is at the same time captivating and translatable. Whether it will win lasting recognition remains to be seen.

Different criteria of appreciation must be applied to Milosz's selection than to Jeleński's. The former is a subjective choice, a poet's confession about his poetic preferences. Nevertheless, it has a great objective value as the first really revealing, promptly done presentation in English of contemporary Polish poetry. Its proper title would be "post-October" or "post-Thaw" poetry (the period of Zhdanovism immediately preceding the "thaw" is presented in an excellent comparative essay of George Gömöri: "Polish and Hungarian Poetry 1945 to 1956", Oxford 1966). Milosz reaches back from the year 1956 to the earlier period after, during and even before the war. He does it sporadically, half-heartedly, haphazardly, distorting thereby the proportions, and doing more harm than service (as in the quoted case of Wierzyński). It would have been more sensible and fair to restrict himself to post-October poetry, as the rest is unsubstantial, scanty and lacks representativeness.

I compared some two thirds of the translations in Jeleński's and Milosz's anthologies with their respective Polish originals. It is a material for a large academic study, fairly unpalatable for the common, even the sophisticated reader—and this is not the place for it. A few most general remarks must suffice.

Polish poetry may seem easier translatable into French than into English, because of the preponderantly syllabic versification of the first and the mainly accentual versification of the second. But to think so would be a sweeping generalisation. Some achievements from Peterkiewicz and Singer's as well as Gillon and Krzyzanowski's anthologies, two renderings of Mickiewicz's "Pan Tadeusz" in the life of one generation (of Watson Kirkconnel in America and of Kenneth Mackenzie in England, not to mention the original attempt at paraphrasing the poem by Donald Davie) militate against such an opinion.

The approximation of the French renderings in Jeleński's anthology to the respective Polish originals, is of varying degree. But where the intuition of the editor directed him towards the right translator of a given poem, whenever it kindled in the chosen translator a spark of interest and sympathy, provoked a mood of musical consonance, the results are astounding; we face almost miracles of transubstantiation.

The idea to marry the baroque "concettista" Andrzej Morsztyn, the brilliant virtuoso of the word with the ascetic poet of the object Francis Ponge, may seem strange but I agree that it was worthwhile, not as a rule, of course, but as an exception. The result is not a translation but a paraphrase ("la mise dans le goût francais" and one could add "aussi dans le goût contemporain"). It will stay as a permanent addition to the history of Polish and French poetry.

I do not risk any generalization about the poetic whole presented in the discussed anthologies. That would be a topic for yet another much longer study than this one. The reader will find some propositions in the prefaces and postscripts written by Claude Backvis (in Pankowski's anthology), by Peterkiewicz, Krzyzanowski, Milosz and Dedecius.* One thing seems to emerge beyond any doubt: the universality of Polish poetry through its centuries-long past and its presence in our troubled times; to use the words of Merton: a presence "independent of ideological imposture, candid, ironic, lucid and sometimes completely shattering".

One practical conclusion impresses itself imperatively. The time is ripe for the build-up of an English anthology equalling, if possible surpassing, in scope Jeleński's French anthology, following his model, whilst avoiding its weaknesses. A great deal of preparatory work has already been done in the aforementioned books and in the two collections of Mickiewicz's "Selected Poems" (The Noonday Press, New York 1957) and "New Selected Poems" (Voyages Press, New York 1957). The method has also been tried out: the first of these collections contains, among many others, a masterly translation done by W.H.Auden, which, most probably, became one of the stimuli and examples for the French anthology. Both these attempts, and others of a similar kind, we owe to the poetic gift, the penetrating intelligence, the holy fire of Clark Mills. For this postulated comprehensive anthology of Polish poetry in the English language—he seems to be the true man of destiny.

*When reading the proofs of this essay, I came across two articles about Polish contemporary poetry (by J. L. Jakubowski and Julian Rogoziński) in "Arena", No. 26, a paper published by the International Writers' Fund of P.E.N. Unfortunately, even their informative value is very restricted, since all Polish poets living outside Poland are passed over in silence, and so is their poetic output, regardless of its character, level and value.

TYMON TERLECKI, historian, essayist and critic of literature, theatre and the fine arts, is now Professor of Polish Literature at the University of Chicago. Before World War II, he was Professor of World Drama at the State Institute of Dramatic Art in Warsaw. After the war, he lectured at the Polish University Abroad (London), the Hebrew University (Jerusalem), the University of Wales (Cardiff). Member of the Philological Commission of the late Polish Academy of Arts and Sciences (Cracow), active member of the Polish Society of Arts and Sciences Abroad (London), the Polish Historical and Literary Society (Paris). Former Chairman of the Union of Polish Writers Abroad. Editor of many periodicals and collective works, including also his personal contributions (among them "Leonardo da Vinci", 1953, "Losses to Polish Culture" 2 vol., Glasgow 1945, "Polish Literature Abroad" 1940-1960, 2 vol. London, 1964/65). Author of numerous essays and studies in Polish, English, French, Italian and Czech, and books, (including "The Social Function of the Theatre, 1937, "Poland and the West", 1947, "Personalistic Criticism" 1957, "Christian Existentialism" 1958, "People Books and the Stage" 1961, "Madam Helena" - a comprehensive biography of the Polish-American actress Helena Modjeska, 1962). Mr. Terlecki is now preparing two monographs for Twayne's World Authors Series on Stanisław Wyspiański, the symbolist dramatist and Kazimierz Wierzyński, one of the most eminent living Polish poets.

translated by Czeslaw Milosz
ALEKSANDER WAT

A damned man

First in my dream appeared a coffee mill.
Most ordinary. The oldfashioned kind. A coffee-brown color.
(As a child, I liked to slide open the lid, peek in and instantly
snap it shut. With fear and trembling! So that my teeth chattered from terror!
It was as if I myself were being ground up in there! I always knew
I would come to a bad end!)
So first there was a coffee mill.
Or perhaps it only seemed so, because a moment later a windmill stood there.
And that windmill stood on the sea, on the horizon's line, in its very center.
Its four wings turned creaking and cracking. They probably were grinding
up somebody.

And at the tip of every one of them
an equilibrist in white
revolved to the melody of "The Merry Widow",
supported by his left hand resting on the wing he floated, fiery, fluid, fleeting,
a silver flame fluttering his feet in the ether.
Then he waned. And so one after the other. It would have been dark if not for a
Oh, where did they come from? Equestriennes?! My marvellous equestriennes!
Lightly on heavy but swift percherons they gallop one after another, I see crowds,
crowds of them—some in ruffles of tulle, others naked, stark naked in black
silk stockings,
still others in beads—golden, truquoise, black and iridescent,
and their thighs white like sugar! Like teeth! And strong, o mighty God, how
strong!
(As a young boy I dreamed : an equestrienne—only an equestrienne!
will saddle the great love in my life! Well, I've never met one.
And it's probably better that way, for what a couple we would have made;
an equestrienne and a bookkeeper in a nationalized funeral parlor.)
Well, nothing lasts forever. Since a moment later
instead of equestriennes, Sabines were parading, armored women much more
vulgar after all
(eleven years ago I fell in love with a certain Sabina,
a divorcee, alas without reciprocity).

Thus the Sabines
not ravished but, let me conceed, ravishing. Taking me where?
Where? How can I know where?
In any case—towards annihilation.
I woke up. I always knew I would come to a bad end.

translated by Lydia Pasternak Slater

To shrink, to be mouse-like. A field mouse. Or one in a garden.
Never a house mouse:
The stench of humans is dreadful!
(Don't we all know it - birds and crabs and rodents)
It causes revulsion and fear.
Trembling.

To nibble wistaria buds, the bark of the palm trees,
Scratching for roots in the cool damp earth, to be dancing
In the fresh clear night. To look at the moon in its fullness,
Our eyes reflecting the agony of the oblique
Moonlight.

To burrow, to go undergound, against the impending
Threat, when the vicious Boreas, with icy skeleton fingers
Looking for me, will knead my small heart with his clasping
Claw,—the timorous mouse-heart,
A palpitating crystal.

ALEKSANDER WAT was one of the first Futurist poets in Poland. During the last war
he lived in the Soviet Union, first as a left-wing refugee, later as a prisoner. Returned to
Poland after the war but could not publish his original verse: his book of poetry published
in 1957 was a minor revelation. From 1959 on, Wat lived in the West; he died in Paris in
the summer of 1967.

translated by Tony Connor
LÁSZLÓ NAGY

Cloud with a woman's face

I awake shuddering, a great pulse
banging inside me, a flame
flickering and jumping inside me,
and the world is burning around me—
up to the purple-trembling sky,
roaring fires of growth in the May sun.
Shine, shine, sun! drag shrieks
from the mouths of flowers as you force
them open! swish sap scalding
through stems and stalks! suck
out sweet leaves from close buds!
hoop growth-ring on growth-ring till
fat trunks burst apart!
Creation drunk on creation!
Female foliage that wants me inside it,
love swinging and ringing my heart
like a deep bell. A blaze, a daze,
a dazzle of glancing lights,
and I've lost all bearings,
I only know it's Spring
raving of truth, beauty, love,—
the murderous, ancient themes
that take the breath away.
O May, May, I have learnt your law;—
only a starving man may know you;
I've gone hungry for a thousand years
to understand your passion.
And I don't want ease and comfort!
the well-fed loll of pestilent shores,
where bright banners turn black
and the roses are worm-eaten.
It's life I cleave to! Slur of silks from flesh,
crackling hair in dark rooms,
Nightingale-songs, and the din of flowers.
Enslave me with sweet music!
Let me sweat with pleasure!

I gather it all to no avail,
and I'm doomed to go on harvesting —
but this is the only life, and it's wonderful.
The flush of youth's gone; my flesh
droops and bulges, and still I cry,
O May, May, your signs are good;
As the year grows I am growing stronger;
I throw back my head to the scent of olive flowers,
and over me leans a cloud with a woman's face.

Squared by walls

Couldn't you have died,
or at least bled,
instead of pacing the floor
stunned with despair?
You kept clear of the trouble:—
bullets, armoured track, emblazoned
girls' screams. Nor for you broken
wheels, scattering rooftiles,
grim gangs of working lads,
and soot-brindled petals.
You did not spill one drop
of blood, and when it stopped,
you had only gone grey and mad.

In usual winter weather
you stand here; no other
but yourself, and wide awake,
squared by walls that echo
a cough like raking
gunfire. It's not merely
your flesh that's cold;
mind and heart are frozen,—crowned
by knives of ice.
You are ashamed of your melting phrases;
as if you had lost the right
to think of spring
and lilacs,—the lung-like trees blossoming.
What agony for a Lord of Life!
Yet, deep in the secret places
of your being, furtive with guilt,
you are breathing on the frosted pane,
that you may look out at the world again.

translated by Anne Cluysenaar
LÁSZLÓ NAGY

Advancing through soot and snow

Advancing through soot and snow
In a dreaming fever,
I looked for another and you
At the sword's edge grew,
My wounded flower.

Those twenty years, though lost,
You can repay me.
In a derelict square, in the smoke
Of suburbs, your urchin music
Delights me.

Tortured by beauty and joy
To miraculous life,
I burn for their sake and wrest
Honey from the rope at my wrist
That they may survive.

My life is a Gordian knot,
My fate is blind.
Arm me from head to foot
And I will cling to your faith
To the bitter end.

LÁSZLÓ NAGY (b. 1925) is an outstanding poet of the first Hungarian post-war generation.
In the last few years he has been evolving towards a synthesis of two-styles: that of old Hun-
garian folk-songs and ballads and a popular-surrealistic stylization of modern urban life.
Last year he won the Kossuth Prize for literature. TONY CONNOR is an English poet living
in Manchester. He has published two collections of poetry *With Love Somehow* and
Lodgers (OUP, 1962 and 1965 respectively) which won him high critical acclaim.

ANNE CLUYSENAAR is an English poet of Irish-Belgian extraction, living at Lancaster
where she teaches English at the University.

translated by Anne Pennington
MIODRAG PAVLOVIĆ

Lament for Smederevo

We are left with no fortress and no law
the fortress has fallen.

We know not where our land begins,
but its end is everywhere.

The stronghold has fallen with our names,
the river has swept them away.

Armies and travellers pass over us,
but no one comes to us.

No more will there be fine fortresses
in our land.

Long nights we wish for, and deep forests,
where the sight is created before the eyes.

Let us sing and remember ourselves,
others have forgotten us.

And may the law of a constant heart reign
by the devastated fortress.

A Slavonic singer beneath Parnassus

I wait for a new robe to be brought me.
My tribe came from afar, shepherds of fire,
and we offered up a torch on the funeral pyre of that people
turned to stone in the fire
and doused in the water of the flood.
Now we take the belts from the waists of the stone
and from its ashes we make pillows
but under our tongues a new warmth arises.

To the warmth of speech the enchanted rock opens
in which the hand finds out honey:
letter by letter returns to my memory
to clothe me in verse, word by word.
Sad are the temples, see, and the eyes of heaven,
they are thinking still of the courts and the courtiers of yore,
and those around me tell me to take off my surplice,
for divinity is no more, in vain I speak.

Come, then, tell me, was anyone at the gods' funeral?
Who saw eternity in its last agony, who?
Was it you, O night? Wait for the dawn on my shoulder!
Though the statues are broken,
You will see their shape on the hill
All shimmering in the light and sound.

I am already devising new names
for the immortals to take when they come down from the mountain,
and a young singer takes the primeval word in his hands
and lifts it to his forehead.

MIODRAG PAVLOVIĆ is a Serbian poet whose work shows the influence of modern English poetry, in particular that of T. S. Eliot. The publication of his *87 poems* in 1952 was hailed as a landmark in the development of post-war Yugoslav poetry. ANNE PENNINGTON is a Slavic scholar, living and teaching in Oxford.

Stanislaw Slonia, "SOCRATES" (Bronze)

Ludovit Fulla

BOYER'S DINNER Tibor Csernus Galerie du Fleuve 1967

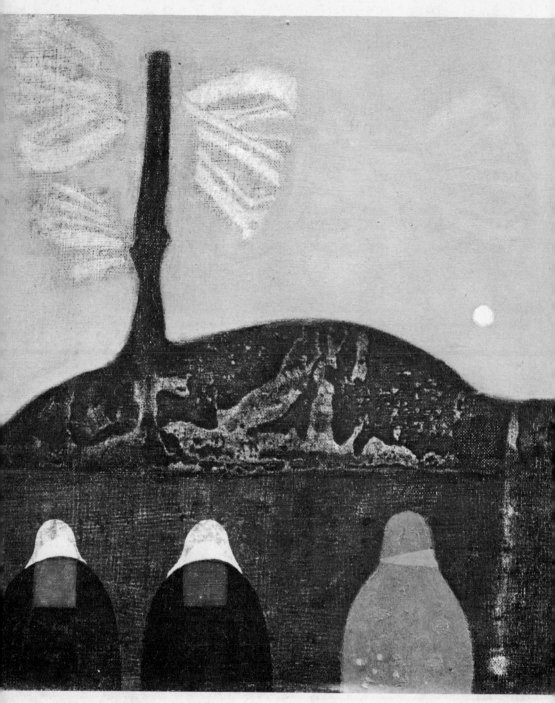

WAITING, Endre Bálint, 1959

ENTRANCE TO THE WAILING WALL IN JERUSALEM, detail; Tivadar Csontváry